Retracing
Major Stephen H. Long's
1820 Expedition

THE AMERICAN EXPLORATION AND TRAVEL SERIES

RETRACING
MAJOR STEPHEN H. LONG'S
1820 EXPEDITION

THE ITINERARY AND BOTANY

BY GEORGE J. GOODMAN
AND CHERYL A. LAWSON

UNIVERSITY OF OKLAHOMA PRESS : *Norman and London*

This book is published with the generous assistance of the Wallace C. Thompson Endowment Fund, University of Oklahoma Foundation.

Book designed by Bill Cason

Library of Congress Cataloging-in-Publication Data

Goodman, George J., 1904–
    Retracing Major Stephen H. Long's 1820 expedition : the itinerary and botany / by George J. Goodman and Cheryl A. Lawson.
        p.   cm. — (The American exploration and travel series ; v. 73)
    Includes bibliographical references and index.
    ISBN: 0–8061–2703–1
    1. West (U.S.) — History — To 1848.   2. West (U.S.) — Discovery and exploration.   3. Southwestern States — Discovery and exploration.
4. Botany — West (U.S.)   5. Botany — Southwestern States.   6. Long, Stephen Harriman, 1784–1864. I. Lawson, Cheryl A., 1947–   . II. Title.   III. Series.
F592.G64   1995
978'.02 — dc20   94–42657
                                                                CIP

Retracing Major Stephen H. Long's 1820 Expedition: The Itinerary and Botany is Volume 73 in The American Exploration and Travel Series.

The paper in this book meets the guidelines for permanence and durability of the Committee on Production Guidelines for Book Longevity of the Council on Library Resources, Inc. ⊚

1   2   3   4   5   6   7   8   9   10

CONTENTS

ILLUSTRATIONS

MAPS

PREFACE

WHEN THOMAS JEFFERSON, A MAN OF EXTRAORDINARY TALENTS AND diverse interests, became president of the United States in 1801, he was, among many things, an accomplished naturalist and scientist. His dream of explorations in the American West became paramount with the purchase of the Louisiana Territory in 1803.

In 1804, Jefferson sent Meriwether Lewis and William Clark, both of whom were army men from Virginia, to explore the Missouri River in the northern part of the Louisiana Territory as well as any such watercourses that led to the Pacific Ocean (these proved to be the Snake and Columbia rivers). Their collections of plants and animals, made without a scientific staff, emphasized just how little was known of the natural history of this vast area. From this expedition would come "the first faunal studies in the newly acquired Louisiana Territory"[1] and "the first studies of plants indigenous to western plains, mountains, deserts, and river valleys."[2]

While the Lewis and Clark Expedition was in progress, Jefferson agreed that William Dunbar (a Scottish scientist who had settled in Natchez, Mississippi)[3] and Dr. George Hunter (a druggist from Philadelphia who had also come to this country from Scotland)[4] should explore the Ouachita River from its mouth in Louisiana to a point not far from what is today Hot Springs, Arkansas. That exploration began in the fall of 1804 and was completed the following January. A few botanical specimens were made, but, more important, Dunbar and Hunter became "the first scientific expedition to report back from Louisiana."[5]

Then, in April, 1806, Jefferson initiated an exploration of the Red River of the South. Thomas Freeman, a surveyor who had emigrated from Ireland, became the leader of this Red River expedition,[6] and

[1]CUTRIGHT, 395.
[2]CUTRIGHT, 396.
[3]FLORES, 15.
[4]MCDERMOTT [2], 5.
[5]FLORES, 45.
[6]FLORES, 49.

Peter Custis, a student from the University of Pennsylvania, became its naturalist.[7] As Dan L. Flores has pointed out,[8] Custis "was not only the first professionally-trained naturalist to work from the Mississippi River westward, he was also the first scientist with American training to accompany a government exploration into the West." In the time before this expedition was turned back by the Spanish near what is now the Texas/Oklahoma/Arkansas border, Custis cataloged many plants and animals; but he returned with only "twenty-six dried plant specimens."[9]

Zebulon Pike, a young army man from New Jersey, in 1806–1807 led "the first explorers to journey from the settled eastern areas to the region now containing the states of Kansas, Colorado, and New Mexico."[10] They explored the Arkansas to its headwaters but made few natural-history collections.

Next came the Long Expedition to the Rocky Mountains in 1820. Led by Major Stephen H. Long, whose career as an army engineer had begun only five years earlier, this landmark in the history of American exploration was more scientifically oriented and better staffed for the purpose of inventorying a portion of the trans-Mississippi West than any previous expedition had been. Long, who had promoted scientific exploration in the West to President James Monroe and Secretary of War John Calhoun, in 1818 received authorization to formulate a scientific group. After some changes were made in the original roster, Long finalized his scientific staff to include Edwin James, M.D.,[11] a twenty-three-year-old Vermonter, as botanist,[12] geologist,[13] and surgeon; Titian Peale, the twenty-one-year-old son of Philadelphia artist Charles Willson Peale, as naturalist; and Thomas Say,[14] a thirty-three-year-old Philadelphian and charter member of the Academy of Natural Sciences of Philadelphia, as zoologist.

Many overviews of the historical impact of Long's expedition and those that preceded it have been written by historians,[15] but the

[7]FLORES, xvi.

[8]FLORES, 212.

[9]JACKSON [1], 233.

[10]JACKSON [2], I, x.

[11]For biographical information on James, see BENSON [2].

[12]Long chose James as botanist and surgeon to replace Dr. William Baldwin, who died in 1819 in Franklin, Missouri, while en route with the expedition up the Missouri River.

[13]The original geologist, Augustus Jessup, remained with the expedition only until October, 1819.

[14]For further information on Say, see STROUD.

[15]CUTRIGHT, FLORES, GOETZMANN, HOLLON, JACKSON [1] and [2], MCDERMOTT [1] and [2], AND NICHOLS and HALLEY.

botanical importance of the Long Expedition, while not overlooked, has received less attention. Unlike the naturalists who had collected specimens in other areas within the Louisiana Purchase, Edwin James returned with hundreds of plant specimens. When one considers the difficulties involved at the time in collecting and preserving plant specimens and in transporting them on packhorse during the one hundred days James was in the field, his accomplishments are remarkable.

The route of the Long Expedition provided James with an opportunity to collect plants in virgin territory. His collections came from short-, mixed-, and tall-grass plains and prairies; from coniferous and deciduous forests; and, for the first time in the Colorado Rockies, from the alpine zones. James's sampling of plants along the route of the expedition provides the reader of Part 2 of this volume with an idea of the plants to be found there today, as well as verification, in most instances, of the occurrence of a plant in a given area in 1820.

James provided the Eastern botanists with the most extensive collections made to date from the lands included in the Louisiana Purchase. Well over one hundred of the plants he collected were previously unknown. When occasionally James noticed the first occurrence of a plant, it often proved to be at its currently known eastern or western limit.

James brought to the botanical world the initial list of species found in the vast ecological areas along the route of the Long Expedition before settlers and accompanying invader plants changed that pristine setting. He published a partial plant list a few years after the expedition.[16] One of the leading botanists in the country, John Torrey of the College of Physicians and Surgeons, New York City, accounted in three publications for many plants collected on the trip.[17] No other list of plants collected on the Long Expedition had appeared for nearly a century when, in 1920, Osterhout[18] published one containing about half the new species collected by James. No comprehensive species-by-species study of the botany has heretofore been presented.

We cite Edwin James's unpublished diary, in which he entered almost daily observations on the vegetation and geography. In this

---

[16]JAMES [4].

[17]Dr. Torrey's first publication listed ten alpine taxa, the second listed eight grasses, and a third listed more than 481 taxa (see TORREY [1], TORREY [6], and TORREY [2]).

[18]OSTERHOUT [1].

diary he named or described many of the plants he had collected. Frequently, the locality given in the literature for the collection of a particular plant is not supported either by our findings in the diary or by the known distribution. The localities published by Torrey were often incorrect, and these have been quoted abundantly in the literature.

Because of the frequent reference to plants in the diary, it was necessary to know exactly where the expedition was each day, and, accordingly, we have attempted to locate their camp for each night of the trip. The recently published diary of Captain John R. Bell,[19] the journalist on the expedition, and certain original paintings made by Samuel Seymour, the artist who accompanied the expedition, proved corroborative. We have located with certainty where the artist made these various landscape paintings, thereby enabling us to determine the exact route of the expedition in areas where historians had believed the task impossible. We have photographed these landscapes as they appear today, and several of those photographs are reproduced in this volume.

The landforms described by James and Bell were also important in locating the route of the expedition. Through our field explorations we saw the country that they described, and their presumed route has been revised in some areas.

We have painstakingly retraced the explorers' route. That was a task never before undertaken during the more than 170 years since Long, James, and their colleagues left the field. During a total of some sixty days, our trips took us more than ten thousand miles in Nebraska, Colorado, New Mexico, Texas, and Oklahoma. During that time we consulted 347 relevant topographic maps. The geological features described by James were checked, and we collected many plants as near to the 1820 collection sites as possible. Only a few localities had been previously traced. These were to ascertain the type locality of a species under study: for example, a *Geranium* by Osterhout[20] or a *Quercus* by Tucker.[21]

We have accounted for all but a few of the approximately seven hundred plants. This involved trying to obtain the correct name and location and date of collection for each. With very few exceptions, the extant James collections are housed in the herbarium of the New York Botanical Garden.

[19]FULLER AND HAFEN.
[20]OSTERHOUT [2].
[21]TUCKER [1].

ACKNOWLEDGMENTS

Throughout the course of this study, many libraries and collections were consulted. For their generous supply of information and materials we gratefully acknowledge the American Philosophical Society ╪ Library; the Coe Collection of Yale University; the Colorado Historical Society; Mr. Ralph Ellenbogen, Assistant Librarian for Rare Books, Columbia University Library; Dr. David Hunt, Curator of Western American Art, Joslyn Art Museum, Omaha, Nebraska; Marcia M. Goodman, Librarian, History of Science Collections, and wife of author George Goodman, Roberta B. Kauskay, Librarian, and the Western History Collection, University of Oklahoma; the Paul Mellon Collection; Anne-Marie T. Schaaf, Manuscripts and Archives Librarian, Historical Society of Pennsylvania; and the Museum of Fine Arts, Boston.

We appreciate the information provided by Dr. Patricia Holmgren, Director of the Herbarium, New York Botanical Garden; Dr. Peter Raven, Director, Missouri Botanical Garden; the Academy of Natural Sciences, Philadelphia; and the British Museum, London.

We thank the Department of Botany and Microbiology, University of Oklahoma, for providing the office space and computer facilities, and Dr. Loren Hill, Director of the University of Oklahoma Biological Station, for generously providing equipment.

Generous donations to our research and travel expenses were made by the University of Oklahoma, the University of Oklahoma Foundation, Dr. Howard W. Larsh, Mrs. Lucille McAnally, and Mrs. Cleo Sliepcevich.

Dr. William A. Weber of the University of Colorado, Boulder, accompanied us for two days in different years on field trips in Colorado. His knowledge of the area added much to our field experiences. Steve Kemper, Superintendent, Fort Atkinson State Historical Park, Fort Calhoun, Nebraska, assisted us in exploring the area of Fort Atkinson and the Missouri River.

Our field explorations took us across much privately owned property. Certain Colorado landowners were particularly helpful in aiding us to find the landmarks we sought. They were Diana K. Braden, Sedalia; the Don Brazeal family, Box Ranch, Branson; and C. R. Troxler, Waterton.

For encouragement and valued advice we acknowledge the assistance of Dr. Savoie Lottinville, Director Emeritus, University of Oklahoma Press.

Dr. George L. Cross, President Emeritus, University of Oklahoma, through the years showed constant interest in and support of our research. For that we express our gratitude.

Lastly, we appreciate Cleo Cross, who encouraged the fieldwork that changed our account of the route of the expedition, and McKinley Lawson, who only once, at the age of two, discouraged his mother's fieldwork by demanding over the telephone, "Come home now!"

GEORGE J. GOODMAN
CHERYL A. LAWSON

Norman, Oklahoma

AUTHORS' PROCEDURES

BECAUSE OF THE GENERAL AVAILABILITY OF THE READEX MICROPRINT OF James's Philadelphia edition of the *Account* and Reuben Thwaites's *Early Western Travels,* volumes XIV–XVII (based on the London edition of the *Account*), our citations are primarily from those sources. They may vary slightly in wording and punctuation, but where the meaning remains unchanged both printings are footnoted for the quotation. Where important, the original Philadelphia and London editions have been cited.

Abbreviations: The standard abbreviations for herbaria have been used. They are as follows:

BM   British Museum
GH   Gray Herbarium, Harvard University
MO   Missouri Botanical Garden
NY   New York Botanical Garden
OKL   Bebb Herbarium, University of Oklahoma
PH   Academy of Natural Sciences, Philadelphia
RM   Rocky Mountain Herbarium, University of Wyoming

Bibliographic Note: Frequent references are made to John Torrey's article in volume II of the *Annals of the Lyceum of Natural History of New York.* The page following 180 of that article is numbered 191. This ten-page error continues to the end of Torrey's article (page 254). The error is corrected at the beginning of the next paper, which begins with page 245. Our citations follow the page numbers as printed in Torrey's article.

The numbers that Torrey gave the plants in this article are his and not those of the collectors. Torrey followed these numbers with his identifications and/or comments. He used a similar format in his articles in volume I of the *Annals of the Lyceum of Natural History of New York.* We have commented on all of Torrey's numbers with the exception of those that involved Baldwin's collections and those of James that were collected prior to reaching Engineer Cantonment or after leaving Fort Smith. We have commented similarly on the plants in Torrey's articles in volume I.

Compass Readings: When a second reading is given in parentheses, it is the reading corrected for magnetic declination.

Quotations: In quotations, any misspellings, English spellings, abbreviations, variations in punctuation, or other printing errors have been retained.

Sites: The sites in the text used to designate locations refer to present-day sites, rather than to sites then existent, because there were few of the latter excepting military posts. In the text the phrase "present-day" is silently omitted.

Sources: In the footnotes, we have indicated sources in capitals using the surname of the author, editor, or compiler. Additional information is given in Sources Cited. When more than one work by the same author, editor, or compiler is cited, the bracketed number following the surname corresponds to the bracketed number of that work in Sources Cited. Similarly, in the case of works by authors with the same surname, bracketed numbers are assigned.

Synonyms: Those that are not otherwise obvious have been accepted from the literature.

PART ONE
THE ITINERARY

CHAPTER ONE

NEBRASKA

ENGINEER CANTONMENT. IN LATE MAY, 1820, MAJOR LONG, WHO HAD spent the winter in the East, mostly in Washington, returned again to the winter encampment of the exploring expedition. With him were Captain Bell and Dr. James. The site for this encampment, called Engineer Cantonment, had been chosen the previous September by Major Long and other members of the scientific party.

According to James,[1] Engineer Cantonment "was on the west bank of the Missouri, about half a mile above Fort Lisa,[2] five miles below Council Bluff,[3] and three miles above the mouth of Boyer's[4] river."

The Missouri River in 1820 must have been close to the hills on the western bank (within a half mile), as Peale's sketch[5] of the *Western Engineer*[6] at Engineer Cantonment would indicate. Today the river holds a course nearly three miles to the east of the western hills. Situated now in what was once the riverbed are fields of corn, farms, and even recreational parks.

Further evidence for the position of the Missouri River in the early 1800s was shown by Karl Bodmer, a Swiss painter who accompanied Prince Maximilian von Wied-Neuwied up the Missouri in 1833. He

---

[1]JAMES [1], I, 146; JAMES [2] in THWAITES [1], XIV, 221.

[2]A trading post was established here by Manuel Lisa in 1812 on the west side of the Missouri River.

[3]The reference is to the bluff on the Nebraska side of the Missouri River. Atop this bluff Lewis and Clark held council with the Otoe and Missouri Indians in August 1804 (THWAITES [2], I, 97). The bluff is located just east of the town of Fort Calhoun, Washington County, Nebraska, in Section 12, T17N, R12E (CARLSON, 1).

[4]The original course of the Boyer River has been changed considerably. Through modern feats of engineering, the mouth of the river has been moved upstream five miles. The meandering river once entered the Missouri from the Iowa side about three-fourths of a mile south of the present-day boundary between Washington and Douglas counties, Nebraska.

[5]The original sketch is now a part of the collection of the American Philosophical Society, Philadelphia.

[6]*Western Engineer* was a stern-wheeler steamboat designed by Stephen Long that carried a portion of the exploring expedition from Pittsburgh to Engineer Cantonment. The long, four-month journey lasted from May to September, 1819.

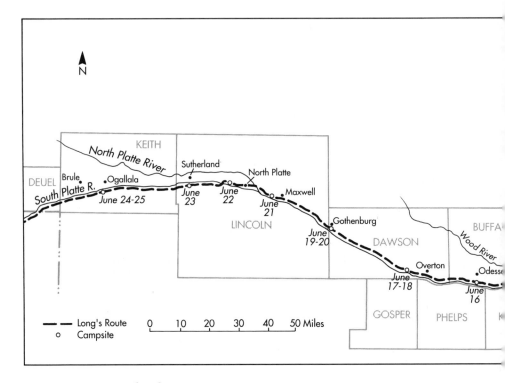

Route in Nebraska

painted Council Bluff with the ruins of Fort Atkinson[7] atop and the river in the foreground, close to the bluff.[8]

While almost nothing remains of the original fortification, Fort Atkinson, a Registered National Historic Landmark, is being reconstructed at the site. Since the locations of Council Bluff and Fort Atkinson are known with certainty, they served as fixed references in locating Engineer Cantonment.

As we viewed Council Bluff in June, 1985, from what would have been the bed of the Missouri River in 1820, we were struck with the

---

[7]A military fort established atop Council Bluff by the garrison from Cantonment Missouri following its inundation in early June, 1820. The flooded cantonment had been located three miles upstream from Council Bluff on the western side of the floodplain of the Missouri River. Fort Atkinson was itself abandoned in 1827.

[8]The original painting is now a part of the collection of the Joslyn Art Museum, Omaha, Nebraska.

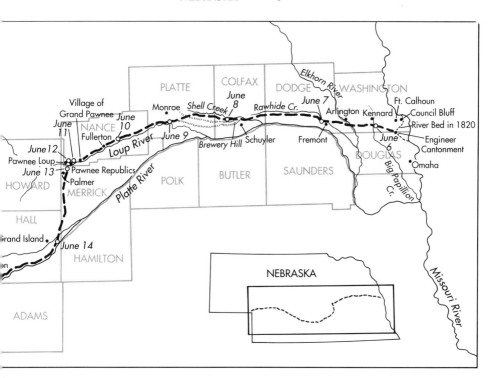

changes that have occurred: The barren bluff in Karl Bodmer's painting is covered by trees that make the outline of the bluff difficult to visualize. A county road now runs down a ravine and east across the old riverbed, which today is rich farmland.

Five miles downstream (now five miles southeast on a county road) from Council Bluff is the bluff beneath which we believe Engineer Cantonment was established. This bluff is in Section 28, T17N, R13E, Washington County. As we compared Peale's sketch at Engineer Cantonment with what we saw before us, the outline of the bluff was again camouflaged by the many trees that covered it. Peale's sketch was made in February, 1820, with the few trees in winter condition.

The remains of a limestone quarry are visible along the bluff less than half a mile southeast of the Cantonment site. These limestone cliffs were noted by James.[9]

[9]JAMES [1], I, 146; JAMES [2] in THWAITES [1], XIV, 222.

Engineer Cantonment was the point of departure for the more than three-month journey of the expedition. Knowing the location of the Cantonment was important in locating the campsites of the first week of travel westward.

June 6, 1820. The twenty-two members of the expedition left Engineer Cantonment at 10:00 A.M., according to both James[10] and Bell.[11]

The Indian trace that the men followed led to the Pawnee villages on the Loup River. In the *Account,* James indicated that the trace led "a little south of west from the cantonment,"[12] but Bell indicated the course direction as "N75°W" (N67°W).[13] Bell's direction, slightly north of west, agrees both with Long's map[14] and the general direction of the Pawnee villages on the Loup.

The expedition traveled "across a tract of high and barren prairie[15] for the first ten miles."[16]

The late start and insecure pack saddles resulted in the party's traveling but a short distance this first day. According to Bell,[17] the men traveled only nine miles before camping for the night on "Puppillion" Creek, a steep-banked creek containing very little water. Today, at the site of their camp near Kennard, Washington County, the banks of Big Papillion Creek[18] are nearly twenty-five feet high and are lined with many Old World introductions, such as fanweed (*Thlaspi arvense*), motherwort (*Leonurus cardiaca*), and hemp (*Cannabis*).

June 7. Leaving their camp on Big Papillion Creek at 6:00 A.M., the party reached the high bluffs above the Elkhorn River[19] in about eight miles. There, just south of Arlington, Washington County, they

[10]JAMES [3], June 6.

[11]FULLER AND HAFEN, 103.

[12]JAMES [1], I, 427; JAMES [2] in THWAITES [1], XV, 193.

[13]FULLER AND HAFEN, 106.

[14]JAMES [6], Map of the Country Drained by the Mississippi—Western Section, atlas; JAMES [7], I, Map of the Country Drained by the Mississippi, fold-in.

[15]Today these beautiful Nebraska hills roll gently with plowed fields of corn, oats, and beans.

[16]JAMES [1], I, 427; JAMES [2] in THWAITES [1], XV, 193.

[17]FULLER AND HAFEN, 106.

[18]This creek heads about three miles north of Orum, Washington County, and flows southeast to join the Missouri River in Sarpy County only a couple of miles north of the mouth of the Platte River.

[19]This river heads near Bassett, Rock County, in north-central Nebraska and flows east-south-east for most of its course before turning south at Washington County to enter the Platte River west of Gretna, Sarpy County.

had a view to the southwest of the sand bluffs on the southwest side of the Platte River, about eight miles distant.[20] From the bluffs on the Elkhorn the skyline lies some twenty-five miles to the west, across the plain that James described as "unvaried"[21] and "with scarce a tree or a shrub to been seen upon it."[22]

Continuing slightly north of west for nine more miles, the men halted for the night on a small creek, which would be Rawhide Creek.[23] The men were told by their guide that they would find no more wood for twenty miles from that point.[24]

Bell estimated the total distance traveled as sixteen miles,[25] which would place their camp on Rawhide Creek, just northwest of Fremont, Dodge County.

June 8. The line of horses and men formed the only prominence on the flat, desolate plain as the party proceeded nearly due west at 6:00 A.M. on a course four or five miles north of the Platte River. Given their line of travel, which would have been essentially along the south side of Rawhide Creek to near its head, they would have reached what James referred to[26] as "the valley of a small river, called La petite Coquille or Muscleshell Creek"[27] in about twenty-two miles (eighteen miles, according to James).[28]

The valley into which their course took them is the valley of Shell Creek, bounded on the south by a ridge[29] that separates this valley from that of the Platte. Traveling westward, they ascended this creek

---

[20]The rolling hills end abruptly at the bluffs along the east side of the Elkhorn River. From there the sand bluffs on the Platte River are no longer visible in the summer months, as the many trees, which mark the watercourses on the flat plain to the west, block the view.

[21]JAMES [1], I, 429; JAMES [2] in THWAITES [1], XV, 196.

[22]JAMES [1], I, 430; JAMES [2] in THWAITES [1], XV, 197.

[23]This creek heads about three miles north of Schuyler, Colfax County, and enters the Elkhorn River four miles north of Waterloo, Douglas County.

[24]Such would not be the case today, as the course of Rawhide Creek, through cultivated fields of corn, wheat, and beans, can be traced by the outline of the trees on its bank. Such trees as black willow (*Salix nigra*), soft maple (*Acer saccharinum*), cottonwood (*Populus*), mulberry (*Morus*), box elder (*Acer negundo*), American elm (*Ulmus americana*), and introduced Chinese elm (*Ulmus parvifolia*) now line its banks.

[25]FULLER AND HAFEN, 107.

[26]JAMES [1], I, 431; JAMES [2] in THWAITES [1], XV, 198.

[27]The creek here is Shell Creek, which they reached some three miles north of Schuyler, Colfax County. This creek enters the Platte River a few miles west of Rogers, Colfax County.

[28]JAMES [1], I, 431; JAMES [2] in THWAITES [1], XV, 198.

[29]The eastern end of this ridge is now referred to as Brewery Hill.

for six miles, according to the *Account*,[30] crossed its muddy, steep banks, and camped.[31]

Bell gave the distance traveled for the day as twenty-four miles.[32] We calculate it at twenty-eight miles, which places their camp on the south side of Shell Creek, six and a half miles northwest of Schuyler, Colfax County.

June 9. According to Bell, the party traveled from 8:00 A.M. to 1:30 P.M. before halting on the bank of Shell Creek.[33] To travel upstream on Shell Creek requires a course somewhat north of west, but both the *Account*[34] and Bell's *Journal*[35] indicate a southwest course. In reviewing the events that followed, during the day before the men reached the Loup River, we believe we can explain this apparent contradiction.

Both the *Account* and Bell's *Journal* indicate that the party crossed "Grape Creek"[36] before reaching their evening's campsite on the Loup River. James's diary indicates a campsite "near the confluence of willow creek and the Loup."[37] For the party to have crossed Looking Glass Creek before reaching the Loup, they must have been traveling southwest. The question is, Southwest from where? A course of S65°W (S74°W) from the campsite of June 8 for the twenty-one miles indicated by Bell[38] would have brought them to Looking Glass Creek and the Loup River, but it does not allow for their having halted on the bank of the "Coquille," or Shell Creek, at 1:30 P.M. Nor does it explain Bell's comment[39] that after halting on the creek bank they "took a course to the left, in order to cross a dividing ridge of the prairie, and to arrive on the Loup fork [of] the river Platte."

If the men did indeed travel up Shell Creek approximately sixteen miles between 8:00 A.M. and 1:30 P.M., however,[40] they then could

[30]JAMES [1], I, 431; JAMES [2] in THWAITES [1], XV, 198.

[31]The *Account* further states that their camp was six miles above where the Coquille (Shell Creek) enters the valley of the Platte. JAMES [1], I, 431; JAMES [2] in THWAITES [1], XV, 199. This junction, of course, is the same place as the lower end of the valley of Shell Creek, which is at Brewery Hill.

[32]FULLER AND HAFEN, 108.

[33]FULLER AND HAFEN, 109.

[34]JAMES [1], I, 432; JAMES [2] in THWAITES [1], XV, 199.

[35]FULLER AND HAFEN, 109.

[36]The creek in reference must be Looking Glass Creek, which at that time entered the Loup River about two miles east of Monroe, Platte County.

[37]JAMES [3], June 9.

[38]FULLER AND HAFEN, 109.

[39]FULLER AND HAFEN, 109.

[40]That would place them about two miles southeast of Platte Center, Platte County.

have taken a course to the left (southwest) over a slightly elevated ridge to cross Looking Glass Creek before reaching the Loup. Such a course would have required only an additional mile or two of travel, if any at all, over and above the twenty-one miles indicated by Bell. As will be seen later (entry for July 7), Bell makes it clear that the course distance and the actual distance traveled were not always the same.[41]

We place their campsite on the Loup River just west of the mouth of Looking Glass Creek, approximately two miles east of Monroe, Platte County.

June 10. Bell states that after seven miles of travel they crossed "Beaver river."[42] The distance to Beaver Creek, which now enters the Loup River near Genoa, Nance County, is given as six miles in the *Account*.[43] There the men halted until 3:00 P.M. "to secure our baggage from the rain."[44]

The next creek they crossed is called Council Creek on most modern-day maps. The *Account* gives the distance from Beaver Creek to Council Creek, which they called "Creek of Souls," as four miles.[45]

At sunset, according to the *Account*,[46] the men crossed a second creek[47] that was eleven miles from the village of the Grand Pawnee. There they camped, having traveled some twenty miles for the day.

We place their camp near Merchiston, Nance County, five miles east and a little north of Fullerton, Nance County.

June 11. A few miles from their last campsite the party crossed Willow Creek,[48] according to Bell,[49] and arrived at the village of the Grand Pawnee[50] about 11:00 A.M. That was the first of three Indian villages the party would visit within this portion of the Loup River valley. Here the valley is broad and bounded by low, rolling hills to the north. The village was located, as we calculate it, about seven miles

[41]FULLER AND HAFEN, 148.

[42]FULLER AND HAFEN, 109.

[43]JAMES [1], I, 434; JAMES [2] in THWAITES [1], XV, 201.

[44]FULLER AND HAFEN, 109.

[45]JAMES [1], I, 435; JAMES [2] in THWAITES [1], XV, 203.

[46]JAMES [1], I, 435; JAMES [2] in THWAITES [1], XV, 203.

[47]This is surely the creek presently known as Plum Creek, which enters the Loup River near Merchiston, Nance County. The names Plum and Council have been interchanged; today, however, traveling west on Nebraska State Highway 22, one encounters Council Creek first.

[48]This is Cedar River, which enters the Loup River a short distance downstream from Fullerton, Nance County.

[49]FULLER AND HAFEN, 111.

[50]This tribe of Pawnee is also known as the Chaui. HODGE, 216.

southwest of Fullerton, or nearly two miles east of Horse Creek on the north side of the Loup River, Nance County.[51]

Lieutenant William H. Swift, the assistant topographer and commanding guard on the expedition, and Captain Bell continued west for nearly two miles with all but eight of the men and set up camp on the bank of a rivulet we believe to have been Horse Creek. From there they had a view of the village of the Grand Pawnee, where Major Long and the seven others had remained in an unsuccessful attempt to visit Chief Long-hair.

Major Long and the men who had remained with him arrived at Horse Creek between 3:00 and 4:00 P.M., and within the hour Chief Long-hair and two other chiefs approached the campsite. After the pipe of friendship was smoked, Major Long explained the objectives of the expedition, the intended route, and the desire to meet the Indians in friendship. Having assured Major Long that friendship would be offered by his war parties, Chief Long-hair and the others returned to their village bearing as presents twists of tobacco and a biscuit.[52] Major Long thus conciliated "the Indians by kindness and presents,"[53] as he had been ordered.

Long's camp on Horse Creek would have been nine miles southwest of Fullerton, Nance County. The total distance traveled for the day was nearly thirteen miles.

June 12. The party proceeded west at 6:00 A.M. In about three miles, according to the *Account,*[54] they reached the village of the Pawnee Republics[55] about 8:00 A.M. This village was about four to five miles from the village of the Grand Pawnee and was located near the margin of the river. The site, according to Bell, was neither so attractive nor so elevated as that of the Grand Pawnee.[56]

We believe that this village was only three miles to the west of Horse Creek.[57] Here there are no steep bluffs along the river, and the land slopes gently for more than a mile to the river's edge.

[51]The location of the Grand Pawnee has been given as "9 miles southwest of Fullerton, on the north bank of the Loup immediately below the mouth of Horse Creek." WEDEL, 37.

[52]FULLER AND HAFEN, 114.

[53]JAMES [1], I, Preliminary Notice, 4; JAMES [2] in THWAITES [1], XIV, 38.

[54]JAMES [1], I, 440; JAMES [2] in THWAITES [1], XV, 209.

[55]This tribe of Pawnee is also known as the Kitkehahki. HODGE, 216.

[56]FULLER AND HAFEN, 116.

[57]The Republican village has been placed just east of the mouth of Cottonwood Creek (see WEDEL, 37). That, however, would locate the second village six miles from where Wedel placed the village of the Grand Pawnee.

The men remained at the village of the Pawnee Republics only a short time, as the chief, Fool-robe, was not prepared to receive them. After dispensing small quantities of tobacco to Fool-robe and a few others, Major Long and the party continued west at noon toward the Pawnee Loup village.[58] That village was located on a high bluff above the river, about four miles, according to Bell,[59] from the Pawnee Republics.

The party camped about a half mile east of the village "on the margin of the high bluff above the confluence of a creek with the river & on a plain with the Village."[60] We believe that Long's campsite was in Nance County on the western bluff above the original confluence of Cottonwood Creek[61] with the Loup River, some four miles north and a mile east of Palmer, Merrick County. The bluff rises some thirty to forty feet above the river.

Wedel gave the probable site of the Skidi village (Pawnee Loup village) as "four miles north and slightly more than a mile west of the town of Palmer, on the north side of the Loup."[62] That location is just over the Howard County line, some two miles farther west than the Nance County location we have calculated.

There is no doubt that Wedel reported a village site that was inhabited during the time that Europeans had contact with it. It should be recalled, however, that in locating the villages as they were in 1820, Wedel had not had the opportunity to read the information in Captain Bell's *Journal,* a journal that at the time Wedel was doing his work had not yet been discovered.

June 13. By midmorning the expedition began crossing the Loup. Because of the sandy bottom, they had considerable difficulty and much of their equipment got wet. Soon after reaching the south side they made camp to allow their equipment to dry and, according to Bell, to await the interpreters, Bijeau and Ledoux, from the Loup village.[63]

We place this camp near the Nance/Merrick county line, three miles north and a half mile east of Palmer.

June 14. With the arrival of the interpreters, the party headed south for the Platte River. The entire day's travel was across flat to

---

[58]This tribe of Pawnee is also known as the Skidi, or Wolf, Pawnee. HODGE, 216.

[59]FULLER AND HAFEN, 117.

[60]FULLER AND HAFEN, 117.

[61]We are told by the current landowners that the mouth of Cottonwood Creek has been moved about 0.2 mile downstream to protect the cornfields above from erosion.

[62]WEDEL, 26.

[63]FULLER AND HAFEN, 123.

slightly rolling countryside. According to Bell,[64] the course for the first fifteen miles was S15°E (S5°E). Having crossed a small stream,[65] the men halted until shortly after 2:00 P.M. to let their horses feed.

The afternoon's course was south (S10°W) for ten miles, which brought them near evening to the Platte River. They would have crossed the Wood River a little more than an hour before reaching the Platte.[66] Curiously, no one mentioned crossing the Wood River this day. To have camped on the Platte without having crossed the Wood River would, of course, have meant meeting the Platte at or below the confluence of the two streams. To have done that would have required following a course twenty degrees east of south from their previous evening's camp, or fifty-five degrees east of south from their noon camp. Such a direction seems highly unlikely not only because it is in sharp disagreement with Bell, but also because it is inconsistent with their westward intent.

Following the courses given by Bell,[67] we calculate the distance traveled to have been twenty-six miles. Bell's estimate was twenty-five miles.[68]

We place their campsite on the Platte, four miles southeast of Grand Island and near the Hall/Merrick county line.

June 15. The map that accompanies the Philadelphia edition of the *Account* shows that the expedition crossed the Wood River on June 15;[69] however, the map in the London edition,[70] which appeared after the Philadelphia edition, shows that it was crossed on June 14. In this instance we believe the London edition to be accurate.

It is stated in the entry for June 15 in the *Account,*[71] "Soon after leaving our camp we crossed a small stream, tributary to the Platte, from the north. It is called Great Wood river." That is the only mention of this river. Neither Bell's *Journal* nor James's diary refers to it. We assume that James included this entry in the *Account* on the basis of notes by Long or Say, and that it was simply made on the

[64]FULLER AND HAFEN, 125.
[65]We take this to be Prairie Creek.
[66]The Wood River, which is slightly more than 100 miles long, originates north of Oconto, Custer County. It flows southeast to near Kearney, where it turns northeast, paralleling the Platte River before joining it in Hamilton County a few miles downstream from Grand Island.
[67]FULLER AND HAFEN, 125.
[68]FULLER AND HAFEN, 125.
[69]JAMES [6], Map of the Country Drained by the Mississippi—Western Section, atlas.
[70]JAMES [7], I, Map of the Country Drained by the Mississippi, fold-in.
[71]JAMES [1], I, 454; JAMES [2] in THWAITES [1], XV, 224.

wrong day. They surely could not have crossed the Wood River on the 15th; they would have had to cross it on the 14th, as explained. That Bell nowhere mentioned the Wood River is surprising, given his penchant for describing the land and the streams in detail.

Bell estimated a southwestern course for twenty-seven miles;[72] we believe, however, that the distance traveled on June 15 was more nearly thirty miles. That is because Bell's courses indicate that two days later they reached the point where the river turns northwest. During those ensuing two days they traveled so few hours that they had little opportunity to travel farther than Bell estimated. There is, too, the possibility that the party had traveled upriver the additional three miles before encamping on June 14.

On that day James described some "low and distant hills which bound the valley"[73] of the Platte on the north.[74] James's description was of the scene as viewed from their campsite at an abandoned Indian camp. There they used for firewood the Indians' poles and stakes, which, according to James, "had been brought from the islands."[75] According to Bell, there was "not a tree or a bush to be seen on this Side of the river, as far as the eye can reach."[76]

We place their campsite for this day on the Platte, about three and a half miles south of Gibbon, Buffalo County.

June 16. During the twenty-one-mile advance this day the party traveled nearly due west, "along the base of the prairie hills."[77] Some fourteen miles into their travel, these prairie hills were only a couple of miles north of the river.[78]

Some eighteen miles from the previous night's encampment, they halted to let the horses feed on the bank of the first of two creeks[79] mentioned this day by Bell.[80]

---

[72]FULLER AND HAFEN, 126.

[73]JAMES [1], I, 454; JAMES [2] in THWAITES [1], XV, 225.

[74]As we drove southwest up the north side of the Platte, we were puzzled by this description. There were no hills to be seen to the north; as we approached the June 15 campsite, however, low, distant hills appeared on the northern horizon some eight miles away.

[75]JAMES [1], I, 454; JAMES [2] in THWAITES [1], XV, 225.

[76]FULLER AND HAFEN, 126.

[77]FULLER AND HAFEN, 126.

[78]U.S. Highway 30, from Kearney west to Odessa, very closely approximates the expedition's route along these hills.

[79]The party would have been less than three miles west of Kearney in the area of Cottonmill Lake, a lake that derives its name from the Kearney cottonmill, which operated at this site from 1892 to 1901.

[80]FULLER AND HAFEN, 126.

In the *Account*,[81] mention is made of only one creek, which they crossed toward evening, "three miles beyond which we arrived at an old Indian camp, where we halted for the night." That creek was evidently Bell's second creek,[82] which he described as "a large creek or bayau."[83]

We place their camp on the river, two miles south of Odessa, Buffalo County.

June 17 and 18. Although no mention was made of crossing creeks, the party must surely have crossed Elm, Buffalo, and Spring creeks as they traveled nearly due west for twenty-one miles. In early afternoon they halted on the river at "an old Indian encampment, opposite an island,[84] on which was some wood."[85] There they remained on the Sunday that followed. Bell described the view to the north of their campsite as "extensive."[86] To the south he described "ranges of prairie hills,[87] seen a considerable distance along the course of the river."

We place their campsite near the point where the Platte valley turns northwestward, some six and a half miles west-southwest of Overton, Dawson County.

June 19 and 20. The morning of the 19th the party began a steady northwestern course which, according to Bell, they continued for twenty-eight and a half miles.[88] James gave the distance traveled as "about thirty miles."[89] They "arrived in the evening at a place where the hills on the north side close in, quite to the bed of the river."[90] The expedition traveled across these sandy hills for a short distance before descending into the river valley to camp.

We believe that the party camped slightly west of Gothenburg, Dawson County, just beyond the area where the Nebraska Sand Hills make their easternmost approach to the Platte River. Gothenburg is situated at the foot of those easternmost hills.

[81]JAMES [1], I, 455; JAMES [2] in THWAITES [1], XV, 226.

[82]FULLER AND HAFEN, 126.

[83]In this area Turkey Creek joins the North Channel of the Platte River, and it is likely the one referred to.

[84]This island is doubtless Jeffreys Island.

[85]JAMES [1], I, 457; JAMES [2] in THWAITES [1], XV, 228.

[86]FULLER AND HAFEN, 128.

[87]These hills begin to appear across the river, southwest of Overton.

[88]FULLER AND HAFEN, 129.

[89]JAMES [1], I, 460; JAMES [2] in THWAITES [1], XV, 231.

[90]JAMES [1], I, 460; JAMES [2] in THWAITES [1], XV, 231.

The provisions were exhausted, so the party remained encamped on June 20 while the hunters were sent out on what proved to be a successful hunt. This two-day campsite was at the place where the Pawnee Indians often crossed the Platte, but high water at the time thwarted Long's attempt to ford here. A few days later the party would cross both forks of the Platte to arrive at the south side of the South Platte River.

June 21. The drying of the meat from the previous day's hunt delayed the departure of the expedition until after 9:00 A.M. According to Bell, the men continued upriver for twenty-two miles without halting during the day.[91] James estimated the distance traveled as "about twenty-five miles."[92]

Their camp that night was approximately six miles upstream from Maxwell, Lincoln County.

June 22. According to Bell, the men reached the junction of the North and South Platte after traveling three miles from their previous night's camp.[93] From there they continued northwest, as Bell indicated, up the North Platte for three to four miles to the point where they crossed it. That is in agreement with James's diary, in which he stated that they traveled six miles from their camp and then crossed the North Platte.[94] It is in disagreement, however, with the *Account*,[95] in which it is stated that they traveled six miles from their encampment to the junction.

After crossing the North Platte, the party continued in a southwesterly direction for eight miles before arriving at the South Platte. Such a course direction would have been possible only if they had continued the few miles up the North Platte before crossing it, as Bell stated.

We place their camp for the night on the north side of the South Platte, six or seven miles west of the city of North Platte, Lincoln County. From that camp, they saw what they estimated to be ten thousand buffalo blackening the plain on the south side of the river,

[91]FULLER AND HAFEN, 130.
[92]JAMES [1], I, 463; JAMES [2] in THWAITES [1], XV, 234.
[93]FULLER AND HAFEN, 130.
[94]JAMES [3], June 22 (erroneously dated June 21).
[95]JAMES [1], I, 463; JAMES [2] in THWAITES [1], XV, 234.

for as far as the eye could see,[96] a spectacle by which James was "highly gratified."[97]

June 23. Not a single buffalo of the thousands seen the night before remained this morning as the men prepared to cross the South Platte. Rain delayed their departure until 11:00 A.M. when, according to Bell, they traveled two miles upriver before crossing to the south side.[98] Once across they continued for another nine miles upriver before camping at 3:15 P.M. The early stop was made at the recommendation of the guide, who informed them that the wood they encountered here for tent poles and stakes would not be available again for some time.

We place this camp on the South Platte, a mile or so southwest of Sutherland, Lincoln County.[99] The distance traveled was likely nearer thirteen miles, as the courses given by Bell apparently do not allow for the two miles they traveled upstream before crossing the river.

June 24 and 25. Leaving at 6:30 A.M., the party, keeping between the river and the undulating prairie to the south, continued nearly west for thirty miles, according to Bell[100] and James,[101] before camping. There they remained on the following day, Sunday, June 25.

We place their camp two miles upriver from Ogallala, Keith County, and reckon the distance at thirty-two miles.

June 26. Shortly after 5:00 A.M., the party again continued west along the river. Before noon they passed an inconsiderable range of hills that they noted extended for several miles north and south of the river.[102]

According to Bell, twenty-four miles were traversed before camping.[103] We believe that this camp was in Colorado, a little more than two miles upstream from the Nebraska/Colorado line, approximately two miles east of Julesburg, Sedgwick County. We think that the distance traveled was more nearly twenty-six miles.

---

[96]For other comments James made concerning the buffalo, see ROE.
[97]JAMES [1], I, 467; JAMES [2] in THWAITES [1], XV, 239.
[98]FULLER AND HAFEN, 132.
[99]Their course is approximated today by Interstate 80.
[100]FULLER AND HAFEN, 133.
[101]JAMES [3], June 25 (erroneously called "Sunday 24").
[102]Evidently, they were very near Brule or Big Springs.
[103]FULLER AND HAFEN, 135.

CHAPTER TWO

COLORADO

JUNE 27. CHOOSING A LESS FATIGUING ROUTE FOR THEIR HORSES, THE party began following the course of the river at 5:00 A.M. The sand bluffs they crossed were described as having the "appearance at a distance of the walls of an edifice in ruins," which Bell attributed to the activities of the buffalo looking for salt,[1] followed by the effects of wind and rain.[2]

The most helpful information given this day is to be found in Bell's comment,[3] "We observed on the opposite side of the river distant about 2 miles, two large mounds situated on a plain, completely insolated from any other high grounds—and also to discover at a great [distance] a chain of bluffs, which must mark the course of a branch coming in from the north."[4]

In northeastern Colorado along the South Platte, there are very few landmarks. It is to Bell's credit that the mounds were noted. Prior to reading Bell's comments, we had been inclined to agree with Thwaites that campsites in northeastern Colorado could only be approximated, given the paucity of landmarks and errors in longitude.[5]

We place their camp on the river, a little east of south of Crook, Logan County, thirty-two miles upriver from their June 26 campsite. Bell estimated the distance traveled, by their courses, as thirty miles,[6] and the same distance is given in the diary.[7]

According to Bell, their campsite for the night was "where is an

---

[1]FULLER AND HAFEN, 136.

[2]Perhaps these "walls of an edifice in ruins" have been completely eroded by now, as there is no trace of them on the sandhills west of Julesburg.

[3]FULLER AND HAFEN, 136.

[4]The mounds proved to be Twin Buttes, located on the north side of the river about four miles north-northeast of Crook, and the chain of bluffs doubtless refers to the breaks off Peetz Table that extend more than twenty miles to the west.

[5]THWAITES [1], XV, 251n.

[6]FULLER AND HAFEN, 136.

[7]JAMES [3], June 27.

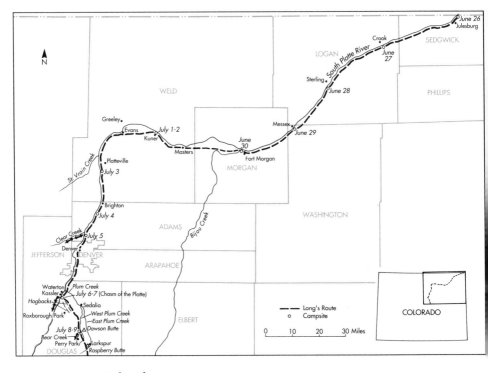

Route in Colorado

other of Indian fortified camp abandoned."[8] This war camp was depicted by Peale[9] and is reproduced by Murphy.[10]

June 28. Both Bell[11] and James[12] noted three creeks coming into the Platte from the north as the party passed upstream during their march, which began at 5 A.M.

Past historians have suggested Pawnee Creek, which enters the South Platte southwest of Sterling in Logan County, for the one called "Cherry Creek."[13] As indicated by James, however, this "con-

[8]FULLER AND HAFEN, 136.
[9]The original watercolor is now a part of the Peale Collection at the American Philosophical Society, Philadelphia.
[10]MURPHY, 525, fig. 5.
[11]FULLER AND HAFEN, 138.
[12]JAMES [1], I, 485; JAMES [2] in THWAITES [1], XV, 260.
[13]THWAITES [1], XV, 117n.; FULLER AND HAFEN, 138, 39n.

siderable branch of the Platte" was passed in the morning.[14] That implies that the creek should have been passed in the first eighteen miles of travel. As we measure it, Pawnee Creek would be some thirty miles from the campsite of June 27 near Twin Buttes, a most unlikely distance for a morning's travel and farther than the twenty-seven miles Bell stated they traveled the entire day.[15] We would suggest Cedar Creek, some eight miles downstream from Sterling, as the one referred to as Cherry Creek. They would have passed Cedar Creek after seventeen miles. Lewis Creek and Corral Creek, downstream from Cedar Creek and also in Logan County, may have been the other two creeks noted.

Their campsite for the night we estimate to have been a couple of miles upstream from Sterling, near the northeast end of Hadfield Island, Logan County.

June 29. With exhausted horses the party pushed on this morning before 5 A.M. According to Bell, they traveled twenty miles before camping "in the middle of the day . . . on a small isleand."[16] According to the *Account,* the party halted at 10 A.M.[17] Perhaps Bell's "middle of the day" is nearer right. Say's horse was so lame that Say dismounted and drove the animal ahead of him. Under such conditions it hardly seems possible to have traveled twenty miles in five hours.

Finding better feed for their horses than they had seen for some time, the party stopped and made camp, which we place a couple of miles south of Messex, Washington County.

June 30. At 8 A.M., after traveling for about three hours, the party at last gained a faint view of the Rocky Mountains.[18] Shortly before encamping late that afternoon, a sighting was made on what was believed to be Pike's "high peak,"[19] which was "distant about 60 miles."[20]

No southern tributaries of the South Platte between North Platte, Nebraska, and Denver are mentioned in the text by James or Bell, even

[14]JAMES [3], June 28.
[15]FULLER AND HAFEN, 138.
[16]FULLER AND HAFEN, 141.
[17]JAMES [1], I, 488; JAMES [2] in THWAITES [1], XV, 263.
[18]This long-anticipated event likely occurred in Morgan County, as the party approached the town of Brush.
[19]The peak, more than 100 miles away, bore S73°W (JAMES [2] in THWAITES [1], XV, 271) (S86°W), and became known as Long's Peak.
[20]FULLER AND HAFEN, 142.

though on this one day alone the party crossed Beaver and Badger creeks[21] before camping near Bijou Creek.[22] This last creek does appear on the map accompanying the *Account*.[23] It is the only tributary entering from the south that is shown along this stretch of the river and is labeled "Bijeaus Cr."

We believe that the party camped near the mouth of Bijou Creek, just west of Fort Morgan, Morgan County, after traveling, according to Bell, twenty-six miles.[24]

July 1 and 2. Near Bijou Creek, the South Platte narrows for about four miles on the eastern end of a fifteen-mile north loop. Both the narrowing of the river and its meandering were noted by Bell.[25] His compass courses indicate a line of travel south of west, across the plain, rather than northwest along the meander of the river.

Traveling sixteen and a half miles before stopping to rest, the party would have arrived again at the river at the western end of the north loop.[26] There, in stagnant pools near the river, a few aquatic plants were noted, their presence being in sharp contrast to the flora of the desolate plain over which they had traveled that morning.

James noted[27] in the *Account* some inconsiderable sandstone ridges[28] extending north and south from the river; they were seen as the party traveled even more westwardly in the afternoon.

The compass course of the final seven and a half miles of the twenty-seven miles traveled on July 1 was N83°W (N70°W), according to Bell.[29] This was their first northerly course for the day and indicates that they continued upriver along another north loop.[30]

We place their camp near Kuner, Weld County, nearly opposite the mouth of Crow Creek. From this camp, the compass reading on Long's Peak was S75°W.[31] This reading is puzzling inasmuch as they are now

[21]Both creeks enter the South Platte in Morgan County, the former to the west of the town of Hillrose and the latter to the west of the town of Brush.

[22]This creek heads in north-central El Paso County, near the divide between the Platte and Arkansas drainages, and flows northeast for over 100 miles before entering the South Platte west of Fort Morgan, Morgan County.

[23]JAMES [6], Map of the Country Drained by the Mississippi—Western Section, atlas; JAMES [7], I, Map of the Country Drained by the Mississippi, fold-in.

[24]FULLER AND HAFEN, 142.

[25]FULLER AND HAFEN, 143.

[26]This is just a few miles east of the town of Masters, Weld County.

[27]JAMES [1], I, 494; JAMES [2] in THWAITES [1], XV, 272.

[28]These ridges are doubtless those that begin just to the west of Dearfield, Weld County.

[29]FULLER AND HAFEN, 143.

[30]This north loop begins, as one follows upriver, some four miles downstream from Hardin.

[31]FULLER AND HAFEN, 143.

north of the location from which they took the reading of June 30. That would result in a reading that is less westwardly, not more so.

July 2 was a Sunday, and they stayed in camp. Seymour's drawing, entitled "Distant View of the Rocky Mountains" in the London edition of the *Account*,[32] was very likely drawn near this campsite. (See fig. 1.)

July 3. Thwaites commented that the route of the expedition this day was "difficult to follow."[33] With the aid of Bell's *Journal,* such is no longer the case. The first compass course given by Bell for the day was west (N76°W) for six miles,[34] which indicates that the party traveled across the plain rather than any farther northwest up the South Platte toward Greeley, Weld County. This westward course would have brought them again to the river just south of Evans, Weld County. From there they continued southwest up the river for the next sixteen miles,[35] which would have brought them near the mouth of Saint Vrain Creek and to the point where the valley of the South Platte turns south. As Bell indicated,[36] the direction of the party for the final six miles of this day's travel corresponds with this southern turn of the river valley.

Both James[37] and Bell[38] noted passing three creeks that entered the South Platte from the northwest. The first of these creeks would have been the Cache la Poudre River;[39] when just east of Greeley they could have seen the valley of the Poudre a couple of miles to the north. The second creek would have been the Big Thompson River, whose valley they would have seen after some eighteen miles of travel.[40] The

[32]JAMES [2] in THWAITES [1], XV, 269; JAMES [7], I, colored plate.

[33]THWAITES [1], XV, 274n.

[34]FULLER AND HAFEN, 144.

[35]FULLER AND HAFEN, 144.

[36]FULLER AND HAFEN, 144.

[37]JAMES [1], I, 495; JAMES [2] in THWAITES [1], XV, 274.

[38]FULLER AND HAFEN, 144.

[39]This river heads near Milner Pass on the Continental Divide within the boundaries of Rocky Mountain National Park. It flows northwestward from the park and then eastward through Fort Collins before entering the South Platte near Greeley, Weld County.

[40]This river also heads near Milner Pass, within the boundaries of Rocky Mountain National Park, and flows southeastward through the park to Estes Park and hence generally eastward through Loveland and Milliken before joining the South Platte in Weld County.

Fig. 1. *Distant View of the Rocky Mountains,* July 2, 1820. From an original sketch by Samuel Seymour. Courtesy Western History Collections, University of Oklahoma.

last would have been the Saint Vrain Creek,[41] which James[42] and Bell[43] called "Potera's creek" and "Potero's Creek" respectively.

James stated that the night's camp was "nearly opposite . . . Potera's creek."[44] We believe that they were about six miles upriver from the mouth of the Saint Vrain. That would place their camp about three miles south of Platteville in Weld County. From there one can look to the northwest, up the valley of the Saint Vrain. The creek turns sharply to the northeast about five miles west of the location where we place their camp and nearly parallels the South Platte for some six miles before entering it. James estimated the mountains to be about twenty miles distant;[45] the distance is more nearly forty miles.

July 4. The party traveled nearly south for seventeen miles up the South Platte and passed a large stream[46] and a rivulet[47] that entered the South Platte on the west, as indicated by Bell,[48] before stopping at midmorning on an island. The morning's ride would have brought them three or four miles south of Brighton, Adams County, near the north end of Henderson Island.

Major Long ordered corn and a gill (4 ounces) of whiskey to be issued to each man to celebrate American independence. Bell wrote of America's forty-fourth birthday:[49]

May the spirit of patriotism and love of country be perpetuated until time shall be no more. May it fire the heart of every American and may those who have adopted it in their country feel its warmth. We are, where, imagination only, has travelled before us—where civilization never existed—yet, we are within the limits of our country, separated hundreds of miles from the companions of our youth, who are commemorating the events of this day in fertive [festive] joy. Absolem, fate, to those who would destroy the tranquility of the United States of America.

[41]The most northern branch of this creek heads on the Continental Divide within Rocky Mountain National Park, just south of Long's Peak. This branch is joined by two others, which head on the Continental Divide south of the southern boundary of the park, near Lyons. From there the Saint Vrain flows eastward toward the plains through Longmont before heading northeast to join the South Platte in Weld County about five miles west of Gilcrest.
[42]JAMES [1], I, 496; JAMES [2] in THWAITES [1], XV, 274.
[43]FULLER AND HAFEN, 144.
[44]JAMES [1], I, 495–96; JAMES [2] in THWAITES [1], XV, 274.
[45]JAMES [1], I, 496; JAMES [2] in THWAITES [1], XV, 275.
[46]The large stream is likely Big Dry Creek, which enters the South Platte near Ft. Lupton, Weld County.
[47]The rivulet might well have been either Little Dry Creek or Todd Creek.
[48]FULLER AND HAFEN, 146.
[49]FULLER AND HAFEN, 144–45.

The early stop would have given Seymour time to sketch his drawing entitled "View of the Rocky Mountains on the Platte 50 Miles from their Base." This illustration (see fig. 2), published in the Philadelphia edition of the *Account*,[50] shows South Boulder Peak, Green Mountain, and the site of Boulder. The high peak in the far right of the drawing is Long's Peak. In the background is the Arapahoe Range.

July 5. The party traveled only ten miles before encamping a short distance upstream from the mouth of Cannon Ball Creek.[51] This creek, which was seen on the opposite side of the South Platte as they ascended the river in the early morning, is one of three mentioned by Bell.[52]

We believe the other two creeks mentioned occur in the gulches found along the west side of the South Platte between the camp of July 4 and that of July 5. One such is Brantner Gulch. Some believe that one of these creeks is Ralston Creek.[53] That, however, is a branch of Clear Creek and joins it near Inspiration Point, some eight miles to the west of the Platte.

In his diary, James commented that he and Peale "went out to examine the cannon-ball river which empties into the Platte a little below our encampment."[54] They were accompanied, as noted by James[55] and Bell,[56] by two other men on this excursion.

For what they perceived to be only a five-mile hike to the mountains, the four men took no provisions. After traveling about eight miles, they found that the mountains still appeared to be about the same distance away and that they could not be reached in one day.

Near some sandstone ledges Peale killed two curlews, which the men ate before returning across country to the main encampment on

---

[50]JAMES [1], I, with engravings following page 503; JAMES [6], atlas. In the "List of the Engravings," this drawing is cited as "View of the Rocky Mountains, on the Platte, 50 Miles from their Base—See Vol. I. Page 495." On page 495, under the date of July 2, is a description of the distant view of the mountains that does not fit this drawing. On the same day in the London edition of the *Account* (JAMES [2] in THWAITES [1], XV, 273; JAMES [7], II, 179), this same description occurs. The accompanying plate, "Distant View of the Rocky Mountains," (JAMES [2] in THWAITES [1], XV, 269; JAMES [7], I, colored plate) is different but much more closely fits the description. That is doubtless the one drawn by Seymour on July 2.

[51]The present name for this creek is Clear Creek, a stream that flows into the South Platte near Denver about two miles north of the Denver County line near Adams City, Adams County.

[52]FULLER AND HAFEN, 146.

[53]FULLER AND HAFEN, 146n.

[54]JAMES [3], July 5.

[55]JAMES [1], I, 500; JAMES [2] in THWAITES [1], XV, 279.

[56]FULLER AND HAFEN, 146.

Fig. 2. *View of the Rocky Mountains on the Platte 50 Miles from their Base*, July 4, 1820. From an original sketch by Samuel Seymour. Courtesy Western History Collections, University of Oklahoma.

the Platte. The sandstone ledges described at a distance of eight miles up Cannon Ball Creek (Clear Creek) are surely those of Inspiration Point.[57]

We explored this point, which rises about two hundred feet above Clear Creek, both for the plants noted by James and for sandstone outcrops; we found that only the rocks have withstood urbanization.

July 6. The place of encampment this day can be located closely, but there is much confusion concerning the creeks the party passed en route.

As noted by James, their camp for July 5 was located above the mouth of Cannon Ball Creek (Clear Creek).[58] Soon after departing the next morning (July 6) they "crossed Vermilion creek, a considerable tributary from the south."[59] We would agree with Thwaites[60] and Fuller and Hafen[61] that this is Cherry Creek.[62]

Sand Creek, which today forms a conspicuous junction with the South Platte only about a mile upstream from the mouth of Clear Creek, is apparently not mentioned by the expedition. It is possible that they crossed it before encamping on the night of July 5.

A stream from the northwest was said to be "[o]pposite the mouth of Vermilion creek"[63] (Cherry Creek) and was called "medicine-lodge creek" by James[64] and "Lodge creek" by Bell.[65] Fuller and Hafen believe that "medicine-lodge creek" or "Lodge creek" may again refer to Cannon Ball Creek (Clear Creek).[66] Since the party passed this creek on the day before and encamped above its mouth, we find it difficult to accept that statement. It seems almost certain that Fuller and Hafen based their statement on an ambiguous footnote of Thwaites's that reads, "Medicine Lodge Creek, Cannon Ball Creek, mentioned above, and Grand Camp and Grape creeks, referred to a few lines below, cannot be certainly identified. Streams

---

[57]Inspiration Point is located just east of the junctions of Colorado State Highway 121 and U.S. Highway 70 in a northwest suburb of Denver in Jefferson County.

[58]JAMES [3], July 6.

[59]JAMES [1], I, 502; JAMES [2] in THWAITES [1], XV, 281.

[60]THWAITES [1], XV, 279n.

[61]FULLER AND HAFEN, 148n.

[62]This creek heads on the plain east of Monument, El Paso County, and flows north and west to enter the South Platte at Denver. In Denver it is a canalled creek paralleled by Speer Boulevard.

[63]JAMES [1], I, 502; JAMES [2] in THWAITES [1], XV, 282.

[64]JAMES [1], I, 502; JAMES [2] in THWAITES [1], XV, 282.

[65]FULLER AND HAFEN, 148.

[66]FULLER AND HAFEN, 148.

most nearly answering the descriptions given are now called Clear, Bear, and Deer creeks."[67]

Having Cannon Ball Creek follow Medicine Lodge Creek in the footnote implies either that it was an alternative name for Medicine Lodge Creek or that Cannon Ball Creek is found farther upstream from Medicine Lodge Creek. Neither implication is tenable. The confusion is added to by the fact that Thwaites gave modern names to three of the creeks, leading the reader to think that two of the expedition's names were alternative ones for the same creek.

There is no creek opposite Cherry Creek; if the party had continued in a more nearly southerly course when the river, as they ascended it, turned toward the southwest, however, they would have crossed Cherry Creek about a mile above its mouth. At that point Lakewood Gulch would have appeared to be opposite Cherry Creek, and we suggest it as possibly being Medicine Lodge Creek.

As the party proceeded a few miles farther upstream, they observed on the opposite bank Grand Camp creek,[68] or Grand creek as it was called by Bell.[69] Fuller and Hafen believed, as do we, that this was Bear Creek.[70]

Two miles farther upstream they observed "the mouth of Grape creek."[71] The first creek entering from the west upstream from Bear Creek is four miles distant. Fuller and Hafen stated, "James' statement that the mouth of the stream was opposite that of Defile Creek (Plum) would identify it as Deer Creek of today."[72] Actually, according to James, Defile Creek was "a little above, on the opposite side" from the mouth of Grape Creek.[73] Defile Creek is surely present Plum Creek.[74]

Since Deer Creek joins the Platte above Plum Creek and is nine miles, rather than two miles, upstream from Bear Creek, its identity as the former Grape Creek seems dubious. We would suggest that Grape Creek is Dutch Creek, which flows from the west into the Platte just south of Littleton. It is downstream from Plum Creek, though its distance upstream from Bear Creek is four miles. That, at

[67]THWAITES [1], XV, 282n.
[68]JAMES [1], I, 502; JAMES [2] in THWAITES [1], XV, 282.
[69]FULLER AND HAFEN, 148.
[70]FULLER AND HAFEN, 148n.
[71]JAMES [1], I, 503; JAMES [2] in THWAITES [1], XV, 285.
[72]FULLER AND HAFEN, 148n.
[73]JAMES [1], I, 503; JAMES [2] in THWAITES [1], XV, 285.
[74]This creek meanders northwest from near Sedalia, where West and East Plum creeks join.

least, is closer to the distance of two miles they mentioned than is the nearly nine miles to Deer Creek.[75]

Why the party did not mention Deer Creek is still a concern. Perhaps Deer Creek was overlooked in their anticipation of reaching the chasm of the Platte, which was not more than two hours' ride away. The view the party had from where they crossed Plum Creek on the east side of the South Platte could well have been spectacular, and surely exciting to explorers eager to reach the mountains.[76]

According to Bell, the party traveled twenty-two miles (by their course they would have traveled nearly twenty-five) this day before encamping at the foot of the mountains through which the South Platte flows onto the plain.[77] Seymour's illustration, entitled "View of the Chasm through which the Platte Issues from the Rocky Mountains," was published in the *Account*.[78] It captures the view from near their campsite, which would have been a little south of Kassler and Waterton, across the river on the east side in Douglas County, some twenty-five to twenty-seven miles as we measure it from their camp of July 5 (see fig. 3). Our photograph (see fig. 4) is presented for comparison.[79]

The party reached their campsite near noon, which allowed time for exploring the area. James and Peale explored the hogbacks on the southeast side of the South Platte as well as the valley between the hogbacks and the foothills of the mountains.

Two inclined, parallel ridges of barren sandstone form the hogbacks in Seymour's illustration entitled "View Parallel to the Base of the Mountains at the Head of the Platte"(see fig. 5).[80] The hogbacks are now covered to the top in many places with oak and juniper (see fig. 6). The narrow valley between them and the foothills that James described as "a little more fertile than the plains along the river"[81] is now so much overgrazed that the "fine and short grasses" have been

[75]Today, both Deer Creek (which heads in the mountains to the west near Phillipsburg) and Plum Creek flow into Chatfield Lake, which was formed by damming the South Platte some four to five miles southwest of Littleton. We have explored this area and easily located both Deer and Plum creeks.

[76]As we stood at the mouth of Deer Creek (or as near as is now possible), we were struck by the magnificent view to the south and west of the mountains and the hogbacks that extend on both sides of the South Platte, parallel to the range.

[77]FULLER AND HAFEN, 148.

[78]JAMES [2] in THWAITES [1], XV, 283; JAMES [7], II, colored plate.

[79]This photograph was taken in June 1983.

[80]This illustration is now a part of the Coe Collection, Yale University, New Haven, Connecticut, and was reproduced by MCDERMOTT [1], plate 7.

[81]JAMES [1], II, 4; JAMES [2] in THWAITES [1], XV, 289.

replaced by invader species. In this valley James noted[82] the "numerous . . . columnar rocks, sometimes of a snowy whiteness, standing like pyramids and obelisks."[83]

Most of the afternoon of July 6 was spent along the hogbacks and among the rocks in the area of Roxborough Park.[84] Even today the area near the chasm of the Platte is exciting and fascinating, and it is little wonder that the afternoon passed into night before James and Peale had scarcely arrived at the foothills to begin their intended ascent of the mountains.

July 7. Some of the party remained at the camp so that others could explore the South Platte as far as possible into the mountains. James, in his diary, told little of this excursion except for the plants collected,[85] but in the *Account* he indicated their decision to travel on the north side of the river.[86] An attempt was subsequently made to wade across, but the river's depth and swiftness made that impossible. A man holding a rope in his teeth then swam across, and the rope was fastened to each bank. Holding onto the rope, James, Peale, and two riflemen (Nolan and Duncan) crossed the river and were on their way by sunrise.[87]

The traveling was slow and exhausting because of the difficult footing and the steepness of the terrain. The direction and distance that they traveled is to be gleaned from their comments: "They could distinguish two principal branches of the Platte, one coming from the northwest,[88] the other from the south."[89] They could see the river as it turned abruptly southeastward, but they were so far above it that it appeared the size of a brook. Nor could they hear it, although it was "white with foam and spray."[90] Peale traveled northeast about six miles when he returned to camp to get aid for

[82]JAMES [1], II, 2; JAMES [2] in THWAITES [1], XV, 287.

[83]These are the rocks that form the picturesque formations in an area now known as Roxborough Park and for several miles to the southeast. These rocks are primarily of sandstone, but the white ones James noted can be seen here and there. The rock formations are easily visible from the northwest end of the hogbacks on the south side of the South Platte. The view from atop the hogbacks is particularly scenic.

[84]The beauty of this area at the foot of the Rockies, with immense, red sandstone formations rising spectacularly (see JAMES [5], 199), was not lost on later arrivals. This beautiful place is now a residential area complete with golf course.

[85]JAMES [3], July 7 (under the erroneous date of July 8).

[86]JAMES [1], II, 5; JAMES [2] in THWAITES [1], XV, 290.

[87]JAMES [3], July 7 (under the erroneous date of July 8).

[88]This would be the North Fork of the South Platte.

[89]JAMES [1], II, 6; JAMES [2] in THWAITES [1], XV, 292.

[90]JAMES [1], II, 6; JAMES [2] in THWAITES [1], XV, 292.

Fig. 3. *View of the Chasm through which the Platte Issues from the Rocky Mountains*, July 6 or 7, 1820. From an original sketch by Samuel Seymour. Courtesy Western History Collections, University of Oklahoma.

Fig. 4. Same location as in figure 3, photographed June 1983. From authors' collection.

Fig. 5. *View Parallel to the Base of the Mountains at the Head of the Platte*, July 6 or 7, 1820. Samuel Seymour, watercolor. Courtesy Yale Collection of Western Americana, Beinecke Rare Book and Manuscript Library.

Fig. 6. Same location as in figure 5, photographed June 1983. From authors' collection.

the sicker of the two riflemen, who had presumably eaten too many wild currants.

The description of what they could see of the river and the distance traveled by Peale indicate that they hiked to the southeast side of Sheep Mountain to an elevation approaching 7,000 feet, a mile or so northeast of the junction of the two branches of the South Platte. Less than a mile downstream from that junction the river turns southeast as Platte Canyon becomes increasingly steeply walled.

Late that evening all the party were safely back in camp, presumably by holding onto the rope and recrossing the river. The men who had been sent out to aid the stricken riflemen had been unable to locate them; they returned to camp even later.

Although the highest elevation attained this day was less than 8,000 feet, James remarked that they were "nearly to the limit of phaenogamous vegetation."[91] That they thought that flowering plants occurred no higher than 8,000 to 9,000 feet is somewhat surprising, inasmuch as they must have realized that the upper timberline they had seen on the mountains for several days was at a far greater altitude than Sheep Mountain.

Our first attempt in 1981 to locate the point from which James and his men made their observations was via Deer Creek Canyon road to Phillipsburg and then south through Critchell. We eventually came to an unimproved road about one and a half miles northeast of Sheep Mountain. This road would have taken us to within a mile and a half of our destination on the mountain, but a padlocked gate blocked this southbound route.

We drove on east another mile and a half and came to a cabin owned by Mr. Kuestler, whose family had settled there years before. He told us that we would not have been able to see the river from the south end of the road on Sheep Mountain. (Later, studying the map, we decided that he was quite right, although we suspected that a hike of a mile and a half from that point to the top of another peak would have brought us to the brink of the canyon, from which point one could see the South Platte a short distance from where the North Fork joins it.)

After retracing our route a couple of miles, we noticed another road leading south. This led us to a mountain home, at 8,000 feet, about one and a half miles north of Sheep Mountain. The owners, Mr. and Mrs. Riley, were most cordial. From the south-facing deck of their home they aided us in identifying various landmarks. The view

[91]JAMES [1], II, 8; JAMES [2] in THWAITES [1], XV, 294.

was magnificent! To the south lay the valley of the North Fork of the South Platte, with the landmarks of Raleigh Peak and Chair Rocks on its south side. To the distant south was the faint outline of Pikes Peak, the peak on which James would make his historic climb one week hence. On the horizon toward the southeast lay Devils Head Mountain, at an elevation of 9,748 feet.

The Rileys offered to allow us to cross their property to reach our destination on Sheep Mountain, but by now it was too late in the day to make the trip. We knew we would need to return to this area again to see the view from the southeast side of Sheep Mountain and to search for the plants James recorded on that day.

Our second attempt to reach our destination on Sheep Mountain came in June of 1983. This time, however, we decided to follow down the northwest side of the South Platte from its junction with the North Fork and to climb from the riverbank up to the southeast side of the mountain.

The river was nearing flood stage, and although it diminished greatly in size as we climbed to a point nearly one thousand feet above the water, it never "appeared to be the size of a brook" or became inaudible. The river's abrupt turn to the southeast, however, and the valleys of the South Platte and the North Fork of the South Platte were clearly distinguishable. We could not see the actual junction of the rivers, and we feel certain it was not seen by James.

July 8. On the previous day, July 7, James lost his vasculum containing the day's plant collections,[92] including at least two plants that would be described as new species. He retrieved it early on the morning of July 8, and the party left camp at 7:00 A.M.

There are discrepancies concerning the exact route of this day's travel. In the *Account,* James, under the erroneous date of July 9, stated that they traveled southeastward along a stream that "lies from south to north along a narrow valley, bounded on each side by high cliffs of sandstone."[93] Such a route could well have been between the two hogbacks.

Bell, on the other hand, stated that the "party travelled along outside the range [that is, the hogbacks] and occasionally passed an opening made by the outlet of a rivulet from the mountain, where we had new and very interesting views of insolated masses of rock laying

[92]FULLER AND HAFEN, 153.
[93]JAMES [1], II, 10; JAMES [2] in THWAITES [1], XV, 298.

in the valley of singular colour and formation."[94] Bell's statement indicates a route to the east of the hogbacks where, through their openings, the rock formations of Roxborough Park are clearly visible. The course directions given by Bell are suited only to a route along the east side of the hogbacks. There the small streams of Little Willow and Willow Creek flow in a south-to-north direction as they descend through the hogbacks toward the South Platte.

The party, according to James, ascended "the small stream . . . to its source . . . [and] crossed an inconsiderable ridge which separates it from the valley of Defile Creek."[95]

Only three miles from the South Platte, Little Willow Creek turns southwestward (as one travels up it) through the hogbacks. Had the party left this creek and continued southeast for yet another two miles, they would have struck the head of the rivulets of Willow Creek just before crossing a ridge[96] over which Defile Creek drainage begins.[97] This ridge would have presented no obstacle before the descent to Defile Creek.[98]

Their last six miles or so they rode nearly south to near the junction of Bear Creek (called by James a "principal branch" of Defile Creek)[99] and West Plum Creek. That would place their camp at the west base of Dawson Butte, about ten miles south of Sedalia, Douglas County.

The distance traveled this day, according to Bell,[100] was fourteen and a half miles southeasterly, an estimate that is very close to the actual distance from their South Platte camp. Thwaites believed that this campsite was at the confluence of East and West Plum creeks near Sedalia.[101] He, of course, did not have the information on distance traveled or the course direction that later became available from Bell's *Journal*.

July 9. This day being Sunday, the party remained in camp and explored the surrounding areas. Major Long and one of his men

---

[94]FULLER AND HAFEN, 153.

[95]JAMES [1], II, 11; JAMES [2] in THWAITES [1], XV, 298–99.

[96]We were able to ascend this ridge about a half mile southeast of the Sundance Ranch (SE ¼ of SW ¼ Section 24, T7S, R69W).

[97]This is the present Plum Creek.

[98]This is the present West Plum Creek.

[99]JAMES [1], II, 11; JAMES [2] in THWAITES [1], XV, 299.

[100]FULLER AND HAFEN, 154.

[101]THWAITES [1], XV, 299n.

climbed an "ensolated natural mound"[102] that James referred to[103] as "one of those peculiar tabular hills."[104] The top of the butte was described as being "of an oval form, about eight hundred yards in length and five hundred in breadth"[105] and about a thousand feet high. The undulating summit was "terminated on all sides by perpendicular precipices"[106] about fifty feet high. Dawson Butte is the only butte in the valley of West Plum Creek that so well fits this description (see fig. 7).[107] In addition, the courses and distance given by Bell for July 8 place their camp at the west base of this butte.[108]

From the top of this butte, Long believed he saw Captain Pike's "High Peak," that is, Pikes Peak; he found it to be "S.50°W"[109] or "S.50.W."[110] It may have been a sighting error, as Pikes Peak, thirty-five miles away, is only about ten or twelve degrees west of south. It seems more likely, however, that the reading is a misprint for S5°W, which, when corrected for magnetic declination, would bring Long's reading very close to that for Pikes Peak.[111] Thwaites, convinced now that the description of the route in the *Account* for the next few days was "an impossible one," did not attempt to pinpoint the butte climbed by Major Long.[112] Since there is no butte where he placed them at Sedalia, that is understandable.

"Several of the party," continued James, "ascended Defile creek until they arrived at the mountains, into which they penetrated as far as was found practicable."[113] It remained for Bell to tell us that it was James, Peale, and Seymour who made this trip, ascending "some distance up a rivulet within the mountains."[114]

[102]FULLER AND HAFEN, 154.

[103]JAMES [1], II, 12.

[104]It might be noted here that the words "butte" and "mesa" were not used by the journalists of the expedition.

[105]JAMES [1], II, 12; JAMES [2] in THWAITES [1], XV, 301.

[106]JAMES [2] in THWAITES [1], XV, 301.

[107]The conspicuous bare stripes visible in our photograph of Dawson Butte are the result of torrential rains that flooded the area in June 1965. During this storm an estimated twelve inches of rain fell, washing ponderosa pines and scrub oaks from the butte's sides and leaving the four great gouges in their place. We learned of this storm from Diana Keene Braden, the present landowner.

[108]FULLER AND HAFEN, 154.

[109]JAMES [6], II, 12.

[110]JAMES [2] in THWAITES [1], XV, 301.

[111]The London edition of the *Account* (JAMES [7], II, 200) adds further to the confusion with this statement: "From the top of this hill, the high peak mentioned by Captain Pike, was discovered, and its bearing found to be S.50.E." The "E" is clearly an error for "W," an error which wittingly or unwittingly was corrected by Thwaites, who makes no comment about the correction.

[112]THWAITES [1], XV, 305n.

[113]JAMES [1], II, 12; JAMES [2] in THWAITES [1], XV, 301.

[114]FULLER AND HAFEN, 154.

Fig. 7. Dawson Butte, as seen in June 1983. From authors' collection.

"The little river," James stated, "pours down from the rugged side of the granitic mountain through a deep inaccessible chasm, forming a continued cascade of several hundred feet. From an elevation of one or two thousand feet on the side of the mountain, we were able to overlook a considerable extent of secondary region at its base. The surface appeared broken for several miles; and in many of the valleys we could discern columnar and pyramidal masses of sand-rock, sometimes entirely naked, and sometimes bearing little tufts of bushes about their summits."[115]

We followed West Plum Creek into the mountains in an attempt to discover once again the cascades and the view seen by James and his companions.[116] The road up West Plum Creek ends in a pasture owned by the Haystack Ranch,[117] named for the haystack-shaped sandstone rocks at the ranch house on the northwest side of the creek. Farther up West Plum Creek, again on its northwest side, there are groups of interesting sandstone rock formations. These rocks did not appear to be "three hundred feet above the common level of the plain," but some were "so steep as to preclude the possibility of ascent."[118] Sketches of rocks were preserved by Peale and Seymour.[119]

With the permission of two cordial ladies and two mean dogs at the ranch we followed the pasture road to its end, up West Plum Creek, and then hiked upstream a half mile or so. We found cascades, but they did not seem so impressive as the ones James had described.

We were not completely satisified that this was the stream that James had followed, particularly since the geology of the area was not as he had described it. Clearly, we would need to see the drawings made by Peale and Seymour. It was now beginning to appear increasingly probable to us that the three had followed a rivulet into the mountains, as Bell had stated. We decided to go up Bear Creek, since this stream joins West Plum Creek in the valley to the west of Dawson Butte very near, we believe, to the site of their camp.

About three miles south from the junction is Perry Park Ranch. Bear Creek tumbles down a steep chasm and right into the park. Here were some of the most spectacular rock formations we had seen. The height of some of them and the geology agreed with James's description.

---

[115]JAMES [2] in THWAITES [1], XV, 302.
[116]We made this trip early in July, 1981.
[117]This ranch is indicated on topographic maps as Perry Park South Ranch.
[118]JAMES [1], II, 13; JAMES [2] in THWAITES [1], XV, 302.
[119]JAMES [2] in THWAITES [1], XV, 302.

An illustration by Seymour[120] reproduced by McDermott[121] unquestionably depicts the huge red sandstone rock that stands just a few hundred yards west of Bear Creek in Perry Park. The illustration is entitled "View Near the Base of the Rocky Mountains" (see fig. 8). The same landscape as it appears today is shown in fig. 9. Unfortunately, the drawings made by Peale this day have not been found.

An Indian legend of this area tells of a great chief turned to stone. Near him "sings the voice of his beloved Wahuneep in the falls of Muaga Canyon where she becomes a fountain of tears at the sight of her silent and stony lover."[122] The falls of Muaga Canyon, or Bear Canyon, which was later referred to as Wahuneep's Falls, is surely the one that James described as "one of the most beautiful cataracts imaginable."[123] Little more than a half century later, William Henry Jackson photographed this same falls in Perry Park.[124] Clearly it was Bear Creek that James, Peale, and Seymour followed into the mountains on that adventure-filled Sunday, and many of the beautiful rocks James described are those in Perry Park.

Perry Park would be hard to believe, could James and his friends see it today. It is still beautiful, very beautiful, but now there are also many homes, the quarter-mile-long Lake Wauconda (formed by damming Bear Creek in the early 1890s),[125] and a golf course lying at the foot of the spectacular red columnar rock shown in Seymour's illustration.[126]

In his illustration entitled "Cliffs of Red Sandstone near the Rocky Mountains" (see fig. 10),[127] Seymour drew what we believe could be the cliff shown in fig. 11. The foothills are now covered with trees and shrubs, and the red sandstone cliff is itself partially camouflaged by vegetation.

With the aid of binoculars, it is still possible to see, through the trees, the white rocks on the barren foothill shown in Seymour's

[120]The original is now part of the Coe Collection, Yale University, New Haven, Connecticut.
[121]MCDERMOTT [1], plate 6.
[122]WEBB, 5.
[123]JAMES [3], July 9 (erroneously dated July 10).
[124]The photograph is now a part of this noted photographer's collection at the Colorado Historical Society, Denver.
[125]WEBB, 30.
[126]Washington Monument was the name given this rock by the Perry family, but it is now known as Sentinel Rock (WEBB, 27). The former name perhaps was given the rock because of its resemblance to the Washington Monument of that time, a flat-topped, unfinished structure 150 feet high.
[127]This illustration is also part of the Coe Collection, Yale University, and was reproduced by MCDERMOTT [1], plate 8.

illustration. Note that the tip of the cliff seen in Seymour's illustration is missing in our picture. It has apparently broken off, as evidenced by a scar that is of a much deeper red than the face of the cliff. The debris lies at the foot of the cliff, located just south (upstream) on Bear Creek from the site illustrated in fig. 8. In all our searching, we found no other cliff that so closely approximates the one shown by Seymour.

Two years later we returned to this area to climb Dawson Butte.[128] The sound created as our feet crossed loose shale near the top of the butte recalled Long's description of "a clinking noise under the feet like fragments of pottery."[129] Once on top we made readings on the visible peaks and were well rewarded with a magnificient view of the country below us. Pikes Peak was snowcapped and clearly visible about twelve degrees west of south. The summit of the Greenhorn Mountains could be seen some five degrees west of south.

The plains visible to the south and east were dotted with buttes and mesas, some of which would become the subjects for Seymour's paintings. In that direction, Major Long could easily have made reconnaissance for his course the next day. Below us to the southwest the course of Bear Creek could be followed from the mountains to its junction with West Plum Creek, also easily traced from the mountains and northward toward Sedalia.

Devils Head Mountain and the faint outline of snowcapped Mount Evans appeared as we scanned the horizon more to the west.

July 10. "Resumed our march," wrote Bell, "at 10 minutes past 5 oclock A.M."[130] The party stayed close to the foot of the mountains and must have left West Plum Creek very near the Haystack Ranch. They passed many buttes, and James remarked again in his diary, "Among the most prominent features of the country through which we are now passing one of the most peculiar is formed by certain elevated tabular hills with perpendicular sides and level summits."[131]

One such "tabular hill," or butte, was drawn by Seymour about four or five miles southeast from where the party left West Plum Creek. The drawing is of Raspberry Butte, which rises some nine hundred feet above the surrounding plain a mile or so southwest of Larkspur, Douglas County. Seymour entitled his illustration "Hills of

---

[128]This visit was in June, 1983.
[129]JAMES [1], II, 12; JAMES [2] in THWAITES [1], XV, 301.
[130]FULLER AND HAFEN, 159.
[131]JAMES [3], July 10 (under the erroneous date of July 11).

Fig. 8. *View Near the Base of the Rocky Mountains*, July 9, 1820. Samuel Seymour, watercolor. Courtesy Yale Collection of Western Americana, Beinecke Rare Book and Manuscript Library.

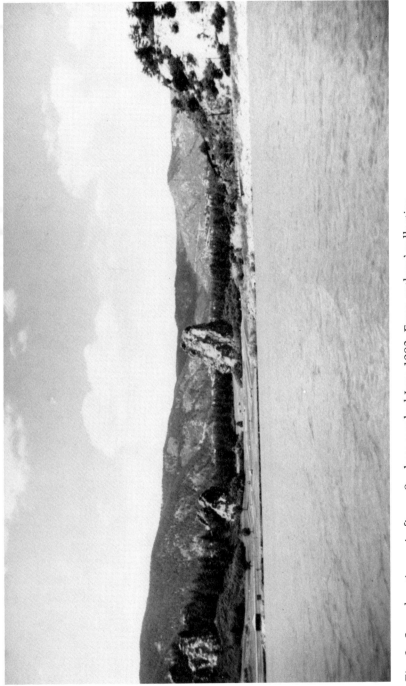

Fig. 9. Same location as in figure 8, photographed June 1983. From authors' collection.

Fig. 10. *Cliffs of Red Sandstone near the Rocky Mountains*, July 9, 1820. Samuel Seymour, watercolor. Courtesy Yale Collection of Western Americana, Beinecke Rare Book and Manuscript Library.

Fig. 11. Same location as in figure 10, photographed June 1983. From authors' collection.

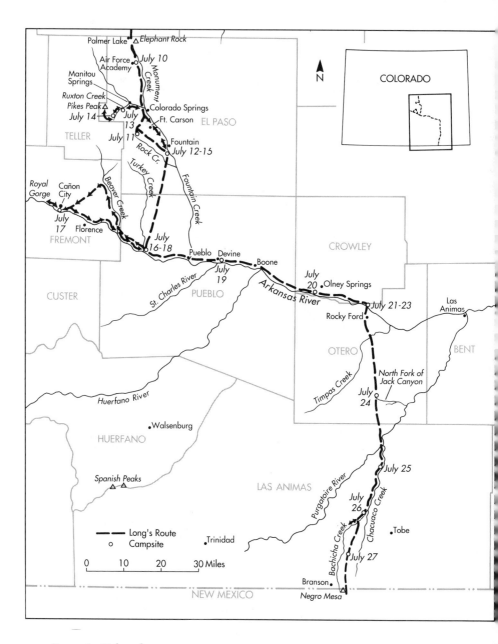

Route in Colorado

the Trap Formation."[132] (See fig. 12 and our comparative photograph, fig. 13.)[133] The stream in the foreground is that of East Plum Creek, which flows through Larkspur and northwest until it joins West Plum Creek at Sedalia.

To the east and southeast of Raspberry Butte is a striking chain of buttes that once again caught the artistic eye of Seymour. His illustration (see fig. 14) was published in the Philadelphia edition of the *Account*[134] and was entitled "View of the Insulated Table Lands at the Foot of the Rocky Mountains."[135] The butte at the left is Larkspur Butte, followed to the southeast by Corner Mountain and Nemrick Butte. (See our comparative photograph, fig. 15.)[136] Highway 85/87 passes north to Larkspur and southward toward Palmer Lake along the western side of this interesting chain of buttes.

At about 8 A.M., having traveled about ten and a half to twelve miles (eleven and a half by Bell's courses),[137] they crossed the last rivulet issuing from the mountains and flowing north to the Platte.[138] An hour later they reached Palmer Lake and made the observation that the lake, when full, drained both north to the Platte and south to the Arkansas River.[139]

In his diary, James stated that the distance from their camp "to the sources of waters discharging into the Arksansaw is about 6 or 8 miles."[140] We cannot account for this statement, as in six or eight miles they would still have been on the Plum Creek drainage. Bell, according to his compass courses, estimated this distance as fourteen miles,[141] which is about right.

Following down the south drainage of Palmer Lake, in less than two miles they came upon a large, distinctively sculptured rock that they named Castle Rock and that Seymour illustrated.[142] Seymour's illustration, entitled "View of the Castle Rock, on a Branch of the

[132]His illustration is also a part of the Coe Collection, Yale University, and was reproduced in MCDERMOTT [1], plate 9.

[133]The photograph was taken in June 1983.

[134]JAMES [1], II, following the index; JAMES [6], atlas.

[135]In the "List of the Engravings" in this edition, the illustration is listed as "View of the Insulated Table Lands at the Base of the Rocky Mountains."

[136]The photograph was taken in June 1983.

[137]FULLER AND HAFEN, 161.

[138]This would be Cook Creek, three miles north of Palmer Lake.

[139]This lake is located at the eastern edge of the town bearing the same name and is about three miles northwest of Monument, El Paso County.

[140]JAMES [3], July 10 (under the erroneous date of July 11).

[141]FULLER AND HAFEN, 161.

[142]This is Elephant Rock, which rises some 400 feet above the surrounding plain and is easily visible from State Highway 105 between Palmer Lake and Monument, El Paso County.

Fig. 12. *Hills of the Trap Formation*, July 10, 1820. Samuel Seymour, watercolor. Courtesy Yale Collection of Western Americana, Beinecke Rare Book and Manuscript Library.

Fig. 13. Same location as in figure 12, photographed June 1983. From authors' collection.

Fig. 14. *View of the Insulated Table Lands at the Foot of the Rocky Mountains*, July 10, 1820. From an original sketch by Samuel Seymour. Courtesy Western History Collections, University of Oklahoma.

Fig. 15. Same location as in figure 14, photographed June 1983. From authors' collection.

Arkansa, at the Base of the Rocky Mountains" (see fig. 16), was published in the Philadelphia edition of the *Account*[143] and reproduced in Bell.[144] In Bell, the editors have included a copy of William Henry Jackson's photograph of this rock.[145] Jackson's photograph (likely taken in 1874) shows considerably more timber than is shown in Seymour's original sketch. Today, that increase in pine timber and scrub oak is very striking (see fig. 17).[146]

At Elephant Rock the party examined the flora, rested the horses, and dined before resuming their journey shortly after 2 P.M.

By pinpointing the location where Seymour painted these illustrations, we can determine their route from the chasm of the Platte to Elephant Rock; it no longer seems the "impossible one" that Thwaites thought.[147]

They named the creek they continued to follow southward Castle Rock Creek.[148] According to Bell, they traveled another three hours, or, according to his courses, six miles, and camped at 6 P.M. in sandy soil "almost surrounded by groves of pine trees."[149] In following the course of the creek they crossed it repeatedly. Their meandering course and the wind squalls and rain they encountered may account for the short distance they traveled that afternoon.

In both Bell[150] and James,[151] twenty miles is given as the distance traveled. That would put their camp in the Air Force Academy grounds, likely in T12S, R67W, Section 12, El Paso County.[152]

We asked permission at the Air Force Academy to drive along Monument Creek, as we wished to see if we could spot likely campsites. Permission was cordially granted, and we followed a series of dirt roads for some distance. For much of the way the stream lies between steeply cut banks ten feet or more high, but, even so, there are many suitable camping places. Ponderosa pine, mostly small, was abundant on the rolling land on either side of the stream.

Among the plants James collected this day was the columbine

[143]JAMES [1], II, following the index; JAMES [6], atlas.
[144]FULLER AND HAFEN, 157.
[145]FULLER AND HAFEN, 156.
[146]Photograph taken in June 1983.
[147]THWAITES [1], XV, 305n.
[148]Now known as Monument Creek, it flows southward along the foothills until it joins Fountain Creek at Colorado Springs.
[149]FULLER AND HAFEN, 160.
[150]FULLER AND HAFEN, 161.
[151]JAMES [3], July 10 (erroneously dated July 11).
[152]That is less than a mile southwest of the cloverleaf intersection of Interstate 25 and the entrance to the Academy, a few miles south of Monument, El Paso County.

(*Aquilegia coerulea*), which would become the state flower of Colorado.

July 11. The itinerary for this day proved to be perplexing, as it is entirely omitted in the diary. In the *Account,* James stated that in the afternoon they followed a bison path, "not in the direction of [their] proper course" (that is, to the west of it).[153] They followed a ravine into the mountains, near to the "romantic scenery" they had long seen from a distance. Toward sunset the guide realized that they had passed Pikes Peak, and so, with a plan to retrace their path the next day, they camped.

Bell's account is much more detailed but nevertheless not easy to follow: Starting out before 5 A.M., they followed down Monument Creek and halted to rest at 10 A.M.[154] A high, snowcapped mountain was in sight. That, as already pointed out by Fuller and Hafen,[155] was Pikes Peak.

At 1 P.M. they left the creek, keeping more to the west along the base of the mountains, which appeared to turn considerably westward. They crossed a number of deep ravines and "passed a valley which appeared to extend a great distance between the ranges of mountains."[156]

Continuing southward and along the base of the mountains, they "entered a valley which appeared to cut off a very considerable spur of the mountain" and followed a buffalo trail along a shelving rock into the valley.[157] "Following up the valley," Bell continued,[158] they "passed some beautiful views of perpendicular rocks on the side of the spur."[159] On ascending from the valley they were surprised not to see Pikes Peak, not realizing that their proximity to the base of Cheyenne Mountain caused it to be hidden from view. Soon they saw the Spanish Peaks and realized that they had gone too far south.[160]

---

[153]JAMES [1], II,17; JAMES [2] in THWAITES [1], XV, 308.

[154]FULLER AND HAFEN, 161.

[155]FULLER AND HAFEN, 161n.

[156]This was surely the Fountain Creek valley, in which Manitou Springs is located; they were traveling across the site of Colorado Springs.

[157]We take this to be Limekiln Valley, which skirts southwest along the foot of Cheyenne Mountain just west of Fort Carson.

[158]FULLER AND HAFEN, 161.

[159]The spur that Bell referred to we take to be the southeastern side of Cheyenne Mountain; today, North American Defense (NORAD) is located within this side of the mountain. Rugged, steep rocks are prominent, and, near the head of Limekiln Valley, these rocks overawe the observer who contemplates their ascent.

[160]These twin peaks, which rise to an elevation of over 13,500 feet about thirty miles northwest

Fig. 16. *View of the Castle Rock, on a Branch of the Arkansa, at the Base of the Rocky Mountains*, July 10, 1820. From an original sketch by Samuel Seymour. Courtesy Western History Collections, University of Oklahoma.

Fig. 17. Same location as in figure 16, photographed July 1981. From authors' collection.

At 6 P.M. they camped on a small stream. We presume the stream to have been Rock Creek or, more likely, a small branch of it.[161] This agrees well with Bell's compass courses and his estimated distance traveled—twenty-three miles.

We place their camp about three or four miles southwest of Fort Carson, El Paso County.

July 12. James stated that they retraced their route of the previous day until a small stream running to the northeast presented a course more nearly in the direction they wished to go.[162] There then follows an account of a perilous trip along a narrow ledge where "a single misstep of a horse, or the sliding of a fragment of stone in our narrow path, would have been sufficient to have precipitated us into the abyss."[163] There is no clue that they reached Fountain Creek, the implication being that they camped on the small eastbound branch of it. A few days later, however, James stated, "On the day after my return from the peak we moved our encampment on Boiling Springs Creek . . . to . . . the Arkansaw."[164] Bell, not having been to Manitou Springs, referred to Fountain Creek as "Castle Rock creek";[165] James, having been there, called it Boiling Springs Creek.

Bell's story is a bit different.[166] There is no mention of the hazardous ledge, of a creek leading to the northeast, or of a compass course in that direction. He stated that they left camp at 6 A.M. and retraced their steps out of the valley for about four miles. They then took a course twenty degrees south of east and traveled down a gentle slope until, at about eleven o'clock, they arrived at Fountain Creek and camped. Bell gave the mileage for the day as twelve and a half.[167] That, with the direction of travel, would place their camp a couple of miles south of the town of Fountain, El Paso County. The location agrees well with the distance (twenty to twenty-five miles) from their base camp to Manitou Springs subsequently estimated by Swift, and with the estimated distance to the Arkansas (twenty-eight miles) when the party reached it four days later.

---

of Trinidad, were pointed out by their guide.

[161]From the elevated ridge above the north side of Rock Creek, the Spanish Peaks and the valley of the Arkansas would have been visible.

[162]JAMES [1], II, 18; JAMES [2] in THWAITES [1], XV, 309.

[163]JAMES [2] in THWAITES [1], XV, 310.

[164]JAMES [3], July 19.

[165]FULLER AND HAFEN, 163.

[166]FULLER AND HAFEN, 163.

[167]FULLER AND HAFEN, 165.

Thwaites, utilizing James's *Account,* believed that the party "followed the general course of Cheyenne Creek,"[168] which does flow in
a northeasterly direction until it joins Fountain Creek at the southern
edge of Colorado Springs. Had the party done so, their camp would
have been less than seven miles from Manitou Springs rather than the
twenty to twenty-five miles they estimated. Also, Swift's compass
reading of N67°W (N54°W) on Pikes Peak[169] is very good for a camp
near the town of Fountain, but from Colorado Springs the peak is
nearly due west. From the camp on Fountain Creek they "had a
distinct view of the part of the mountains called by Captain Pike the
highest peak. It appeared about twenty miles distant, towards the
northwest."[170]

In the early afternoon, James observed a dark storm cloud advanc-
ing toward the peak; it "remained nearly stationary over that part of
the mountains, pouring down torrents of rain."[171] The scene was
captured by Seymour in an illustration entitled "View of James Peak
in the Rain" (see fig. 18), which was first identified as a Seymour[172]
painting by Trenton.[173] The rain washed immense quantities of
buffalo dung into the streams, and soon Fountain Creek was swollen
and tainted, although little rain had actually fallen at their campsite.
The flavor of dung in the water was so strong that little of the supper
could be eaten, even though the water from the creek had been boiled
before the meat was put into the kettles.

July 13. On this day James started for the peak. He was accompanied by four men, two to attend the horses at a camp near "Boiling
Springs" (Manitou Springs), and two to make the ascent with him.
Lieutenant Swift and a guide, Bijou, were also in the group as they left
the base camp on Fountain Creek early in the morning. Swift was to
make observations to aid in ascertaining the height of the peak.
Major Long and the rest of the party were to remain at the base camp
on Fountain Creek during the three days that James would be gone.

After establishing the horse camp in the valley of Fountain Creek,
some twenty to twenty-five miles from the base camp, they continued

---

[168]THWAITES [1], XV, 314n.
[169]JAMES [1], II, 36; JAMES [2] in THWAITES [1], XVI, 27.
[170]JAMES [2] in THWAITES [1], XV, 314.
[171]JAMES [1], II, 22; JAMES [2] in THWAITES [1], XV, 314.
[172]We believe that Seymour drew this painting from their Fountain Creek camp on the
afternoon of July 12. In front of and slightly to the right of the snowcapped "James Peak" is
Cheyenne Mountain.
[173]TRENTON AND HASSRICK, 346 n.23 and 348 n.61.

Fig. 18. *View of James Peak in the Rain*, July 12, 1820. Samuel Seymour, watercolor. M. and M. Karolik Collection. Courtesy Museum of Fine Arts, Boston.

up the valley a short distance to the springs. There they had lunch at about noon, and at 3 P.M. James and his two climbers, Verplank and Wilson, left Swift and the others and started their difficult climb. They traveled about two miles and then, remarked James, "[W]e laid down to rest for the night, having found few plants or anything else to reward us for our toils."[174]

Their camp this night would have been on Ruxton Creek between Minnehaha and Midway. Because of the steep sides of the ravine,[175] the men placed a pole on the ground between two trees; by laying their beds on the uphill side, they were thus prevented from rolling down into the creek during the night.

July 14. Lieutenant Swift, having completed his duties at Manitou Springs, returned with his guide to the base camp on Fountain Creek,[176] while at daylight James and his two men continued the climb. Hoping to reach the summit and get back to this campsite by dark, they first hung their blankets, spare clothing, and food in a tree. The route they took was up Ruxton Creek, which they understandably continued to refer to as Boilings Springs Creek because these two creeks join at Manitou Springs.

The route James took and that of the cog railway are almost the same. The railway leaves Ruxton Creek and ascends westward up Lion Creek. James and his men turned along the dividing ridge between Lion and Ruxton creeks, where, as James described, "a level tract of several acres" occurs.[177]

By about 2 P.M. they were so exhausted that, according to James,[178] they stopped to rest and eat on a stream about a mile above timberline.[179] Their goal was nearly attained, but they now realized that they could not get to the summit and return to their campsite by dark. Nevertheless, they decided to continue the climb.

Their historic ascent was completed by 4 P.M., and James and his men are recorded as the first people known to have climbed this peak. James was also the first botanist to collect the flora above timberline in Colorado. Major Long, a few days later, named the peak

---

[174]JAMES [3], July 13 (erroneously dated July 14).

[175]The steepness of the canyon sides is clearly seen as one goes up the cog railway.

[176]Swift estimated the distance to the springs as twenty-five miles; taking a more direct route on the return, he thought the distance to be twenty miles. FULLER AND HAFEN, 165.

[177]JAMES [1], II, 26; JAMES [2] in THWAITES [1], XVI, 15.

[178]JAMES [2] in THWAITES [1], XVI, 17.

[179]They were doubtless now near the head of Boehmer Creek and scarcely a mile from the summit.

for James, but popular usage resulted in the peak's becoming known as Pikes Peak.

James mentioned seeing from the summit the vast plains to the east and a lake to the south that drained into the stream they had followed from the springs.[180] The lake,[181] he said, lay between him and a lesser peak eight or ten miles to the south and timbered to the top.[182] Valleys that he saw to the northwest and and far north James correctly took to be that of the Arkansas and one that drains into the South Platte.

In less than an hour they started their descent, and they were down to timberline by sunset. Realizing that they had missed their way and overtaken by darkness, they were forced to spend the night by their campfire, cold and without food.

After our own trip on the cog railway we reflected upon the determination James exhibited in climbing this rugged peak and upon our regret that the peak does not still bear his name. If in such a reflective mood one is permitted to draw conclusions, one might determine that James has not received his just credit.

July 15. As soon as it was light enough to see, James and his two men continued their descent. Within about three hours they sighted a dense column of smoke ahead and soon found it was coming from their camp of the 13th, where their campfire had spread and burned their blankets, clothes, and most of their provisions. They made their breakfast from fragments of charred but not completely burned buffalo meat.

About noon they arrived at Manitou Springs and at the horse camp shortly thereafter. Here were provisions, including fresh venison, so at last they dined on ample food. Afterward they mounted their horses and continued down Fountain Creek to the base camp, where they arrived at 7 P.M.

While at the base camp on Fountain Creek, Major Long and Lieutenant Swift had made observations to ascertain the height of the peak. They established a baseline nearby and calculated the peak to be 8,507.5 feet above them. Long apparently assumed that their baseline was at the same elevation as their camp at the chasm of the Platte. In this he was correct, each being about 5,600 feet above sea

---

[180]JAMES [1], II, 30–31; JAMES [2] in THWAITES [1], XVI, 20.

[181]This would be Lake Moraine.

[182]This is the peak that James thought Pike had climbed. It is identified now as Cheyenne Mountain, but there is some debate whether Pike came this far north.

level. Long took these two elevations to be 3,000 feet, however, and, hence, the peak to be at 11,507.5 feet. He obtained the 3,000-foot estimate by assuming a 19-inch drop per mile down the Platte to the Missouri River, 16 inches per mile down the Missouri to the Mississippi, and 12 inches per mile down the Mississippi to the Gulf.[183] He does not tell what mileage he used for these three courses. The latter two calculations introduce much smaller errors than does the first — the 19-inches-per-mile drop down the Platte.

Allowing 600 miles (probably a bit much) from the chasm to the mouth of the Platte, a drop of 19 inches per mile would total a drop of 950 feet. The actual drop is 4,400 feet, or 7.3 feet per mile. (The Platte drops 15 feet per mile from the chasm to Denver.) The difference in the two calculations of the drop is roughly 3,400 feet. If this figure is added to the 3,000 feet that Long estimated as the elevation of his baseline, the resultant 6,400 feet is too much by 800 feet.

Where all this error lies we are not sure, but a foot per mile is clearly too much for the drop in the Mississippi from the mouth of the Missouri to the Gulf. The distance is around 1,000 miles, and the elevation at the mouth of the Missouri is about 420 feet — a drop of 5 inches per mile. That would cut the error in half, giving the baseline an elevation of 6,000 feet — not so very far from the 5,600 feet that we take it to be. If one adds the elevation of the baseline (5,600 feet) to Long's estimate of the height of the peak above it (8,500 feet), the sum, 14,100 feet, is very good. Clearly, the measurements made by Long and Swift by triangulation on the peak were accurate.

July 16. The reunited members of the party began their southward march toward the Arkansas River at 5 A.M.[184] They came upon the precipitous wall of the Arkansas valley, but by going back to the north a quarter of a mile on the plain, they found a ravine down which they made their way to the river, although not without difficulty. They camped there at 2 P.M. The distance traveled, by Bell's courses, was twenty-three miles.[185] It should be noted that even when corrected for magnetic declination, Bell's courses leave the party out on the plain some five miles short of the Arkansas River.

The direction, distance, and time of travel differ somewhat in the *Account*. There, James stated that the party traveled twenty-eight

[183]JAMES [1], II, xxxviii; JAMES [2] in THWAITES [1], XVII, 258.
[184]FULLER AND HAFEN, 168.
[185]FULLER AND HAFEN, 169.

miles in a southwestwardly direction for twelve hours without having once dismounted from their horses.[186] Twenty-eight miles in that direction would have brought them to the Arkansas River.

Based on information given by Bell[187] and James,[188] we believe that the party made its way down to the Arkansas River near the mouth of Turkey Creek.[189] From the plain, the valley of the Arkansas and the trees that lined it were hidden at this point by the steep, perpendicular precipices that rise abruptly some 120 feet or more above the level of the river. It is not surprising that the party found itself on the brink of the precipices with no prior warning. Here the steep walls of the valley with their masonry-like appearance were captured by Seymour (see fig. 19). His "View on the Arkansa near the Rocky Mountains" shows a steep wall on the river near Turkey Creek.[190] We were able to locate a portion of the wall on the Arkansas River, nearly opposite the mouth of Turkey Creek, characteristic of the one Seymour drew (see fig. 20).

July 17. After the very fatiguing trip of the previous day, James, Bell, Landeau (that is, LeDoux), and Parish set out to follow the Arkansas to the mountains.[191] Upon his return from this excursion up the Arkansas, James summarized in the diary entry for July 19 the events of July 16 and the two days following.[192] The details of the events of July 17 are scanty and give hardly a clue as to the route. It is clear, then, that the entries in the *Account* for July 17 and 18 were drawn from memory,[193] because Bell's *Journal* was not available to James. The details that are included in the *Account* are fewer and in a different (we think impossible) sequence than in Bell's *Journal*. We have relied, then, upon Bell for interpreting the route for these days.

Finding the Arkansas valley-bottom too heavily timbered and difficult, they went up to the north rim, where they met with deep ravines coming into the valley. To avoid these they chose a northwest course across the plains, where soon they discovered an easily

[186]JAMES [1], II, 39; JAMES [2] in THWAITES [1], XVI, 30.

[187]FULLER AND HAFEN, 168.

[188]JAMES [3], July 17, 18, and 19.

[189]This creek enters the Arkansas River from the north, thirteen to fourteen miles west of the mouth of Fountain Creek, which enters the Arkansas River at Pueblo, Colorado.

[190]His illustration is also a part of the Coe Collection, Yale University, and was reproduced in MCDERMOTT [1], plate 10.

[191]FULLER AND HAFEN, 169.

[192]JAMES [3], July 19.

[193]JAMES [1], II, 42–50; JAMES [2] in THWAITES [1], XVI, 32–42.

traveled Indian trace that they followed into the mountains, although it took them much more northerly than they wished to go. As the trace started to follow a creek that came through a valley from the northeast, the men turned southwest and made their way along a valley within the mountains. They stopped to rest at 3 P.M.

Beaver Creek flows out of the mountains through a northeastern valley in its descent to the Arkansas. At the mouth of this valley, there is another secluded valley within the mountains that from this point turns southwest to near where Eightmile Creek cuts through to the plains toward the Arkansas. It is through this valley that we believe the men traveled after leaving the Indian trace on Beaver Creek.[194] This mile-wide valley is covered mostly with grass, piñon pine, juniper, hop tree, and cactus.

About a mile west of Eightmile Creek begins the valley of Six Mile Park, which extends to the northwest and through which flows Six Mile Creek. In this valley is apparently where the men expected to find the Arkansas River. Bell stated that their intent was to direct their course "for a valley of the mountains, where it appeared most probable to us, the river had is [sic] course bearing from our camp N70°W."[195] Such a course, when corrected to N56°W, puts them very near to Six Mile Park. James had viewed the northwestern valley of the Arkansas from the top of Pikes Peak, so for the men to have headed northwest in search of the place where the Arkansas comes out of the mountains was logical.

As we stood on the plain above the mouth of Turkey Creek and viewed the mountain ranges to the northwest, it was exceedingly apparent why James and Bell chose this direction. The Royal Gorge area, some fourteen degrees more to the west, is not clearly the only valley, through which the Arkansas could escape the mountains.

After their afternoon rest on Six Mile Creek at the east end of the valley, they continued southwestward out of this valley and soon could see the Arkansas, still about eight miles away. According to Bell, they kept "close on our right the exterior range of the mountain, generally about 120 feet high."[196] The *Account* states that near the base of the mountain argillaceous sandstone occurs, resting in an inclined position against the primitive rocks.[197] This sandstone was

[194]Today upper Beaver Creek Road traverses this valley, crossing Eightmile Creek near the University of Oklahoma Summer Geology Camp.
[195]FULLER AND HAFEN, 169.
[196]FULLER AND HAFEN, 170.
[197]JAMES [1], II, 42–43; JAMES [2] in THWAITES [1], XVI, 33.

Fig. 19. *View on the Arkansa near the Rocky Mountains*, July 16 or 17, 1820. Samuel Seymour, watercolor. Courtesy Yale Collection of Western Americana, Beinecke Rare Book and Manuscript Library.

Fig. 20. Same location as in figure 19, photographed July 1981. From authors' collection.

said to resemble the mountains at the Platte, and to be separated from the mountains by a narrow, secluded valley. The references are apparently to the hogbacks near the chasm of the Platte and to similar rocks, along whose base they traveled, to the west of Six Mile Creek. The party covered the eight-mile distance and camped at the springs, which Long later named Bell's Springs.[198]

We made some inquires about these springs, since they are no longer visible at the western edge of Cañon City, Fremont County. Of the seven springs (thirty according to Bell),[199] we learned from a local historian in Cañon City of only two. These springs, soda and iron, were tourist attractions for years, but with the widening of U.S. Highway 50 and the necessary blasting off of rocks at the southwest corner of the grounds of the Colorado State Penitentiary, the springs were destroyed. Very close by is a historical marker telling of the location of Captain Pike's blockhouse, built in the winter of 1806–07.

The length of the route to Cañon City that we have suggested is within a mile or two of the thirty-four miles Bell gave as the distance traveled.[200]

July 18. In the early morning, the men continued about three-quarters of a mile up the river from the springs to the entrance of the canyon (Royal Gorge). They described the geology and the beauty of the country and commented on the seeming impossibility of ascending farther up the canyon.[201] James wrote in his diary, "In the excursion I found a few new plants which I have no time to examine."[202]

In the early morning they started eastward for the main camp, a long day's ride ahead. Downstream about seven and a half miles was a massive rock, which they described as being on the north side of the river and about one hundred feet high.[203] "James' Peak" they noted, was visible from here, lying due north.[204] This is the correct reading for Pikes Peak, before correcting for magnetic declination.

[198]JAMES [1], II, 43; JAMES [2] in THWAITES [1], XVI, 34.

[199]FULLER AND HAFEN, 171.

[200]FULLER AND HAFEN, 171.

[201]Even today as we viewed the area, its magnificence remains nearly pristine. The Denver and Rio Grande Railroad, which wends its way through the gorge, makes only a minuscule scar in the vastness of the surroundings.

[202]JAMES [3], July 19.

[203]It is with ease that we located this landmark about a mile northwest of Florence, Fremont County. On topographic maps of the area this huge rock is named Castle Rock. It rises at its highest point 280 feet above the river, however.

[204]JAMES [1], II, 45.

Thirteen miles from the springs, Bell noted[205] a stream entering from the south.[206] In another seven miles a stream came in from the north.[207]

After traveling thirty-two miles, Bell estimated, they arrived at the main camp at 7 P.M., "fatigued and hungry."[208] Twenty-eight and a half miles is the distance reported by Bell,[209] a distance that would have brought them back to very near Turkey Creek.

July 19. Beginning at 6 A.M., the party ascended to the plains on the north side of the Arkansas.[210] The compass readings given here for the Spanish Peaks (S15°E) and Pikes Peak (N30°W) lend further evidence that their camp was near Turkey Creek, as these readings, when corrected for magnetic declination, are very good.[211]

Eight or ten miles from their camp, James noted the disappearance of the perpendicular precipices along the river.[212] On the south side of the river this occurs at the western edge of Pueblo, in an area denoted as Goodnight on the topographic map, a little more than nine miles from Turkey Creek. On the north side, the precipices end within another mile downstream.

The emotions among the party as they turned eastward down the Arkansas were interestingly different. True to the feelings of a naturalist, James, as he turned his back on the mountains, stated, "It was not without a feeling of something like regret that we found our long contemplated visit to these grand and interesting objects, was now at an end."[213] From Bell, the artilleryman, came quite a different feeling: "The anticipation of again enjoying the benefits & pleasure of civilized society and the fond welcome of our friends, cheers our hearts & gives full scope to fancied imagination in anticipated pleasures perhaps never to be realized."[214]

Before noon the party had crossed two creeks. The first was likely Dry Creek, which enters the Arkansas three miles above Fountain

[205]FULLER AND HAFEN, 172.
[206]This would be Hardscrabble Creek.
[207]This must have been Beaver Creek, although it is but four miles from Hardscrabble Creek.
[208]FULLER AND HAFEN, 172–73.
[209]FULLER AND HAFEN, 173.
[210]FULLER AND HAFEN, 177.
[211]These snowcapped peaks, in addition to the Wet Mountains, the Greenhorn Mountains, the Sangre de Cristo Mountains, and Cheyenne Mountain, would have created a panoramic view for the expedition just as they did for us as we stood on the plains north of the mouth of Turkey Creek.
[212]JAMES [1], II, 51; JAMES [2] in THWAITES [1], XVI, 44.
[213]JAMES [1], II, 50; JAMES [2] in THWAITES [1], XVI, 43.
[214]FULLER AND HAFEN, 177.

Creek. The second was Fountain Creek, which they called Castle Rock Creek, which enters the Arkansas in Pueblo. In the afternoon they passed the mouth of the Saint Charles River, which enters the Arkansas from the south near the town of Devine. By 5 P.M. the party had camped.

We place this camp only a mile and a half or so southeast of Devine, Pueblo County. The mouth of the Saint Charles is only a mile upstream from there, and James commented that they camped nearly opposite it. The estimated distance traveled, twenty-five miles, is reasonable given the extra distance traveled in avoiding the ravines.

July 20. Soon after 5 A.M. they continued their way down the river. During the forenoon they noted the mouth of "Pike's 2nd. fork," (that is, the Huerfano River) coming in from the south. Both Bell[215] and James[216] described the natural mounds visible on the prairie. These are plainly seen from the river two or three miles east of Devine, Pueblo County, often less than a mile north of State Highway 96. They show up again six or eight miles west and east of Boone, Pueblo County.

Boone is about a mile north of the Arkansas River and nearly opposite the mouth of the Huerfano. We think that near the mounds east of Boone is where the party rested from 10 A.M. to 2 P.M.; James would have had time to examine the mounds closely, as is evidenced from his detailed description of them. After their rest they continued for another three hours and camped. They estimated the distance for the day at twenty-six miles.[217]

We place their camp for this day about two and a half miles southwest of Olney Springs, Crowley County.[218]

July 21. Again they started at 5 A.M. They shortly met the first Indians, a man and his wife, that they had seen since leaving the Pawnee villages on the Loup River in central Nebraska. The Indians were persuaded to accompany them a few miles to point out a suitable ford on the Arkansas River.

The ford was reached about 10 A.M. That places them almost without doubt at the original site of Rocky Ford, Otero County. The crossing site is shown on topographic maps; it is about three and a

[215]FULLER AND HAFEN, 179.
[216]JAMES [1], II, 59; JAMES [2] in THWAITES [1], XVI, 53–54.
[217]JAMES [1], II, 59; JAMES [2] in THWAITES [1], XVI, 54.
[218]The route the party took is closely approximated by that of State Highway 96.

half miles north and a little west of the town of Rocky Ford. The distance the party traveled this day was fourteen miles.

They would stay for three days (July 21–23), making astronomical observations and arranging the packs preparatory to dividing the party into two groups. One group, headed by Captain Bell, would continue down the Arkansas River. The other, led by Major Long, would go southward in search of the sources of the Red River.

July 24. Major Long, accompanied by James, Peale, and seven other men, forded the Arkansas River before 7 A.M. and began their southward march.[219] They were entering Spanish Territory, according to the Adams-Onis Treaty.[220] Until August 18 they would remain in Spanish domain.

The party traveled for twenty-seven miles slightly east of south and noted several paths leading toward the Spanish settlements.[221] They camped at the head of a dry ravine that joined the Purgatoire River eight or ten miles to the southeast. We take their camp to have been near the head of the North Fork of Jack Canyon, near an area known as Packers Gap in Otero County. Jack Canyon does join the Purgatoire eight miles to the southeast.

The rounded junipers, which James described in his diary on the next day as "small but beautifully shaped," are abundant here on the plain.[222] To the southeast the canyons leading toward the Purgatoire are conspicuous, and on the distant southern horizon Mesa de Maya can be seen.

July 25. Continuing southward, the party encountered the head of Minnie Canyon or Iron Canyon. Both lead southeastward to the steep-walled canyon of the Purgatoire, which they reached by midday after traveling nine or ten miles.[223] That distance agrees with James's remark that they arrived at this river after traveling thirty-six miles from where they had left the Arkansas.[224] Twenty-seven of those miles, James stated, were traveled the previous day.[225]

[219]JAMES [1], II, 63; JAMES [2] in THWAITES [1], XVI, 58.

[220]This treaty was signed in 1819 but was not ratified until 1821.

[221]These paths were likely the ones that only a few years later would become abundantly used by wagons on the Santa Fe Trail, a few miles northeast of the junction, near Timpas, of Colorado State Highway 71 and U.S. Highway 350.

[222]JAMES [3], July 25.

[223]We entered the valley of the Purgatoire on July 5, 1981, by following Iron Canyon down to its mouth, near which is the Roark Ranch. Heavy rains had fallen near Trinidad and the Purgatoire was in flood, just as James had found it.

[224]JAMES [1], II, 69; JAMES [2] in THWAITES [1], XVI, 66.

[225]JAMES [1], II, 68; JAMES [2] in THWAITES [1], XVI, 65.

Midday halt was made upon, or very soon after, reaching the Purgatoire. After the halt they continued up the stream. "A few miles above our mid-day encampment," James continued, "we entered the valley of a small creek, tributary from the south-east to the stream we had been ascending;[226] but this we found so narrow and so obstructed by fallen masses of rock, and almost impenetrable thickets of alders[227] and willows, as to render our progress extremely tedious and painful." They tried traveling along the bed of the stream, but the mud was so deep that they decided instead to attempt to climb out of the canyon. They "attained nearly the elevation of the precipitous ramparts"[228] but still could not get out. "Counselled therefore by necessity, we resumed our former course, ascending along the bed of the creek."[229] These difficulties indicate that they could not have traveled up the canyons very far before making camp.

Thwaites,[230] Chittenden,[231] and Tucker[232] all surmised that the branch the expedition followed was Chacuaco Creek (referred to as Chaquaqua Creek by Thwaites and Chittenden), and we feel certain that it was. Chacuaco Creek enters the Purgatoire about three miles above, or south, of the mouth of Iron Canyon.

According to the *Account*[233] they traveled fifteen miles. The distance is not mentioned in the diary. They would now be at the lower end of the sinuosities, which they mentioned encountering on July 26.

Tucker placed their camp for this day at the head of the sinuosities on Chacuaco Creek, about twelve miles above its mouth.[234] Allowing an additional three miles (as would we) on the Purgatoire, the fifteen miles agrees with their estimated distance for the day. But Tucker apparently overlooked the nine miles they traveled that morning from their camp of the previous night to the Purgatoire. We think that the estimated fifteen miles they mentioned more likely refers to the total for the day. We think that they traveled seventeen or eighteen miles and camped near the *lower* end of the sinuosities,

[226]JAMES [1], II, 71; JAMES [2] in THWAITES [1], XVI, 68.
[227]This doubtless is a slip for "elder," as the party was out of the known range of alder in Colorado.
[228]JAMES [1], II, 71; JAMES [2] in THWAITES [1], XVI, 68.
[229]JAMES [1], II, 72; JAMES [2] in THWAITES [1], XVI, 69.
[230]THWAITES [1], XVI, 69n.
[231]CHITTENDEN, II, 581.
[232]TUCKER [2], 195.
[233]JAMES [1], II, 73; JAMES [2] in THWAITES [1], XVI, 70.
[234]TUCKER [2], 195.

about six miles above the mouth of Chacuaco Creek. That is in Las Animas County, about a mile north of the southern edge of T29S, R56W.

July 26. We believe that on this day the party actually passed upstream along the sinuosities above which Tucker placed their camp of the preceding night.[235] In the *Account* James commented that the actual distance they traveled this day must have been much greater than the fifteen miles he had estimated, because their course followed the sinuosities of the valley.[236] The sinuosities would have added nearly five miles to the distance.

In the diary, James mentioned ascending above the red sandstone to a greyish or yellowish-white sandstone and arriving the evening of July 26 at the place where the red sandstone ends.[237] The red Triassic sandstone is overlaid by a grey Jurassic sandstone at the point indicated by Tucker above the sinuosities on Chacuaco Creek.[238] He credits Elmer H. Baltz, however, for pointing out to him that this Jurassic-age sandstone is stained red in many places. The possibility remains that the campsite was in an area where a red-stained, Jurassic-age sandstone is overlaid by sandstone of Cretaceous age. Such an area can be reached fifteen miles (in a straight line) upstream on Chacuaco Creek from where we believe they camped on the preceding night.

That would place their camp of July 26 in Chacuaco Canyon about thirteen miles east-northeast of the junction of State Highway 389 and U.S. Highway 160, Las Animas County. Such a location would be about five miles downstream from where Tucker placed them,[239] but our own exploration of the area would prove neither location to be correct. As will be seen, our interpretation of events that occurred on the following day enabled us to place their camp for July 26 in a different place.

July 27. Expecting to ascend to the plains at the head of the canyon, the party continued upstream at sunrise. The canyon was very crooked: They remarked that they traveled no fewer than ten different courses and estimated that their straight-line travel was

---

[235]TUCKER [2], foldout map.
[236]JAMES [1], II, 75; JAMES [2] in THWAITES [1], XVI, 72.
[237]JAMES [3], July 27.
[238]TUCKER [2], 196.
[239]TUCKER [2], foldout map.

three miles.[240] They then discovered that the passage was blocked by huge masses of rock in the narrow canyon floor. The men waited until the scouts found a place to lead the horses out of the canyon, a mile and a half back downstream.

Following the route the scouts had discovered, the party climbed out of the canyon onto the prairie. After having been closed in by precipitous walls for thirty miles, the party experienced a feeling of exhilaration to again have the expanded view of the plain. James commented, as they left the canyons of the Purgatoire, "We emerged from the gloomy solitude of its valley, with a feeling somewhat akin to that which attends escape from a place of punishment."[241]

The bearings of several points were taken after the party had proceeded due south on the plain for a mile and a half,[242] at which point James commented, "Due east was a solitary and almost naked pile of rocks towering to a great elevation above the surface of the plain. James's Peak [Pikes Peak] bore north 71° west; the west Spanish Peak, south 87°. West magnetic variation, 13½ deg. east."[243]

The anomaly of Pikes Peak being N71°W has been discussed by Tucker.[244] The reading that Long took on Pikes Peak from near Rocky Ford on the Arkansas was N68°W. Of course, as one goes southward the direction of the peak would become more northerly, yet their reading was three degrees more to the west. The direction of Pikes Peak from their present location is approximately N32°W, or N45°W as they would have read it when not allowing for magnetic declination. We agree with Tucker: They were actually sighting on Greenhorn Mountain, a snowcapped peak about twenty miles northwest of Walsenburg.

In early July 1981, we arrived, after opening and closing no fewer than five obstinate pasture gates, at Chacuaco Canyon, at a point about ten miles east-northeast of the junction of State Highway 389 and U.S. Highway 160. We were eager to view the massive boulders blocking the canyon three miles above the party's previous campsite. To our complete surprise there were no boulders blocking the canyon floor at this point—certainly not enough to have made travel by horseback impracticable. The canyon walls were still two hundred

[240]JAMES [1], II, 75; JAMES [2] in THWAITES [1], XVI, 73.

[241]JAMES [1], II, 76n.; JAMES [2] in THWAITES [1], XVI, 74n.

[242]JAMES [2] in THWAITES [1], XVI, 75.

[243]In the Philadelphia edition (JAMES [1], II, 77; JAMES [6], II, 77) the west Spanish Peak is said to be "south, 87°W; magnetic variation, 13½° east."

[244]TUCKER [2], 197.

feet high, and lying between them was a valley floor a quarter mile or more wide. Chacuaco Creek wound its way through the valley with no apparent evidence that its head was near, as James had indicated.

Perplexed by the view below us, we decided to travel from here a mile and a half south on the plain to make our own compass readings on the landmarks James had noted. Owing to the slightly rolling nature of the plain, no "naked pile of rocks" could be seen to the east. Instead, the eastern horizon was simply uninterrupted grassland plain. To the southwest the Spanish Peaks were not visible, and the view to the northwest was equally unrewarding.

We were now certain that we and others had misinterpreted the events on Chacuaco Creek. After passing back through the pasture gates, with both of us struggling with one particularly recalcitrant one, we drove back to U.S. Highway 160 and headed west to a ranch we would learn was the Howard Sumpter Ranch. We had questions to ask about Chacuaco Creek! Luckily for us, Jim Sumpter, the son of the owner, and Jim's children had pulled up to the ranch just before we arrived. Talking with the man, we learned that there would have been no problem in traveling by horse out the head of Chacuaco Canyon.

Thanking Mr. Sumpter for his help, we left the ranch at sunset and spent the evening studying the topographic maps for other canyons through which the expedition could have passed. We concluded again that there were no canyons that the party could have taken that enter the Purgatoire from the southeast at the proper distance other than Chacuaco Canyon. We were convinced that the party had traveled up Chacuaco Canyon along its sinuosities on the morning of July 26, but until now we had not considered the possibility that the expedition could have taken some other canyon, whose mouth opened into Chacuaco Canyon above the sinuosities.

There are several large canyons that enter Chacuaco Canyon, but James mentioned none of them. The three branch canyons that appeared the most likely choices for a southbound expedition were Poitrey, Tobe, and Bachicha canyons. We eliminated the first two, which come in from the southeast, on the basis that the party could not have traveled the given distance (ten miles) "nearly due south" (corrected to S12°W) without having ascended the precipitous wall of Mesa de Maya. That they clearly would not have done, especially when the western end of the mesa was plainly in sight. To skirt this western end, however, required traveling in a southwesterly direction of S30° to 50°W.

Bachicha Canyon, which comes in from the southwest, would have brought the party out on the plain far enough to the west to miss the mesa entirely, even though they were traveling S12°W. Our hope was now that this canyon was blocked near its head and that the landmarks we had been unable to see a mile and a half out on the plain from Chacuaco Canyon would be visible from the same distance on the plain south of Bachicha Canyon.

Early the next morning we headed for Bachicha Canyon. We had noted on the topographic map the Box Ranch. It was very near where we wanted to go. We decided to visit the ranch, a decision that proved rewarding.

As we pulled up in front of the house we were quickly greeted by a small boy and girl. Following shortly behind and bounding from the kitchen door came their pet goat.

We had scarcely begun our conversation with the children when their mother appeared at the gate. We talked to her and explained our mission. She cordially invited us in to talk to her husband about the canyon. We were served ice tea as we sat in the living room of the ranch house, a solidly built structure built, we learned, in the late 1800s. The rancher, Don Brazeal, was very interested in the history of the area and was fascinated with the possibility that the expedition had passed through Bachicha Canyon—Chi Chi Canyon, as it is known locally. He assured us that it is impossible to travel by horse out the head of the canyon. The canyon is so well blocked that in the winter he takes his cattle into it without fear of their coming out the head.

He pointed on our topographic maps to the place where the canyon becomes blocked by boulders and to some arms on the east side of the canyon where exit by horseback is possible. These arms were about a mile and a half downstream from the blockage.

The Brazeals then volunteered to take us to the east edge of the canyon to show us the boulders blocking it. We followed their pickup truck across the pastures to view firsthand the blocked canyon floor. On our map we measured three miles downstream from this point. In those three miles the direction of Bachicha Creek changes ten times, as James had indicated, and at the end of these three miles the Cretaceous sandstone overlies the Jurassic sandstone in the canyon bottom.

By now the evidence strongly supported our hypothesis that Bachicha Canyon was the one that the expedition had ascended. If the landmarks James mentioned could be seen from the proper distance out on the plain, our hypothesis would be well established.

We then went to a point about one and a half miles southward out on the plain, from where we believed the expedition had left Bachicha Canyon. There, a few degrees south of east, a mesa showed plainly about ten miles away. This isolated prominence, which rises about four hundred feet above the plain, is known as Fowler Mesa. The readings on the easily seen Spanish Peaks and Greenhorn Mountain corresponded very closely to James's readings when his were corrected for magnetic declination. We had finally found a canyon that was impossible to exit at the head and from which the proper landmarks could be seen from the nearby prairie.

Back at the ranch house, Don told us of initials carved on the wall of a shallow cave he had pointed out to us on the west side of the canyon, very near to where it becomes blocked. Before we left we gave him the names of the men on the expedition, as he was interested in checking the initials on the wall of the cave.

It is in Bachicha Canyon, twelve miles northeast of the junction of State Highway 389 and U.S. Highway 160, Las Animas County, in Section 6, T32S, R56W, that we place their camp of July 26. The distance back from there to their camp of July 25 is fifteen miles, which was their estimated distance, and the distance upstream to the massive boulders on the canyon floor is three miles in a straight line. On the prairie, the landmarks viewed by James are plainly seen.

We wondered what factors had influenced their decision to take Bachicha Canyon rather than continuing up Chacuaco Canyon. From a point just above the sinuosities on Chacuaco Creek, their course would have been twenty to thirty degrees west of south as they followed up the canyon. Their direction would have remained unchanged in following up Bachicha Canyon. To have continued up Chacuaco Canyon from the mouth of Bachicha Canyon, however, would have resulted in a notable change in direction to about thirty degrees east of south, an overall change of about sixty degrees.

Both Poitrey and Tobe canyons would have presented the same considerable change in direction to the east of south, seemingly indicating that the party was tending to hold a course to the south and slightly westward, avoiding the canyons that entered from the southeast. It will be recalled that they found the Purgatoire in flood. Whether Bachicha Creek was drier than Chacuaco Creek, and hence more easily traveled, there is, of course, no way to know.

In late October 1981, and again in June 1983, we returned to the Box Ranch and made our way to the rim of the canyon, at a point where we could look down on the junction of the two creeks some three hundred feet below us.[245] Neither time could we see any apparent reason for choosing one canyon over the other except for the reason mentioned earlier—that they wished to hold a course a little west of south.

The camp for July 27, James stated, was about ten miles "nearly due south" from where they left the canyon.[246] That would have placed their camp eight miles northeast of Branson, possibly in Section 3 or 10, T34S, R57W, Las Animas County. The party camped on the plain near a pool of stagnant water and dined long after dark upon a bison they had recently shot.

[245]Our October exploration was an episode in itself. By the time we made it back from the canyon rim to the Box Ranch it was dark, and no one was home. We were very, very low on gasoline. We managed to reach Des Moines, New Mexico, with what gasoline we had. There we stopped, and Goodman went into a beer joint and left Cheryl in the Jeep across the street. A large woman behind the bar asked if she could help him. Noting the two men sitting to his left, he said, "Yes, I need two things—a little encouragement and some gasoline." One of the men tipped back his Western hat and said, "Well, maybe we can help you. There are no gasoline pumps in town available. Do you have an Oklahoma credit card?" An Oklahoma credit card, we soon learned, is a piece of hose, so I didn't say anything. The man sitting next to him said that he had a piece of hose in his car. He went out and got it and gave it to the man in the Western hat, who then drove his car around to the Jeep. We had to siphon the gas out of his car into a cup and then pour it into the Jeep with a funnel we made from newspaper. One of the payoffs came when we insisted on paying. He declined, saying he knew what it was like to be out of gas. When we offered to at least buy him a beer, he said, "No, it's not that I don't like the stuff, but I own the joint." We made it back to Clayton that night because of the help of these people. The Jeep is now equipped with an Oklahoma credit card and a real funnel.

[246]JAMES [1], II, 78; JAMES [2] in THWAITES [1], XVI, 76.

CHAPTER THREE

NEW MEXICO

JULY 28. THEIR MORNING'S RIDE BROUGHT THEM TO AN ELEVATED POINT[1] some eight miles from their previous night's camp. From there James again noted what he believed to be Pikes Peak.[2]

Their course, which according to James was "a little east of south"[3] (nearly due south or even slightly west of south when corrected for magnetic declination), likely took them along the east base of Negro Mesa, across Long Canyon near its head, and to the precipices above the valley of the Dry Cimarron.

As we viewed the area around Negro Mesa we felt certain that the party must have swung southwestward to avoid the vertical walls of Negro Canyon and Long Canyon. Had they negotiated those canyons they would have struck a high, conic hill, Devoys Peak, rather than Negro Mesa, but the former is several miles farther from their campsite than they say they traveled.

About ten miles beyond and toward evening they made their way to the Dry Cimarron. To judge by their course direction, we believe they likely descended into the valley by way of Gleasons Canyon, although Tollgate Canyon, a little more than a mile farther to the west, is another possibility. The descent, said James, was "accomplished, not without danger to the life and limbs of ourselves and horses."[4] Either canyon would have presented difficulties.

Based on the events of the next morning, we place their camp on the Dry Cimarron at or near the mouth of Briggs Canyon, Union County.

July 29. Traveling the next morning for about three miles on a course of S35°E (S23°E) brought them "to the foot of the cliff which

---

[1]The only "elevated point" the proper distance from their camp is Negro Mesa, a basaltic hill that rises 600 feet above the plain just south of the Colorado/New Mexico line.
[2]He was again seeing Greenhorn Mountain.
[3]JAMES [1], II, 81; JAMES [2] in THWAITES [1], XVI, 79.
[4]JAMES [1], II, 81; JAMES [2] in THWAITES [1], XVI, 79.

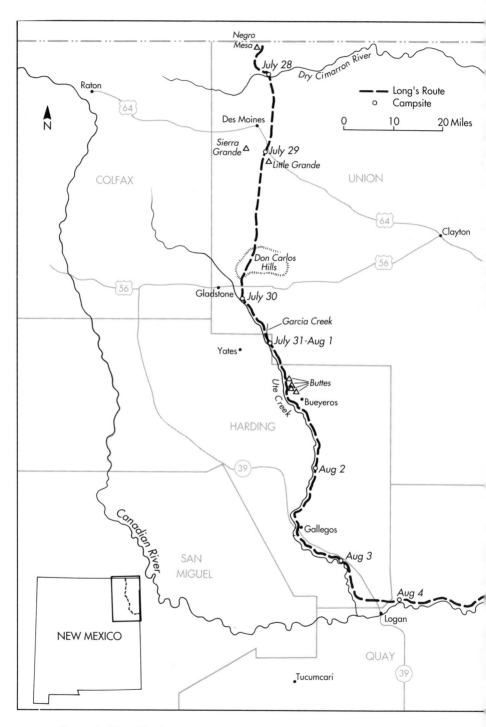

Route in New Mexico

separates the valley from the high plain."⁵ To do so they would have had to camp the previous evening (July 28) at or within about a mile of the mouth of Briggs Canyon, as that is the only place where they could have traveled so nearly south for about three miles before coming to the cliff. This cliff, James noted, was "impassable, except at particular points, where it is broken by ravines."⁶ It forms walls of Briggs and Brown canyons (Sections 5 and 6, T30N, R30E). On the Brown Canyon wall of the cliff there are ravines, one of which must have been their means of ascent to the plains. They estimated the height of the cliff at about two hundred feet. Frustratingly, the cliff, or wall of the canyon, is nearer four hundred feet.

We believed for some time that the party traveled south through Briggs Canyon to its head in their ascent to the plain. We examined this canyon and its vegetation. It is a beautiful, broad canyon with high walls lined in piñon pine, juniper, and an occasional western yellow pine nearer the head of the canyon. Only a few cottonwoods line the intermittent stream. From the Dry Cimarron through Briggs Canyon would have been a toilsome though scenic march and would certainly have brought comments from James. Perhaps it was the fear of becoming boxed in once again as they had been in Bachicha Canyon that persuaded the party to climb the "mural barrier"⁷ some four and a half miles northeast of where the present road through Briggs Canyon becomes a cattle trail leading to the high plain. In trying to answer why the party chose one route over another, we are often left to mere conjecture.

Brown Canyon, without basalt but with vegetation similar to that of Briggs Canyon, heads nearly due south; ascent to the plain could have been made in a mile and a half from the "cliff." It is fortunate that the party did not choose to follow this canyon to its head, as the valley becomes very narrow and the walls exceedingly steep.

Just before noon the party, now upon the high plain, were delayed by two storms. The second storm, a hailstorm from the northeast, was so severe that the horses would travel only with the wind; they waited it out with their backs to the wind rather than be carried off course. The party continued in the rain until dark when, wet, hungry, and without firewood, they set up their tent.

We suspect that James's diary entries for this day were actually made on the following day, since the night would have afforded little

⁵JAMES [1], II, 82; JAMES [2] in THWAITES [1], XVI, 81.
⁶JAMES [1], II, 82; JAMES [2] in THWAITES [1], XVI, 81.
⁷JAMES [1], II, 82; JAMES [2] in THWAITES [1], XVI, 81.

time or light for such labor. Also, James's description of the view before them and to the west after they climbed the "cliff" to the high plain does not entirely fit with what they would have been able to see. James said, "[W]e again caught a view of the distant summits of the Andes appearing on the verge of our horizon."[8] This must surely have been the Sangre de Cristo Mountains, which are not visible from this point. The mountain range would have been clearly visible, however, on the next day. The party would have skirted to the east side of Carr Mountain (Gaylord Mountain). From there, Sierra Grande, Little Grande, and Mount Dora (Cieneguilla del Burro Mountain) are easily seen to the south and fit well into James's description of "high conic hills, and irregular knobs, scattered in every direction as far as the eye could comprehend."[9]

The general location for their campsite this night (July 29) can be derived only from what proved to be a fairly certain campsite for July 30 on Ute Creek. Reckoning their mileage for July 29 at seventeen miles (it is forty-seven miles from their camp on the Dry Cimarron to Ute Creek, and James's diary specifies that they traveled thirty miles on the 30th)[10] places them at the east base of Sierra Grande in Union County, six or seven miles southeast of Des Moines. That agrees essentially with Tucker's interpretation of their movements on this day and the next.[11]

Sierra Grande is the largest volcanic mass in Union County, rising about 2,100 feet above the plain and spanning nearly eight miles in diameter. Basalt fragments are scattered on the plain surrounding the east edge of Sierra Grande, as they are on the east side of Carr Mountain. James noted that these fragments retarded their travel in some places.

July 30. They left their "comfortless camp at an early hour"[12] and crossed "a dividing ridge."[13] The only ridge they could have met with in a southerly direction is the Don Carlos Hills. The approach to the hills from the southeast base of Sierra Grande is gradual and easily traversed. The ascent gives no clue to an escarpment that bounds the southeast end and the south side of the hills westward for about six

[8]JAMES [1], II, 82; JAMES [2] in THWAITES [1], XVI, 81.
[9]JAMES [1], II, 82; JAMES [2] in THWAITES [1], XVI, 81.
[10]JAMES [3], July 30.
[11]TUCKER [2], 206.
[12]JAMES [1], II, 84; JAMES [2] in THWAITES [1], XVI, 83.
[13]JAMES [3], July 30.

miles. Had they discovered this, it certainly would have discouraged them from descending this basalt cliff, several miles in length. Whatever their reason, we think that they traveled across the hills toward the southwest end.

We have traveled in a Jeep nearly the length of the hills. They are readily negotiated.[14] Occasional volcanic cones protrude from the plateau, and antelope, just as James saw them, are still there— although doubtless less abundant. From here the Sangre de Cristo Mountains to the west and Mount Capulin to the northwest are clearly visible. Toward the southwest end a descent is easily made, even by Jeep. The expedition would then have been on a sloping plain, and by traveling another five miles only slightly west of south, would have come to Ute Creek. Their camp that night would have been about twenty-five miles south and six miles west of their camp of the previous night. That fits well with James's remark: "Our sufferings from the want of provisions, and from the late storm, had given us a little distaste for prolonging farther than was necessary our journey towards the south-west."[15]

Precipitous basalt walls bound both sides of Ute Creek, just as James described, beginning about two miles southeast of where New Mexico State Highway 56 crosses Ute Creek just east of Gladstone and running for about another two miles downstream. For part of this distance, the basalt is in three or four terraces and can be descended by foot to the creek with only some difficulty.

It is in this area (beginning in the southeast quarter of Section 25, T24N, R28E, and running through the northwest quarter of Section 6, T23N, R29E) that the expedition must have camped on the evening of July 30. From here, to the northwest and southeast, columnar basalt does not bound both sides of Ute Creek. South-easterly, the valley quickly becomes gradually undulating with occasional precipitous basalt walls visible only on the west side.

As we drove across the grama grassland toward Ute Creek, it was impossible to tell that the columnar basalt would bound the creek until we were right upon its edge. We think that the party arrived at Ute Creek about midway the length of the bounding basalt; otherwise, it would have been easy to see that this basalt disappeared in a short distance one direction or the other.

[14]Except when overcome by darkness. It then becomes necessary, to avoid gullies and to find one's way, to count the windmills that show up in the night sky. These windmills are indicated on the topographic maps.

[15]JAMES [2] in THWAITES [1], XVI, 84.

About ten miles after leaving their camp of July 29 they would have struck the upper reaches of Carrizo Creek (Gallegos Creek) where it is so small that it is understandable that they did not mention it. Nothing on Carrizo Creek fits the description they gave for the stream upon which they camped on July 30 or of the direction they took. Tucker has pointed out that the geology described does not fit Carrizo Creek;[16] neither does the direction of flow (southeast to east) nor the depth of the canyon. Additionally, they would cross no "dividing ridge" in the first ten or eleven miles.

Had they traveled south or east of south, the thirty miles that they report having covered on July 30 would have brought them to Tramperos Creek (a branch of Major Longs Creek). The name Major Longs Creek was understandably sufficient to cause many to think that this creek was the one that the expedition followed to what they supposed to be the Red River—actually the Canadian. Again, Tucker's arguments are excellent for rejecting this choice.[17] He pointed out that Major Longs Creek and its branches have no "columnar basalt nor, indeed, any other volcanic formations" and, therefore, do not fit James's description. In addition, Major Longs Creek ultimately joins the Canadian River in Oldham County, Texas, a few miles west of Tascosa (Boys Ranch). The distance from there to the Antelope Hills is 70 miles less than the estimated distance they traveled (243 miles). If, however, one moves them up the Canadian those 70 miles, they are a little east of Logan, New Mexico, not far from the mouth of Ute Creek. Convincingly, four round mounds, later described in the *Account,* occur only on Ute Creek.

Their report on the plants of Ute Canyon where they camped contains a curiosity. In the London edition of the *Account* one finds this statement: "The common choke cherry, and the yellow and black currants, are almost the only woody plants met with in this valley."[18] We searched all except a portion of the central part of the cliff-bounded canyon where they camped and found not a single specimen of either. Even though we may have overlooked some of the plants, they are certainly not "almost the only woody plants" there. We saw an abundance of cedar (*Juniperus*), considerable grape (*Vitis*), sumac (*Rhus trilobata*), willow (*Salix exigua*), and hackberry (*Celtis reticulata*), infrequent salt cedar (*Tamarix*), and occasional cotton-wood (*Populus sargentii*). Two explanations come to mind to account

---

[16]TUCKER [2], 211.
[17]TUCKER [2], 211.
[18]JAMES [2] in THWAITES [1], XVI, 84.

for the absence of the choke cherries (*Prunus virginiana*) and currants (*Ribes*): (1) Livestock has eradicated them, or (2) Perhaps the remark was based on memory, and the wrong canyon was in mind. The earlier Philadelphia edition does not contain this statement.

July 31 and August 1. Leaving their camp on the morning of July 31, they climbed out of the canyon, whose floor was so obstructed by rock "as to be wholly impassable."[19] Within a few hours, by "continuing along the brink of the precipice" they arrived "where the substratum of sandstone emerges to light at the base of an inconsiderable hill."[20] They would have been along the "brink of the precipice" for only a mile or so. The sandstone appears in much less than a few hours' ride, but they may have stayed far enough up on the plain to have not noticed it for a few hours.

At about 1:00 P.M., having traveled about ten miles, they arrived at a tributary coming in from the east side. They descended it "by a precipitous declivity of about four hundred feet"[21] and camped. That would have been Garcia Creek Canyon. It is about four hundred feet deep at its confluence with Ute Creek (T22N, R29E, north-central part of Section 13). Precipitous it truly is, and a chore, indeed, it would have been for their horses to descend. Viewing this beautiful valley and attractive campsite, we were not surprised that they wrote, "As several of our horses had been lamed in descending into the valley . . . it was thought necessary to allow ourselves a day of rest."[22] The party, then, remained here on August 1. Their Garcia Creek camp is about six miles east and a little north of Yates, Harding County.

The road that follows from New Mexico State Highway 120 along the northeast side of Ute Creek to the Miller Ranch (southeast quarter of T23N, R29E), across whose pasture we traveled to reach the mouth of Garcia Creek, puts one in sight of the ravines leading into Ute Creek and the occasional basalt outcrops on the southwest side of the creek. The view from the sandstone cliffs above Garcia Creek is breathtaking. Below lies the confluence of the two creeks: To the distant north the mounds atop the Don Carlos Hills are still visible; to the south lies the broad valley of Ute Creek with Mesa Quitaras and four unnamed peaks, south of Bueyeros, on the far horizon.

[19]JAMES [1], II, 86; JAMES [2] in THWAITES [1], XVI, 86.
[20]JAMES [1], II, 86; JAMES [2] in THWAITES [1], XVI, 86.
[21]JAMES [1], II, 87; JAMES [2] in THWAITES [1], XVI, 86.
[22]JAMES [1], II, 87; JAMES [2] in THWAITES [1], XVI, 87.

Junipers and oaks, bent and twisted by the winds, are scattered along the top of the cliffs. The sides of the cliffs and the floodplain below are dotted with junipers, and in some places large boulders of sandstone have broken away and plummeted to the bed of the creek.

August 2. The expedition continued down Ute Creek, starting at an early hour. "At sunrise we collected our horses and proceeded down the valley."[23] As the *Account* states,[24] the valley soon widens and "a conspicuous change in the sandstone precipices" bounding the creek occurs.[25]

In about ten miles they came to "an immense circular elevation . . . apparently inaccessible upon all sides."[26] Having passed this butte (located in the northwest quarter of the southeast quarter of Section 28, T21N, R30E, about four and a half miles northwest of Bueyeros, Harding County), they very shortly encountered three other buttes.[27] The four buttes, composed, too, of Exeter sandstone and some capped with the Morrison Formation, are separated by intervals of a mile or less along the east side of Ute Creek and constitute seemingly incontrovertible evidence, which Tucker discussed fully,[28] that the party did descend Ute Creek.

Continuing down the widening valley they stopped to eat, the meal consisting solely of a small portion of roast venison, then continued for another thirteen miles in a southeasterly direction and camped. Their early-morning start would readily have enabled them to travel about eighteen miles before lunch. That plus the thirteen miles they traveled in the afternoon gives a total of thirty-one miles for the day and places their camp in the east-central part of T18N, R31E, Harding County. This is about thirteen miles south, in a direct line, and a couple of miles east of Bueyeros.

Supper consisted of one-eighth of a sea biscuit each. The hunters had killed a badger, but nothing with which to start a fire could be found. Their sufferings from lack of water and food are mentioned here, as it may explain their failure to note landmarks, particularly

---

[23]JAMES [1], II, 90; JAMES [2] in THWAITES [1], XVI, 90.

[24]JAMES [1], II, 90; JAMES [2] in THWAITES [1], XVI, 90.

[25]This is the Exeter sandstone, which here begins to appear.

[26]JAMES [1], II, 90; JAMES [2] in THWAITES [1], XVI, 90.

[27]These last three buttes are interestingly weathered, particularly on the north and east sides. We have found a name for but one of these buttes, the middle one, which is Cerrito de los Muertos. We are told there was a man buried there.

[28]TUCKER [2] 211–13.

the Black Hills, a north-south range about six miles long that rises 600 feet above the plain and at whose southern end they surely camped that night.

We decided that we could make it to Bueyeros via Bueyeros Canyon. The road looked tolerable on the map. It was not an improved road by any means, but with four-wheel drive we thought we could do it. From the top of the canyon, we could hardly see the road as we started down. Cheryl did the driving; Goodman did the admiring of the scenery. The road was steep. We dropped five or six hundred feet in almost no distance. There were places where the cliffs would tower nearly vertically above us for fifty feet. Traveling in the narrow little wash between the cliffs, we could have touched the sides of the canyon. Down, down we went. We had never traveled so far in four-wheel drive or needed it as much as we did that day.

Finally we came to the bottom at the mouth of the canyon, and right away we hit the first gate; it was easy to open. We ran across a fence every two or three miles. We would just go down the length of the fence and hope that at the corners there would be a gate. We were hitting it all right; we'd find the gate. One of the last gates we came upon had a padlock on it. Before Cheryl got out of the Jeep to see if it were locked, she had already decided to pry off the lock and tie a twenty-dollar bill to it rather than return up Bueyeros Canyon. Fortunately, the gate was not locked.

Before we got very much farther we could see a butte that fit the description of one of the four buttes that James had seen. This was exciting! Here was one of them; where were the rest? We drove a little farther, and the top of another showed up, and finally the top of yet another (see fig. 21). All we needed was a fourth butte. We knew we were in the right location now, but how to reach them? We could tell from the map that we were not very many miles from an improved road; that meant it was graded at least. We drove across what we hoped would be the last pasture with a fence, just ahead of us. As we approached, we could see where a road was graded. It looked rather wide. We got through the gate onto this road, and it was a landing field! We couldn't have been more puzzled to see a landing field out there, for the town of Bueyeros has little more than a church and a house. We were right at the foot of the buttes. This was wonderful! Down one arm of the landing field we saw a building, a rather large building that had been out of sight over a tiny hill. We drove over to this building, which proved to be a carbon dioxide plant. A friendly workman of Spanish descent came out.

Fig. 21. Three buttes at Bueyeros, photographed October 1981. From authors' collection.

We were still looking for the fourth butte—the first butte James had seen. The workman suggested that we take a certain road. He also confirmed that there really had been a man buried on top of Cerrito de los Muertos. We asked him some more questions. In answering these he said, "Well, you just take the road you came in on."

"No," we said.

"You came in from Bueyeros didn't you?" the workman asked.

"No," we said.

"Well, how did you get here?"

We responded that we had come down the landing strip.

"You flew in!" He couldn't believe it.

"No," we said. "We drove through Bueyeros Canyon and came in."

His eyes got big, and he said, "Nobody can do that!"

We took the road the company had built up Ute Creek and got a much better picture of the country that Major Long's people had seen. After traveling a little more than a mile north on this road we were able to look south and view the first butte, which James had described as "an immense circular elevation." We had now seen for ourselves all four buttes.

August 3. Having found no potable water for twenty-four hours, and breakfast having consisted of another eighth part of a biscuit, they started early from camp. No mention is made of a midday stop. They camped that night where they found some muddy, brackish, but drinkable water. They also found some firewood, and they cooked their badger and a young owl.

In their travels today the party would have viewed many mesas to the west of Ute Creek, but no comment is made about them. James does mention "passing an extensive tract, whose soil is a loose red sand."[29] In his diary for this day,[30] James noted that the prevailing rock of the country was red sandstone.[31]

James's diary for August 3 states that they traveled "yesterday and today a distance of about 60 miles."[32] We calculate their mileage of August 2 to have been thirty-one miles, leaving nearly another thirty miles to be traveled on August 3. We place their camp in the western

[29]JAMES [1], II, 93; JAMES [2] in THWAITES [1], XVI, 93.

[30]JAMES [3], August 3.

[31]In this area red sandstone is particularly noticeable at Rincon Colorado, a 900-foot buttress at whose base Ute Creek passes near Gallegos, New Mexico.

[32]JAMES [3], August 3.

half of T15N, R32E, in Harding County. An arroyo enters the valley of Ute Creek in Section 17,[33] and the water they found may well have been there. As will be seen, the distance traveled down Ute Creek the next day also would place their camp of August 3 here. The site is about fifteen miles northwest, in a direct line, of Logan.

August 4. They ate the rest of the badger and owl for breakfast and continued down Ute Creek. James stated, "Our morning's ride of sixteen miles brought us to a place where the water of the river emerges to view."[34] James also remarked on their "falling in with a large and much frequented Indian trace, crossing the creek from the west, and following down along the east bank."[35] They supposed that the trail led to an Indian village on the Red River (on a branch of which they thought they were).

The only clue they give us about the rest of the day is to be found on their map.[36] It shows them camped on the Canadian River. The river was correctly labeled "Canadian River" although at the time they camped there they believed the river to be the Red.

Tucker's comments on their travels of August 4 seem to us to explain the day very well.[37] When they struck the Indian trace, they were but a few miles — probably five or six — from the junction of Ute Creek and the Canadian River and, as they say, sixteen miles below their camp of August 3. Evidence of Indian trails can still be found near the banks of the Canadian River and Ute Creek near Logan. These are in an area where the Ute Reservoir is now located. The reservoir dam, on the Canadian River, is about two miles west of Logan. A little more than two miles above the dam, Ute Creek enters the reservoir.

The map accompanying the *Account* shows the trace,[38] labeled "Great Spanish Rd.," crossing Ute Creek (erroneously called "Rio Mora") just north of the Canadian River.[39] The map does not indicate

[33]New Mexico Highway 39 now crosses the mouth of this arroyo.

[34]JAMES [1], II, 94; JAMES [2] in THWAITES [1], XVI, 94.

[35]JAMES [1], II, 94; JAMES [2] in THWAITES [1], XVI, 95.

[36]JAMES [6], Map of the Country Drained by the Mississippi—Western Section, atlas; JAMES [7], I, Map of the Country Drained by the Mississippi, fold-in.

[37]TUCKER [2], 216–18.

[38]JAMES [6], Map of the Country Drained by the Mississippi—Western Section, atlas; JAMES [7], I, Map of the County Drained by the Mississippi, I, fold-in.

[39]This is a name applied later when the map was made. No name is given to the stream in either the diary or the *Account*. The Rio Mora joins the Canadian about sixty-five miles above the Ute Creek junction, and, like Ute Creek, flows southward for most of its length. The two streams are separated by the valley of the upper waters of the Canadian.

that they followed the trace at all; both the diary[40] and the *Account,*[41] however, speak of following it. In the *Account* for August 7 James stated, "On leaving our camp, we endeavoured to regain the trace on which we had for several days travelled." That the trace cut across eastward to the Canadian River seems certain. Otherwise, there is no explanation for their failure to comment on Ute Creek's joining the Canadian River—a right-angled junction in what was then a precipitous canyon.[42] In following the trace they missed the junction, and when they came upon the Canadian they did not immediately realize that they were on a different stream. The next day, however, James wrote in his diary, "[We] believe, that we are now on the main Red river and not on one of its branches as we had at first supposed."[43]

Just where on the Canadian they camped on the night of August 4 one cannot tell, but a ten- or twelve-mile ride, following their morning ride of sixteen miles, would have brought them to a northerly bend of the river (T14N, R34E, Section 33) about four miles northeast of Logan, Quay County. That is a logical point for the trail, which led eastward, to have struck the river after crossing Ute Creek.

That night they ate more amply, the hunters having killed a deer, as noted in the diary[44] and the *Account.*[45]

August 5 and 6. In his diary for August 5, James specified, "Yesterday our hunters joined us soon after our encampment for the evening having captured a small deer. This small supply revived our spirits and we resumed our journey this morning hoping for better fare hereafter."[46] This, then, is direct evidence for travel on August 5.

As noted in the diary, on the following morning, Sunday, August 6, they were forced to kill and eat a wild horse in order to satisfy their hunger.[47] They remained encamped on this day and continued their journey on August 7.

In the *Account*, confusion has long existed regarding their activities on August 5 and 6. This is partly occasioned by the omission, in

---

[40]JAMES [3], August 5.
[41]JAMES [1], II, 97; JAMES [2] in THWAITES [1], XVI, 98.
[42]Today, inundation from Ute Reservoir obscures all except the upper portion of the cliffs of the canyons of Ute Creek and the Canadian River.
[43]JAMES [3], August 5.
[44]JAMES [3], August 5.
[45]JAMES [2] in THWAITES [1], XVI, 96.
[46]JAMES [3], August 5.
[47]JAMES [3], August 7.

both editions, of dates for August 5 and 6, with the events for these two days included with those of August 4.

Thwaites attempted to clarify the dates in the London edition of the *Account* by indicating "[5]" for the events surrounding the killing of the horse.[48] He was thereby compelled to add "[next]" to a sentence in the middle of the same paragraph: "The [next] day being Sunday . . . we resolved to remain encamped."[49] It seems likely that this editing was based on information given in the *Account* on August 9,[50] which we believe is simply in error, that the horse was killed on August 5. James contradicted his previous statement that the horse was killed on August 6 when, on August 9, he commented about eating the last of the horse killed on August 4.[51] We believe that Thwaites's interpolation of "5th" should be "6th," and that the comments about the wild horses in the previous paragraph of the *Account* constitute the entry for August 5.

The distance traveled on August 5 can be estimated on the basis of geographical features of the land along the river and its course direction as given later in the *Account* and diary. For approximately eighteen to twenty miles east along the north side of the Canadian from their campsite of August 4 (twenty-five following the meanders of the river), the terrain is of rolling, sandy hills covered in varying densities with mesquite, yucca, cactus, sandsage, and grama grasses. After this distance, ravines begin to occur on the south side of the river. The party would note the ravines and avoid them on their next move.

The campsite for August 5 and Sunday, August 6 must have been approximately three miles east of the New Mexico/Texas line in Oldham County, Texas. We attempted to reach this campsite, approaching it from the north via Nara Visa. We crossed the Nara Visa Arroyo less than a mile northwest of its junction with the Canadian. Shortly thereafter, numerous sand dunes impeded our travel.

From the top of one of the sand dunes we could see ravines on the south side of the river and trees along the valley. We saw a few antelope in these sandhills, perhaps more than the starving expedition saw over a century and a half earlier. James was likely right when he attributed the scarcity of game through this area to the frequent Indian hunting parties.

[48]THWAITES [1], XVI, 96.
[49]THWAITES [1], XVI, 97.
[50]JAMES [1], II, 101; JAMES [2] in THWAITES [1], XVI, 102.
[51]JAMES [3], August 9.

CHAPTER FOUR

TEXAS

AUGUST 7. AFTER RETRIEVING SOME OF THE HORSES, WHICH HAD strayed in search of pasture, the party attempted in vain to regain the Indian trace on which they had been traveling. The attempt took them several miles off course across a difficult tract of sand covered with sandsage and other plants.

According to the *Account*,[1] "In order to shun the numerous ravines which now began to occur, we chose our route at some distance from the bank of the river, where we found the vallies deeper and more abrupt, though less frequent." The party must have crossed the river near their campsite of August 5 and 6, as the river was kept on their left during the morning's ride of nearly twenty miles. Their travel must have taken them across Trujillo Creek and one of its branches, Agua de Piedra Creek, the two creeks joining at Trujillo Camp.[2]

Turning, then, toward the river for about nine miles, the party encamped at 2 P.M. At the site of the encampment the precipices which bound the river were 100 to 200 feet high. We believe that this campsite must have been just west of the mouth of Las Arches Creek on the Canadian, some eighteen miles north-northwest of Adrian in Oldham County. In this area the walls along the Canadian are precipitous and rise to the heights described.

August 8. The party started the morning's travel eastward in an area where the Canadian makes many meanders,[3] the bed cutting close into the precipices and wrapping around the promontories. From the mouth of Las Arches Creek eastward for about fourteen miles the precipices continue to flank the river, a feature that surely must have prompted the following comment: "[W]e continued our journey, crossing and recrossing the river several times. This we

---

[1]JAMES [1], II, 97; JAMES [2] in THWAITES [1], XVI, 99.

[2]A small ranch house located in Oldham County, about nineteen miles northwest of Adrian, constitutes this camp.

[3]Catfish Bend is the largest meander in this area, and is the only one named on topographic maps.

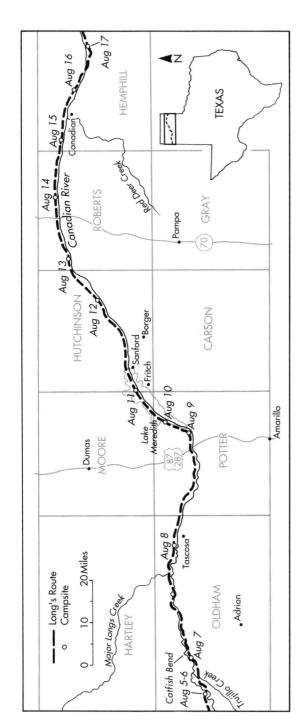

Route in Texas

found necessary, as the occurrence of steep and rocky ravines made it impossible to pass along the bank, parallel to the course of the river, which here became more meandering, winding about the points of rocky and impassable promontories."[4]

As noted by James, "The river valley became wide, and bounded on both sides by low and rounded hills instead of abrupt and perpendicular precipices."[5] This description of the change in geographical features agrees with what is found some fourteen miles east of where we place their campsite of August 7.

In his diary, James stated, "In the afternoon we continued our journey about 16 miles making the whole distance for the day nearly thirty."[6]

In the *Account,* James noted that they crossed several dry creeks, apparently in the afternoon.[7] There are at least eight creeks that enter the Canadian from the north and south in the area traversed that afternoon. One such creek, twenty-two miles east of the previous campsite, is Punta del Agua Creek, or Major Longs Creek, down which many historians have believed the expedition traveled. The nearly thirty miles traveled (twenty-six miles due east according to the *Account*)[8] would place their campsite of August 8 a couple of miles west of Boys Ranch, Oldham County.

We succeeded, though with some difficulty, in getting to Catfish Bend. Our route, on the south side of the Canadian River, took us across Las Arches Creek. This creek was our major, but certainly not our only, obstacle in reaching the bend. The creek is in a V-shaped canyon, and the exceedingly steep road into and out of it was badly washed. With extreme caution, and the Jeep in four-wheel drive and compound low gear, we prevailed.

Ascending the bank of the creek, we traveled east for a few more miles and then north toward Catfish Bend. Less than a half mile north, the road was so nearly washed away that we left the Jeep and hiked the last couple of miles to the precipices along the bend. We wound our way over sandy, rolling hills, noting the vegetation as we went.[9] The steep slopes of the cliffs were covered predominantly with

---

[4]JAMES [1], II, 99; JAMES [2] in THWAITES [1], XVI, 100.
[5]JAMES [1], II, 99; JAMES [2] in THWAITES [1], XVI, 101.
[6]JAMES [3], August 8.
[7]JAMES [1], II, 99; JAMES [2] in THWAITES [1], XVI, 101.
[8]JAMES [1], II, 100; JAMES [2] in THWAITES [1], XVI, 101.
[9]Mesquite, yucca, scattered juniper, at least three species of prickly pear (*Opuntia*), lace cactus (*Echinocereus reichenbachii*), hairy grama (*Bouteloua hirsuta*), galleta (*Hilaria jamesii*), tumblegrass (*Schedonnardus paniculatus*), false buffalo grass (*Munroa squarrosa*), sunflower (*Heli-*

juniper. The floodplain on the headland across the river from the cliffs was rimmed with salt cedar and occasional willow. From Catfish Bend we could see the windings of the river and the broadening valley and low, rolling hills a few miles to the east.

August 9. For breakfast the party ate the last of the wild horse. This meat, now a few days old, had been carried in temperatures over 90° F, so their description of the flavor was hardly necessary.

The *Account* contains the added sentence, "In the morning our course was east, thirteen and a-half miles, at the end of which we found a large spring of transparent and almost pure water, where we halted to dine."[10] Unfortunately, we have been unable to locate this spring with any certainty.

James also mentioned crossing a stream of running water, and the sandy bed of a dry stream, sixty yards in width.[11] There are five dry streams satisfactorily fitting the latter description. These enter from the south along the stretch of river traversed this day. Because he mentioned but one stream, however, perhaps they traveled on the north side of the Canadian where but one creek fitting the description enters.[12]

In the *Account,* James gave the distance traveled as twenty-eight miles.[13] In the diary he gave "about 30."[14] We place their campsite four miles east of where U.S. Highway 87–287 crosses the Canadian River in Potter County.[15]

August 10. Having breakfasted on grapes and two ounces of sugar, the party continued downriver. At 10:00 A.M., the hunters sighted a buffalo, and the party encamped immediately. Shortly afterwards the hunters returned with their trophy, a diseased animal that was eaten in "urgent necessity."[16] Although August 10 is not clearly denoted in the *Account,* the hour of the buffalo kill coincides with James's August 10 entry in the diary.

---

anthus), and clammyweed (*Polanisia*) dominated the landscape. Scattered among them were wild buckwheat (*Eriogonum tenellum*) and nailwort (*Paronychia jamesii*).

[10]JAMES [2] in THWAITES [1], XVI, 102.

[11]JAMES [1], II, 102; JAMES [2] in THWAITES [1], XVI, 104.

[12]This is John Ray Creek, eleven miles in a direct line from the west edge of Potter County.

[13]JAMES [1], II, 101; JAMES [2] in THWAITES [1], XVI, 103.

[14]JAMES [3], August 9.

[15]At this campsite the expedition was the closest it would come to the Red River, which was a little over thirty miles to the south.

[16]JAMES [1], II, 102; JAMES [2] in THWAITES [1], XVI, 103.

The *Account* also mentions that the party "crossed a tributary affording a little water, and a dry channel communicating opposite to our encampment with the bed of the river."[17] The running stream could have been Bonita Creek; the dry one, McBride or Plum Creek.

It seems likely that the party would have traveled some ten to twelve miles by 10:00 A.M. Soon after leaving their camp of August 9, the party would have entered a steep-sided canyon of the Canadian whose walls rise nearly three hundred feet above the bed of the river and are topped with limestone caprock.[18]

We would place their campsite just west of Plum Creek and possibly near the mouth of McBride Creek in Potter County some ten miles southwest of Fritch.[19]

August 11. The party continued downriver and at 11:00 A.M., according to the diary, met a band of Indians traveling upstream.[20] At the insistence of the chief, the party returned a short distance and encamped "for the remainder of the day and the ensuing night."[21] It is possible for the party to have traveled some fifteen miles before meeting the Indians in the steep, narrowing canyon along the Canadian. Assuming that three or four miles were traveled back upstream, we place their campsite at the mouth of Blue Creek near its west bank, some three miles north-northwest of Fritch in Hutchinson County.

The campsite chosen by the Indians was described in the *Account*[22] as "a beautiful open plain, having the river in front, and a small creek on the left."[23]

August 12. At 8:00 A.M. "we took our leave of the Kaskaias," stated James.[24]

Some five or six miles below where we believe they left the Indians, the canyon of the Canadian becomes a half mile or less wide.[25]

[17]JAMES [1], II, 102; JAMES [2] in THWAITES [1], XVI, 104.

[18]They were now, as we believe they had been since the evening of August 9, within the present boundaries of Lake Meredith National Recreation Area.

[19]Interestingly, in this area recessed salt domes and flint are known to occur. The Alibates flint occurring for some ten square miles around Lake Meredith is unknown anywhere else in the Texas panhandle.

[20]JAMES [3], August 11.

[21]JAMES [1], II, 103; JAMES [2] in THWAITES [1], XVI, 105.

[22]JAMES [1], II, 104; JAMES [2] in THWAITES [1], XVI, 106.

[23]This site is now inundated by Lake Meredith.

[24]JAMES [1], II, 114; JAMES [2] in THWAITES [1], XVI, 119.

[25]Across this narrow portion of the canyon, the Sanford Dam on Lake Meredith has now been erected.

Within another four miles downstream, in an area northwest of Borger, the Canadian once again becomes a mile and a half wide. This change must have brought forth the following comment: "The river valley spread considerably a little below the point where we had encamped."[26]

Limestone is abundant in the sandstone canyons of the Canadian throughout the Lake Meredith area and for some distance east of Borger along the Canadian. The red color of the sandstone and the veins of limestone, which give the canyon walls and hills an interesting contrast of color, are mentioned this day in the *Account*.[27]

The party traveled twenty-eight miles in temperatures nearing 100° F and, after crossing "the bed of a large river at least two hundred yards wide,"[28] encamped in an area of many halophytic plants. The large river is shown on Major Long's map and is labeled "Dry Fork."[29] It is likely Moore Creek, which enters the Canadian on the north side. We place their camp some four miles east of this creek near some marshes that begin to appear along the Canadian. This location in Hutchinson County is sixteen miles northeast of Borger.

August 13. In an area beginning near their campsite of August 12, many former watercourses of the Canadian are indicated on the topographic map. These may be remnants of meanders of the river. That the river had become serpentine is noted in the *Account*: The party "turned off from the river and ascended the hills" to avoid the circuitous route of the river.[30] The hills over which the party traveled are low and rolling, dissected with occasional ravines.

If we assume—based on the geographical features noted by the party on the afternoon of this day and over the next two days—that they traveled across the hills on the north side of the river, then their path would have led them across Bent and Adobe creeks. One of these creeks may have been the one they crossed at 10:00 A.M. There they noted traces of a large Indian party, and, in spite of some fears, they regretted not having met them.

For their midday stop (12:00 noon to 3:00 P.M.) the party erected a tent partially shaded by a few trees, but that did little to bring them

---

[26]JAMES [1], II, 114; JAMES [2] in THWAITES [1], XVI, 120.
[27]JAMES [1], II, 114–15; JAMES [2] in THWAITES [1], XVI, 120.
[28]JAMES [1], II, 116; JAMES [2] in THWAITES [1], XVI, 121.
[29]JAMES [6], Map of the Country Drained by the Mississippi—Western Section, atlas; JAMES [7], I, Map of the Country Drained by the Mississippi, fold-in.
[30]JAMES [1], II, 116; JAMES [2] in THWAITES [1], XVI, 122.

relief from the intense heat and glare of the sun. After three hours the party moved on and soon observed a grove of timber at some distance downriver. We believe this timber was on the south side of the river near Garden Springs and Henry Spring. Here an extensive grove runs east for about five miles from the Hutchinson/Roberts county line.

Mr. Peale and another man were sent across the river to what we believe was this forested area to hunt, an episode detailed in the *Account*.[31] Peale lost the tracks of the party and spent a miserable night alone.

It seems likely that the main body of the party encamped around 5 P.M. The probable distance traveled after 3 P.M. would have been some four to five miles. We place their camp on the north side of the Canadian near the mouth of Pat's Creek in Roberts County, about nine miles west of where Texas Highway 70 crosses the river.

The total distance traveled this day by the party would have been fifteen or sixteen miles.

August 14. Unable to find any tracks, Mr. Peale concluded correctly that the party was upriver from him. Turning in that direction, he located the party at 7 A.M. A bit of time was alloted Mr. Peale to resuscitate himself, and the party left camp later than usual.

The river valley here on the north side of the river is wide and is covered with a mixture of tall and short grasses.[32] According to the *Account*[33] the party moved "along a wide and somewhat grassy plain" before halting to dine by a "grove of cottonwood trees, intermixed with a few small-leaved elms."[34] James noted rocky precipices on both sides of the river,[35] and while there are some precipices and mesas on both sides, they are much less prominent than those upriver in the Lake Meredith area.

"At the place where we encamped . . . the valley of the river is very broad and the river hills distant and low. The valley is considerably well timbered and the soil in many places fertile, being covered with

[31]JAMES [1], II, 118; JAMES [2] in THWAITES [1], XVI, 124.
[32]Species of bluestem (*Andropogon*) and grama (*Bouteloua gracilis* and *B. curtipendula*) are common, along with large clumps of sand sage (*Artemisia*), a few mesquite (*Prosopsis glandulosa*), a very few *Yucca*, and an occasional hackberry (*Celtis*).
[33]JAMES [1], II, 119; JAMES [2] in THWAITES [1], XVI, 125.
[34]The elm is a small-leaved variant of *Ulmus americana. Ulmus alata* is unknown in western Texas and western Oklahoma. In this location, in the direction of the river, we noted cottonwoods (*Populus*), buttonbush (*Cephalanthus*), a few willows (*Salix*), indigo-bush (*Amorpha fruticosa*), stenosiphon (*Stenosiphon*), and salt cedar (*Tamarix*), a shrub that in 1820 had not yet invaded here. We found no elm.
[35]JAMES [3], August 14.

a heavy growth of grasses and herbaceous plants."[36] This encampment we believe to have been near the mouths of Pickette Ranch Creek and Three Corrals Creek, approximately six miles east of where Texas Highway 70 crosses the Canadian in Roberts County.

August 15. According to the *Account,* the morning was "advanced" when the party started their journey.[37] Their horses had broken loose and some had strayed, causing an "unusual delay." The party crossed the dry riverbed twice during the day and halted at 4 P.M. near "a scattering grove of small-leaved elms."[38]

We searched the north and south sides of the Canadian River in this area for elms. We were unsuccessful in finding a single tree on the south side, but a grove was finally located on the north side along Morgan Creek. The leaves of these trees were small compared with those of the typical *Ulmus americana.* James described "the whiteness of the trunk,"[39] a characteristic that did not show on the trees we saw. The trees were flat-topped, and those standing alone did have a broad diameter with branches close to the ground, as James had described.[40]

We place this campsite just east of the mouth of Morgan Creek on the north side of the river, approximately six miles northwest of the town of Canadian in Hemphill County. The mileage for the day would have been fifteen.

August 16. The party passed a large tributary from the southwest soon after leaving the campsite of August 15. This tributary, Red Deer Creek or Dry River, enters the Canadian no more than a mile northwest of the town of Canadian and is one of the few certain landmarks along their route in west Texas. Strangely, as revealed in the *Account,* they concluded that this tributary was the one on which the Indians had encamped the night before the party met them on August 11.[41] Red Deer Creek is some seventy to seventy-five miles east of where they had camped with the Indians.[42]

[36]JAMES [3], August 15 (discussed here as "last evening").
[37]JAMES [2] in THWAITES [1], XVI, 126.
[38]JAMES [1], II, 121–22; JAMES [2] in THWAITES [1], XVI, 128.
[39]JAMES [1], II, 122; JAMES [2] in THWAITES [1], XVI, 128.
[40]JAMES [1], II, 122; JAMES [2] in THWAITES [1], XVI, 129.
[41]JAMES [1], II, 123; JAMES [2] in THWAITES [1], XVI, 130.

[42]We think it is more likely that the Indians had camped on Antelope Creek, which intersects the Canadian River just east of Sanford in Hutchison County. This would have meant that the Indians had traveled some four miles before meeting the party, and three or four miles upstream

Just east of the town of Canadian the course of the river changes from east to southeast. James noted this change with the comment, "This morning we have made a great bend to the south."[43]

The campsite of the next day, August 17, opposite sand dunes, can be located with some certainty, although no specific distance traveled or geographical features (except for Red Deer Creek) were given for August 16.

We are arbitrarily allotting them half the distance from their August 15 camp to their August 17 camp. That gives them twelve miles for the day and places their camp six miles east of the town of Canadian in Hemphill County.

August 17. At 1:00 P.M., according to James, the party encamped to hunt.[44] Their camp was on the "southwest side of the river, under a low bluff" (the south side, according to the diary),[45] opposite "a range of low sand hills."[46]

These sand dunes, which we have viewed from the north and south sides of the river, are conspicuously indicated on the topographic maps and begin some twenty miles downriver from the town of Canadian.

We place their campsite this day about eighteen miles downstream from the town of Canadian in Hemphill County. The placement of this camp is also based upon the course direction the party took the following morning. That course direction convinced us that the party crossed into Oklahoma near the Antelope Hills on August 18 rather than the day before, as indicated by Thwaites.[47] Perhaps Thwaites concluded that because the map in the *Account* places their camp of August 17 on the east side of the 100th meridian,[48] which here is the Texas/Oklahoma boundary.

---

with the party, for a total of seven or eight miles for the day. Indians traveled approximately ten miles per day when in large groups with families.

[43]JAMES [3], August 16.

[44]JAMES [3], August 17.

[45]JAMES [3], August 17.

[46]JAMES [1], II, 126; JAMES [2] in THWAITES [1], XVI, 133.

[47]THWAITES [1], XVI, 133n.

[48]JAMES [6], Map of the Country Drained by the Mississippi—Western Section, atlas; JAMES [7], I, Map of the Country Drained by the Mississippi, fold-in.

CHAPTER FIVE

OKLAHOMA

AUGUST 18. WE BELIEVE IT WAS ON THIS DAY THAT THE PARTY CROSSED the 100th meridian into present Oklahoma, leaving Spanish territory, in which they had been since crossing the Arkansas River near Rocky Ford, Colorado.

Leaving camp at 5 A.M., the party followed courses "regulated entirely by the direction of the river."[1] Before their midday stop they had traveled "north fifty-five east, eleven miles; then north, ten east, seven miles; in all eighteen miles before dinner."[2]

Following a (corrected) reading of N65½°E for eleven miles, the expedition would have crossed into Oklahoma within five or six miles of the campsite of August 17. Another five miles on this course would have brought them to the point where the Canadian River turns abruptly north to begin its first of three distinctive meanders in western Oklahoma. The second northerly course (corrected to N20½°E) for seven miles would have brought them to the top of the first meander, which follows north around the Antelope Hills, a prominent landmark in Roger Mills County (Section 32, T17N, R25W).

Curiously, no mention of these hills is made either in the *Account* or the diary. That omission becomes even more puzzling when one considers that on this very day James commented on "the want of ascertained and fixed points of reference."[3] James further stated, "There are no mountains, hills, or other remarkable objects to serve as points of departure, nearer than the Rocky Mountains and the Arkansa."[4]

The party was somewhat perplexed, according to James, by the northerly course of the river, which did not fit their ideas about the course of the Red River.[5] Their concern was assuaged somewhat when their afternoon's course along the eastern side of the loop took

[1]JAMES [1], II, 130; JAMES [2] in THWAITES [1], XVI, 138.
[2]JAMES [1], II, 130; JAMES [2] in THWAITES [1], XVI, 138.
[3]JAMES [1], II, 128; JAMES [2] in THWAITES [1], XVI, 136.
[4]JAMES [2] in THWAITES [1], XVI, 136.
[5]JAMES [1], II, 130–31; JAMES [2] in THWAITES [1], XVI, 138–39.

them in a southerly direction. The description of the next two or three days of travel accounts so sufficiently for the last two meanders of the river that there is no doubt as to their location.

In his diary the next day James stated, "Yesterday we travelled something more than thirty miles."[6] At sunset they encamped on the north side of the river. We place this camp in Ellis County near or only slightly west of the point where the Pack Saddle Bridge (U.S. Highway 283) crosses the Canadian River.

We have endeavored to view the Antelope Hills from several points along the river, which encircles the hills except at the southern end. At the southwestern end, just before the river turns north (this northern turn was plainly visible to us) the Antelope Hills show up prominently. We were on the north side of the river, but it appeared certain that the hills could have been seen quite as well from the south side. We could not cross to the south side because the river was in flood stage—a contrast indeed to the dry bed that the expedition followed in 1820.

Three miles farther north and east the river flows almost due north. From here, too, the hills show prominently from the floodplain. A mile and a half farther north the hills can be seen, so we were told, from the floodplain.

Nowhere around the north end would the hills be visible from the river. Even when we were one to two miles north of the river and a hundred feet above it, the hills did not show. Similarly, there are few if any places along the south-flowing river on the east side of the hills where they are visible.

By the time one gets to the Pack Saddle Bridge, near where we think they camped, the hills can be plainly seen nine miles to the northwest. With the hills easily visible from the floodplain from several places along the southwest and west side, one cannot be sure why no remark was made of this conspicuous landmark.

The river does vary its course over the years, however, from one side of the broad, half-mile or so floodplain to the other. There is no way to know where the river was in 1820, but if it had been close to the bluffs on the inside of the meander it is very possible that the party would not have seen the hills while traveling around this loop.

August 19. According to James, "In the afternoon, finding the course of the river again bending towards the north . . . we turned off on the right hand side, and choosing an east course, travelled across

[6]JAMES [3], August 19.

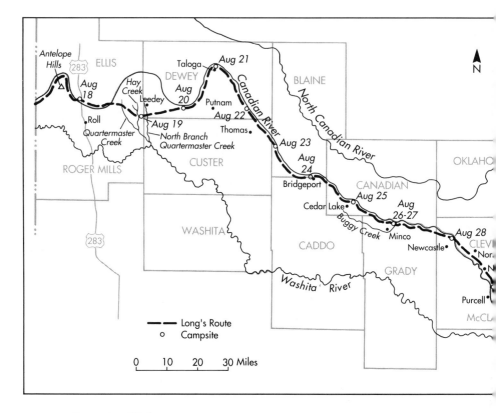

Route in Oklahoma

the hills, not doubting but we should soon arrive again at the river."[7]
In the twelve to fourteen miles they covered from their previous
night's camp they would have come to the point where the river turns
north on its second of the three meanders.[8]

Leaving the river and traveling east, they would have topped the
dividing ridge between the Canadian and Washita river drainages in
about two miles. James described the scene — the expanse of rolling
plains intersected by numerous wooded valleys leading to the southeast.[9] From near where the party must have topped the dividing ridge

[7]JAMES [1], II, 132; JAMES [2] in THWAITES [1], XVI, 140.
[8]This occurs about twelve miles northeast of Roll, Roger Mills County.
[9]That would have been at the upper reaches of Quartermaster, clearly visible from the ridge,
and its tributaries, such as Hay Creek. Quartermaster Creek enters the Washita River about twenty
miles to the southeast.

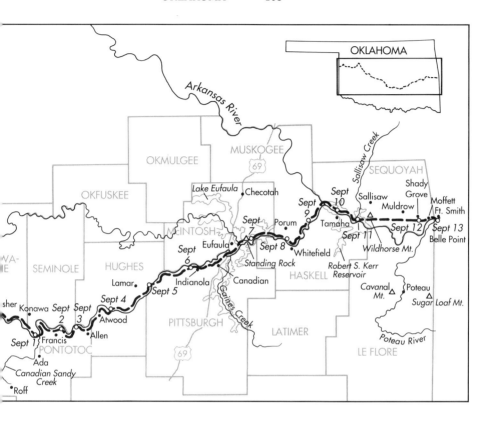

are visible the Canadian to the north, with red sandstone ravines leading to it, and the Antelope Hills to the distant west.

The party must have headed southeast soon after ascending to the dividing ridge, for the next morning they changed their course "from S.E. to N.E."[10] Inasmuch as they had expected the river to turn to the south after bending north, such a course was not illogical. They continued their march to the southeast, across the elevated, grass-covered plain, until sunset.[11] When it became obvious that night would fall before they found the river again, they began to search for a suitable campsite. They found some water dripping from the side of a cliff of sandstone, and there they camped, having traveled eighteen to twenty miles for the day.

[10]JAMES [1], II, 134; JAMES [2] in THWAITES [1], XVI, 144.

[11]Today, as likely then, the dominant grasses are buffalo grass (*Buchloe dactyloides*), grama grasses (*Bouteloua*), and Canada wildrye (*Elymus canadensis*).

Their southeasterly course would have taken them down onto the Washita drainage. While it is not possible to ascertain which of the branches of Quartermaster Creek they had reached, that it was one of them is certain. The red sandstone walls of the ravines along with the outcrops of limestone of a "snowy whiteness"[12] are visible in many places, and the distance they traveled northeast to the river on the following morning gives evidence that they camped in a ravine in Roger Mills County, near the Roger Mills/Dewey/Custer county line, some six to ten miles southwest of Leedey, Dewey County.

August 20. The lack of water obliged them to find the Canadian, so this morning they changed their course from southeast to northeast. They "travelled about fifteen miles, and encamped at noon on the bank of the river."[13]

The *Account* states that they followed a buffalo path because it would be "the easiest and most direct route" to the river.[14] The path led them to the only pool of water "that could be found within a very considerable distance."[15] Near the pool was a grove in which they planned to camp. Standing in the pool and lying in the grove were a herd of buffalo, two of which they shot. Camp was set up. There is little likelihood today that the pool would be in the same place during periods of low water.[16]

Another clue as to where they struck the river appears in the diary for the next day, where James stated, "Almost our whole ride today has been nearly due north."[17] Clearly, they camped at noon at or near the bottom of the meander between the second and third loops, about five to ten miles east of Leedey, Dewey County. That location is the proper distance (fifteen miles) from the ravines of Quartermaster Creek.

August 21. Evidently by now they realized that the course of the river was impossible to anticipate. An easterly course here across the prairie would not have been difficult. At any rate, when the river again turned north, they followed it.

A ride of twenty to twenty-five miles, five to nine miles of which

12JAMES [1], II, 133; JAMES [2] in THWAITES [1], XVI, 142.

13JAMES [1], II, 135; JAMES [2] in THWAITES [1], XVI, 144.

14JAMES [1], II, 135; JAMES [2] in THWAITES [1], XVI, 135.

15JAMES [1], II, 136; JAMES [2] in THWAITES [1], XVI, 136.

16As has been mentioned before, the Canadian was in flood when we visited it. The river is well lined with trees, with no particularly prominent grove.

17JAMES [3], August 21.

being to the east and northeast and the rest nearly to the north, would have placed their camp for the night just north of Taloga, Dewey County, at the north end of the third and last loop.

August 22. As is indicated in the *Account* on August 23, their ride "for the last two days . . . inclined considerably to the south."[18] James stated in his diary that "the greater part" of their travels on August 22 had been "nearly due south,"[19] indicating that the party rounded the northeast-to-east bend of the river at Taloga before heading south.

There is no information given that helps pinpoint with certainty the campsite for this day. We are allotting only eighteen miles for this day's travel, based upon the known distribution of plants collected in the days that follow. That would place their camp near the mouths of One Horse and Yellow Bull creeks, eleven miles east of Putnam, Dewey County. The hills on the southwest side of the river here are interestingly shaped mesas topped with caprock and cones of bright red sandstone; no comment about them, however, is made by James.

August 23. As the party continued southeast today, James collected an evening primrose that would later become the type of *Oenothera jamesii*. His plant collection is our only clue to their location, as no geographical features are given. That is despite the fact that there are many conspicuous bluffs along the southwest side of the river, notably near Thomas, Custer County. *Oenothera jamesii* is presently unknown in Dewey and Blaine counties, but it does occur in Custer County. We believe that this presents some evidence that on this day the expedition followed the Canadian on its course through northeastern Custer County as they passed from Dewey County downstream into Blaine County.

We allot seventeen miles for the day and place their campsite near the mouth of Bear Creek, Blaine County, about nine miles southeast of Thomas.

The noted occurrence of Texas buckeye (*Aesculus glabra* var. *arguta*) two days later (August 25) is further evidence, along with distance, that the party had not yet proceeded downstream into Caddo and Canadian counties, where buckeye begins to occur on the hills and some ravines on the south side of the Canadian.

---

[18]JAMES [1], II, 140; JAMES [2] in THWAITES [1], XVI, 150.
[19]JAMES [3], August 23.

August 24. Again for this day no information is given concerning their exact route or the distance traveled.

The abundance of game in the area gave them the "power to kill as many bison, bear,[20] deer, and turkies"[21] as they wished. James stated, "Our game today has been two bears, three deers, one turkey, a large white wolf, and a hare."[22]

Based again on the known distribution of Texas buckeye, we would place their campsite a little west of the recorded sites for *Aesculus* on the Canadian, a mile or so west of Bridgeport on the Blaine/Caddo county line. That would make the distance traveled this day some seventeen miles.

August 25. On this day in his diary, James first noted the occurrence of a few plants,[23] most notable of which was the Texas buckeye.[24]

There is no indication as to the number of miles the party traveled downstream today. Certain geographical features at the campsite of August 26 and the following Sunday, August 27, help to locate it some thirty-four miles downriver from the campsite of August 24. It seems likely that the party would have traveled at least half of this thirty-four-mile distance on August 25, although their exhausted horses much impeded their progress. We can only surmise that the campsite for August 25 was northeast of Cedar Lake, Canadian County. Here, too, along the south bank of the Canadian, the *Aesculus* is abundant.

No plants are mentioned today in the *Account,* and it is not until August 27 that *Aesculus* is mentioned among the plants observed. Because the field entry in the diary for *Aesculus* was made on August 25, we feel that this date is the more accurate.

The buckeye when in flower is a conspicuous tree. The trees were long past their flowering stage, however, when the expedition noted their occurrence. In May 1983, we had an opportunity to search for the westernmost limits of this species along the Canadian in Oklahoma. From Bridgeport we crossed the river and headed northwest for some twenty-five miles along the river, arriving at the bridge at

---

[20]The many bears in this area may be the reason for the name Bear Creek, near the spot where we believe they camped on the previous evening.

[21]JAMES [1], II, 142; JAMES [2] in THWAITES [1], XVI, 151.

[22]JAMES [2] in THWAITES [1], XVI, 151.

[23]JAMES [3], August 25.

[24]Called by James *Aesculus flava.*

Thomas, Custer County, without having found an *Aesculus*. Crossing the bridge to the south side of the river and traveling southeast, we again found no *Aesculus* until we searched the ravines at Bridgeport on the south side of the Canadian. In the floodplain forest at the mouth of a ravine but a half mile east of Bridgeport we found a stand of *Aesculus*. We believe that this stand represents its most westward occurrence on the Canadian. Since James did not note the occurrence of Texas buckeye until August 25, the campsite of August 24 must surely have been upstream, west of Bridgeport as we had previously surmised.

August 26 and 27. The men headed southeast at an early hour on the morning of August 26 and rode "at a small distance from the river."[25] For the first time in over a week James voiced concern about their location. In his diary on this day James wrote that by now the party had expected to be near the settlements, but that there were no indications of them.[26]

For their campsite the men chose "a delightful situation at the confluence of a small creek from the south."[27] There, on the hills that rose one above another from the river, herds of bison, elk, wild horses, and deer grazed. This beautiful campsite, we believe, was at the mouth of Buggy Creek, a creek that parallels the Canadian for over twenty miles before turning north to enter it near Minco, Grady County. The estimated total distance traveled is seventeen miles.

August 28. Since August 22 the course of the party had been predominantly to the southeast, but near Minco the eastward turn in the river's course was noted by James, and he commented that "the aggregate of our courses for the day was about east, and the distance twenty-one miles."[28]

There are a number of streams that enter the Canadian along these twenty-one miles, but James recorded only two in addition to "several springs on the south side at the base of a rocky hill, rising abruptly from the bed of the river."[29] The rocky hill is likely that on the Canadian River five miles northeast of Tuttle, Grady County. It is approximately ten miles downstream from their previous night's camp.

[25]JAMES [1], II, 142; JAMES [2] in THWAITES [1], XVI, 152.
[26]JAMES [3], August 26.
[27]JAMES [2] in THWAITES [1], XVI, 153.
[28]JAMES [1], II, 147; JAMES [2] in THWAITES [1], XVI, 158.
[29]JAMES [2] in THWAITES [1], XVI, 159.

In late afternoon or early evening the party left the river and traveled across the open plain before returning to the river to camp. We place their campsite near the McClain/Cleveland county line, two miles or so east of the U.S. Highway 62 bridge across the river and three to four miles northeast of Newcastle.

In his diary, James recorded honey locust (*Gleditsia triacanthos*).[30] Once again James observed a species at its westernmost range on the Canadian River.

August 29. The Canadian again begins a turn to the southeast near their previous night's campsite; hence, the party chose to ride this morning a little "south of east"[31] a mile or so north of the river. As they traveled, James commented about the forests on the distant horizon. They are the post oak–blackjack forests easily seen from near Noble southward to Lexington.

The distance the party traveled this day can only be approximated. We estimate it as twenty to twenty-one miles and place their camp approximately three miles north of Lexington, Cleveland County, where for a few miles the Canadian flows nearly due south.

This camp, according to James,[32] was on the "left" bank of the river near a bee tree, which made them think that they would arrive soon at the settlements. Their estimate was doubtless based on information from their hunters that bees rarely migrate more than three hundred miles from the settlements.

August 30 and 31. The men traveled laboriously for a time through the sand of the riverbed, almost blinded by the sun's reflection upon it, before they ascended to the open plain.

The penetration of the forest along the river bottom was accomplished with great difficulty, as the vines of many species greatly impeded their progress. Of the vines encountered, James noted three species of "Cissus" growing together.[33] One such species he called *Cissus bipinnata,* which is peppervine (*Ampelopsis arborea*). This species gives some clue that their ascent from the river was in Pottawatomie County, where the species occurs near Wanette. No records of *A. arborea* are known upstream in either Cleveland or McClain counties. James also observed a change from red sandstone

[30]JAMES [3], August 28.
[31]JAMES [1], II, 148; JAMES [2] in THWAITES [1], XVI, 160.
[32]JAMES [3], August 30.
[33]JAMES [1], II, 150; JAMES [2] in THWAITES [1], XVI, 161.

to a dark-grey sandstone as they ascended the hills. This geologic change, which occurs near the western edge of Pottawatomie County, is an additional clue to the party's location.

They camped, we believe, about four miles southwest of Asher, Pottawatomie County, where, as described by James, the river valley is "much contracted in width, and the bed itself occupying less space by half than where we had left it above."[34] The total estimated distance traveled is twenty-four miles. The men remained there on the following day, August 31, to make observations.

September 1. The river, just south of Asher, begins a serpentine course southward. Near the same point the grey sandstone is replaced by a Pennsylvanian marine shale with interbedded sandstone, limestone, and coal. Both the serpentine course of the river and the geologic change were observed by James as the party proceeded downstream this morning.[35]

After their midday halt they ascended some hills with very characteristic limestone caprock and eroding sandstone bases. These are the hills that occur near Konawa. From the summit of these hills, near the river, James described the mountainous regions to the south and east.[36]

We estimate the distance traveled as nineteen miles and place their campsite on the Canadian in Seminole County, a couple of miles west of the mouth of Canadian Sandy Creek, or approximately six miles southeast of Konawa.

September 2. Soon after leaving their camp at sunrise they passed "a large tributary from the south."[37] We believe the creek to have been Canadian Sandy Creek,[38] a helpful landmark in pinpointing the party's location, but there is no indication how far downstream the party proceeded past the creek before encamping.

On this day in the *Account* and on the following day in the diary, James noted many of the trees of the river valley and highlands.[39] Of the species cited, none have a distribution in Oklahoma that is helpful in further ascertaining the party's location.

[34]JAMES [1], II, 151; JAMES [2] in THWAITES [1], XVI, 162.
[35]JAMES [1], II, 152–53; JAMES [2] in THWAITES [1], XVI, 164–65.
[36]The mountains to the east are doubtless the Shawnee Hills.
[37]JAMES [1], II, 153; JAMES [2] in THWAITES [1], XVI, 165.
[38]This creek heads near Roff in extreme southwestern Pontotoc County and flows north and west for over twenty-five miles before entering the Canadian River some six miles north of Ada, Pontotoc County.
[39]JAMES [1], II, 155; JAMES [2] in THWAITES [1], XVI, 168; JAMES [3], September 3.

Based on events and noted changes in the river's course in the days to follow, we allot seventeen miles for the distance traveled this day and place their campsite three miles northeast of Francis, Pontotoc County, or across the river in Seminole County.

September 3. As their last night's campsite did not have suitable grass for their horses, they moved downstream in search of pasture. According to James such a place was located in six to eight miles.[40]

Their campsite would be about five miles northwest of Allen near the junction of Seminole, Hughes, and Pontotoc counties where, to the southeast, there is a broad floodplain.

From this campsite James "made an excursion into the adjoining forest to collect plants."[41]

September 4. About four miles below the previous night's campsite the Canadian turns northeastward toward the Arkansas River. In his diary for September 6 James stated, "The course of the river for two or three days has been more northerly than for a considerable distance above."[42] With the exception of the noted reappearance of running water in the riverbed, very little information is given in the *Account.*[43]

We estimate seventeen miles as the distance traveled and place their camp about three miles northeast of Atwood, Hughes County.

September 5. Again no information on the distance traveled is given, but James noted[44] that the cedars on the rocky hills were "sometimes so numerous, as to give their peculiar and gloomy colouring to the landscape."[45]

We have allotted nineteen miles for the distance traveled, which places their campsite five miles east of Lamar, Hughes County.

September 6. In the *Account,* events that occurred on both

[40]JAMES [3], September 3.
[41]JAMES [1], II, 156; JAMES [2] in THWAITES [1], XVI, 168.
[42]JAMES [3], September 6.
[43]JAMES [1], II, 157; JAMES [2] in THWAITES [1], XVI, 170.
[44]JAMES [1], II, 158–59; JAMES [2] in THWAITES [1], XVI, 171.
[45]Here in Hughes County the hills rise on both sides of the river, and juniper (*Juniperus virginiana*) occurs abundantly. The party is now in the area of the Shawnee Hills, which occur "in northwestern Pittsburg and eastern Hughes counties" (GOULD, 36) or "between present McAlester, Pittsburg County, and Atwood, Hughes County" (DOTT, 164).

September 6 and 7 are combined under the entry for September 6.[46] The distance traveled is not given, but, in his diary entry for September 7, James stated, "Yesterday evening we . . . encamped at an early hour. The country about our encampment was a beautiful plain in part covered with timber and having a good soil."[47] A ride of fifteen miles would have brought them to the Choate Prairie on the south side of the river about three miles west of Indianola, Pittsburg County. This prairie is the stated distance from the known campsite of September 7, which was just below the junction of the Canadian with the North Canadian River near Eufaula.

September 7. The nearly twenty-eight miles of travel today, as given by James, brought the expedition past several landmarks.[48] The first of these James called the "falls of the Canadian."[49] It was "marked by the occurrence of a peculiar bed of rocks crossing the river, and by the rapid descent of the current." The falls, now inundated by the Lake Eufaula Reservoir, was located a mile upstream from the mouth of Gaines Creek, a then-unnamed stream that, James noted, entered the Canadian from the south.[50] The map accompanying the *Account* calls this stream the "South Fork of the Canadian R."[51] Today it forms an arm of Lake Eufaula. The northern end of the arm, and thus the mouth of Gaines Creek, is located about five miles northeast of Canadian, Pittsburg County.

James gave little encouragement to future travelers as he described the land over which they had traveled from the Rocky Mountains to the falls.[52] "Though the soil," he wrote, "is in some places fertile, the want of timber, of navigable streams, and of water for the necessities of life, render it an unfit residence for any but a nomade population. The traveller who shall at any time have traversed its desolate sands, will, we think join us in the wish that this region may for ever remain the unmolested haunt of the native hunter, the bison, and the jackall."[53]

---

[46]JAMES [1], II, 159–62; JAMES [2] in THWAITES [1], XVI, 172–76.

[47]JAMES [3], September 7.

[48]JAMES [3], September 7.

[49]JAMES [1], II, 160–61.

[50]JAMES [1], II, 161; JAMES [2] in THWAITES [1], XVI, 174.

[51]JAMES [6], Map of the Country Drained by the Mississippi—Western Section, atlas; JAMES [7], I, Map of the Country Drained by the Mississippi, fold-in.

[52]JAMES [2] in THWAITES [1], XVI, 174.

[53]In the Philadelphia edition (JAMES [1], II, 161), James chose to leave the country to "the native hunter, the bison, the prairie wolf, and the marmot."

Much of the land that James described became a large part of the state of Oklahoma and the Texas panhandle. Perhaps its present-day inhabitants, who have experienced the heat of late summer and its accompanying insects, can sympathize with James and understand his uncomplimentary remarks. As Thwaites pointed out, "The myth of the Great American Desert lived for half a century."[54]

The next easily located landmark was the mouth of the North Canadian River, which they reached "six or eight miles farther down."[55] In his diary James called this river "Verplank's River," after one of their hunters.[56] It joined what James continued to call in his diary the Red River.

The North Canadian, which was designated as the "North Fork" on the map accompanying the *Account*,[57] joins the Canadian six miles downstream from Gaines Creek. It, too, now forms an arm of Lake Eufaula Reservoir. The original mouth of the North Canadian was three and a half miles east of Eufaula, McIntosh County.

"[T]hree and a half miles" below the mouth of the North Canadian, James noted[58] that the party passed "a remarkable rock, standing isolated in the middle of the river, like the Grand Tower in the Mississippi. It is about twenty-five feet high, and fifty or sixty in diameter,[59] and its sides so perpendicular as to render the summit inaccessible." According to Foreman, Captain Bonneville in 1830 referred to this rock as "Mary's Rock" and gave its height as "sixty five feet . . . and 20 in diameter and nearly round."[60]

This landmark is Standing Rock, which is presently about twenty-five feet underwater in Lake Eufaula. Modern topographic maps show the rock to be located about two miles below the mouth of the North Canadian River. Along the shore of Lake Eufaula at the foot of Standing Rock Mountain is another rock, presently called Standing Rock. It is north and slightly east of the inundated rock.

A mile or so below Standing Rock the men camped on a sandy beach in either McIntosh or Pittsburg County.

[54]THWAITES [1], XVI, 174n.
[55]JAMES [1], II, 161; JAMES [2] in THWAITES [1], XVI, 174.
[56]JAMES [3], September 7.
[57]JAMES [6], Map of the Country Drained by the Mississippi—Western Section, atlas; JAMES [7], I, Map of the Country Drained by the Mississippi, fold-in.
[58]JAMES [2] in THWAITES [1], XVI, 175.
[59]In the Philadelphia edition of the *Account* (JAMES [1], II, 162) the rock is said to be "about seventy-five feet high, and fifty or sixty in diameter."
[60]FOREMAN, 329.

September 8. A log canoe was discovered by the party near where they made their midday halt. As the canoe appeared to be long abandoned, they placed their packs and heavy baggage in it, and two of the men began to float it down the river.

Their evening's camp was on the north side of the river. We estimate the distance they traveled today to have been thirteen or fourteen miles and place their camp four or five miles south of Porum, Muskogee County.[61]

Being forced to wade the shallow water of the river and drag the canoe much of the way, the two men and the canoe arrived much later at camp.

September 9. A mile or two downstream from the previous night's camp, the men left, on a projecting point of rock, the meat of an elk the hunters had killed that morning and a note instructing the men in the canoe "to add this supply of provisions to their cargo."[62]

The bed of the river at this location and for a short distance downstream was formed by "a soft green slaty sandstone."[63] This sandstone occurs along the south side of the river northwest of Whitefield, Haskell County, upstream only a short distance from where Oklahoma State Highway 2 crosses the river. A ledge two hundred to three hundred feet long and fifty feet above the river is found there.[64]

At noon the party took a measurement to approximate the latitude. The resulting reading of 35°30' was greater than what the men had anticipated for the Red River.[65] Once again they wondered if they could be instead upon a tributary of the Arkansas.

Unbeknownst to them, the men had camped this night only eight to ten miles from the junction of the Canadian with the Arkansas. We estimate they were in the vicinity of Holt Mountain and Harris Mountain, in extreme-southeastern Muskogee County.

The total distance traveled was eleven to thirteen miles.

September 10. The party's arrival in eight or ten miles at the

---

[61]That is about six miles below the Lake Eufaula dam.

[62]JAMES [1], II, 166; JAMES [2] in THWAITES [1], XVI, 180.

[63]JAMES [1], II, 166; JAMES [2] in THWAITES [1], XVI, 180.

[64]We visited with a longtime resident of Whitefield, Mr. Arthur Rouse, who aided us in finding this ledge.

[65]In the Philadelphia edition (JAMES [6], II, 66) the reading is 35°80', clearly an error.

confluence of the Canadian with the Arkansas River brought "disappointment and chagrin."[66]

Of this error Major Long commented, "We were led to the commission of this mistake in consequence of our not having been able to procure a guide acquainted with this part of the country. Our only dependence in this respect, was upon Pike's Map which assigns to the head waters of Red river the apparent locality of those of the Canadian."[67]

In reviewing Pike's map,[68] Long could have easily concluded that a southwesterly course from near Pike's First Fork on the Arkansas River would have brought his party to a branch of the Red River, as it is the only river shown south of the Arkansas and east of the mountains and was plainly labeled the "Rio Rojo." The course direction of the upper reaches of the Red River, as indicated on Pike's map, and that of Ute Creek are very similar.

Misled by Pike's map and the assurances of Indians as to their location, Long and his men had spent over a month traveling down the Canadian River. Because the men and horses were exhausted and because of the lateness of the season, they would forgo a return trip of an unknown distance in search of the headwaters of the Red River. Thirty-two years would pass before the Marcy Expedition would locate what was thought to be the head of the Red River in the canyons southeast of Amarillo, Texas. The actual headwaters of the Red, however, begin in eastern New Mexico, a location not determined until the present century.[69]

Once across the Arkansas the party began to search for a suitable campsite, but found themselves surrounded by dense cane brakes. Until sunset the exhausting journey through the cane continued with no end in sight. A mile and a half upstream the men had passed a small open woods. To this they returned for the night so much exhausted that even "the irritation of the ticks"[70] went unnoticed as they slept.

It seems unlikely that the men would have traveled more than six miles through the cane brakes before returning the mile and a half upstream. That would place their camp not more than five miles downstream from the junction of the Canadian with the Arkansas.

[66]JAMES [1], II, 167; JAMES [2] in THWAITES [1], XVI, 180.
[67]LONG, 8–9.
[68]JACKSON [2], I, Map 4, fold-in between 388 and 389.
[69]FLORES, 332.
[70]JAMES [1], II, 168; JAMES [2] in THWAITES [1], XVI, 182.

We estimate the camp to have been on the north side of the Arkansas River opposite the mouth of Pheasant Creek and Tamaha in Sequoyah County, an area presently inundated by the Robert S. Kerr Reservoir.

September 11. According to James, an hour or two were spent this morning laboriously emerging from the cane brakes of the riverbottom to the open woods.[71]

From there they continued north almost at right angles to the river, where they soon found a path that they correctly assumed to be the one that would lead them to the settlements. James estimated, presumably upon arriving at this night's campsite, that they were now ten to twelve miles beyond the junction of the Canadian with the Arkansas.[72]

We estimate the campsite to have been on Sallisaw Creek about six and a half miles southwest of Sallisaw, Sequoyah County,[73] and twelve miles from the junction of the Canadian with the Arkansas.

September 12. The party, surely in high anticipation of reaching Belle Point, began their eastward march at sunrise. James described the undulating course of the Arkansas River, which lay on his right (to the south).[74] A sun-filled mist rose along the course of the river, giving it a distinctive outline.

James also described a ridge on the north side of the Arkansas that paralleled the course of the river.[75] This ridge we believe to have been Wildhorse Mountain, a narrow ridge less than a mile wide that rises approximately three hundred feet above the prairie and runs northeast to southwest for some six miles along the Arkansas River about four miles south of Sallisaw, Sequoyah County.

The blue summits of the Sugar Loaf Mountains and Cavanal Mountain[76] south of the Arkansas River were noted by James.[77] By 11:00 A.M. the men halted along the path to Belle Point to hunt. No

---

[71]JAMES [3], September 11.

[72]JAMES [3], September 11.

[73]Captain Bell's party camped on this same creek on September 7 (FULLER AND HAFEN, 273), a little north of Long's campsite. The routes of the Missouri Pacific Railroad and U.S. Highway 64 from near the junction of the Illinois River with the Arkansas River to near Ft. Smith, Arkansas, closely approximate the path which led Bell's party to Belle Point.

[74]JAMES [1], II, 169; JAMES [2] in THWAITES [1], XVI, 183.

[75]JAMES [1], II, 169–70; JAMES [2] in THWAITES [1], XVI, 183.

[76]Referred to by James as "Point Sucre and Cavaniol mountains."

[77]JAMES [1], II, 169; JAMES [2] in THWAITES [1], XVI, 183.

game was found, but the ripened fruits of the pawpaw trees (*Asimina triloba*) provided a delicious repast.

Their afternoon's journey was impeded by a failing mule that necessitated an early encampment. We estimate that the party traveled no more than four miles this afternoon, which would place their campsite about two miles south of Shady Grove, Sequoyah County. The total distance traveled for the day was about nineteen miles. In the evening Hugh Glenn visited.[78] He was returning from Fort Smith to his trading post and was camped only a short distance from Long's party. Mr. Glenn was the first white man the party had encountered since leaving Engineer Cantonment on June 6. From him they learned that Captain Bell's party had already arrived at Fort Smith.

We wondered how far north and east the party could have traveled on September 11 after emerging from the cane brakes on the river and still have had the river, the ridge, and the mountains in view the following morning. In our own exploration we discovered that the Arkansas River and the summits of Cavanal and Sugar Loaf mountains are not visible from the north side of Wildhorse Mountain. From this side it is obvious that this mountain is a ridge, but its direction with respect to the Arkansas is clear only from the south side. From near the campsite of September 11 and eastward for a few miles, James would have had a clear view of the ridge that constitutes Wildhorse Mountain.

When we viewed the probable route it seemed evident that in the early morning they had traveled east between the Arkansas River and Wildhorse Mountain upon the wooded hills a couple of miles north of the river valley.[79] After two or three hours of travel eastward the Cavanal Mountain would have been clearly visible some twenty miles due south.[80]

Pawpaw has not since been recorded in Sequoyah County. We calculate that by 11:00 A.M. the party would have been about five

[78]Glenn was the sutler to Fort Smith. According to Bell (FULLER AND HAFEN, 270), his trading post was located "nearly equidistant from the Verdegris and Grand rivers and about 200 yards from the Arkansas" in an area known as Three Forks (in reference to the junction of the Verdigris, Grand (Neosho), and Arkansas rivers). This area is just west of Fort Gibson and northeast of Muskogee, Muskogee County, Oklahoma.

[79]James would have seen species of oak, elm, hackberry, plum, maple, ash, hickory, and hawthorn. Black willow, black walnut, river birch, honey locust, red mulberry, sassafras, serviceberry, redbud, possumhaw, box elder, buckeye, blackgum, chittamwood, and persimmon are also found in the forests of this area.

[80]This mountain rises 2,385 feet above sea level in Le Flore County, Oklahoma, about three to four miles west-northwest of Poteau on the west side of the Poteau River.

miles south of Muldrow, Sequoyah County. We searched unsuccessfully for miles in all directions from this site in search of the pawpaw. Most of the land in the Arkansas River bottom in this area has been cleared for cultivation. Current topographic maps still refer to this area as the Paw Paw Bottom, surely in reference to the trees that once grew there. Noticeable in this area of the Arkansas River bottom, however, were the summits of Sugar Loaf Mountains, visible some twenty-three miles south and only slightly east.[81]

September 13. In heavy rain the men continued eastward for about four or five miles until they arrived at a plantation[82] opposite Belle Point,[83] the site of Fort Smith.

The members of Long's party were eager to converse with other people. They accordingly sought directions to Belle Point from those at the plantation, even though knowing they "were not ten rods from the ferry."[84] A discharged pistol alerted the fort's occupants to their arrival. Captain Bell, whose party had arrived at Fort Smith on September 9, expressed surprise at the arrival of Long's party on the Arkansas River opposite Belle Point.[85] He would soon learn that the Canadian River had been confused for the Red.[86]

By 9:00 A.M. all members of the party had been ferried across the Arkansas to the fort, where they were greeted by officers and by members of Captain Bell's party. Their 1,550 to 1,600 miles of travel, from Engineer Cantonment to Fort Smith, had taken one hundred days. It ended in a breakfast feast.

James remained at Belle Point for one week. During that time he ascended the Poteau for less than two miles. Near this point he was able to step across the river in almost a single step, "so inconsiderable was the quantity of water it contained."[87]

---

[81]Sugar Loaf Mountain rises about 2,560 feet above sea level in Le Flore County, Oklahoma, about nine miles east-southeast of Poteau on the east side of the Poteau River. Less than two miles northeast of Sugar Loaf Mountain two other peaks of this range rise along the Oklahoma/Arkansas state line.

[82]The town of Moffett, located on the north side of the Arkansas in extreme-southeastern Sequoyah County, Oklahoma, would be very near the location of the plantation.

[83]The site, so-called by the French hunters, was chosen by Major Long in 1817 for the establishment of Fort Smith. Belle Point is located on the south side of the Arkansas on a rise about fifty feet above the river and just downstream from the mouth of the Poteau.

[84]JAMES [1], II, 172; JAMES [2] in THWAITES [1], XVI, 186.

[85]FULLER AND HAFEN, 280–81.

[86]Had Long's party descended the Red River, they would have arrived at Belle Point via the Poteau River.

[87]JAMES [1], II, 261; JAMES [2] in THWAITES [1], XVI, 189.

Fig. 22. *Fort Smith, Arkansas*, September, 1820. Samuel Seymour, watercolor. From the Collection of Mr. and Mrs. Paul Mellon, Upperville, Virginia. Courtesy Academy of Natural Sciences of Philadelphia.

Fig. 23. Same location as in figure 22, photographed October 1989. From authors' collection.

James's description of the land between the confluence of the Poteau and the Arkansas rivers as "low and fertile bottom land . . . covered with dense and heavy forests" that included the pawpaw trees[88] is in sharp contrast to the inundation we observed. It is our opinion that this fertile bottomland between the Poteau and Arkansas rivers is shown in Seymour's sketch of Fort Smith (see fig. 22). In addition, in this view to the southwest from the then-incomplete fort, we believe that the south blockhouse and one adjacent building are shown. At the foot of the hill below this blockhouse the "inconsiderable" Poteau flowed northward toward its junction with the Arkansas. The view today is seen in fig. 23.

According to Bell, on September 13 "Mr. Seymour completed two views of Belle Point."[89] Whether this includes the one he started on September 11 is not clear.[90] Only the one shown has been located.

On September 20, James,[91] along with Lieutenant Swift and Captain Kearny,[92] left Fort Smith for Cape Girardeau via Hot Springs and Little Rock. By October 12 the members of the exploring expedition were all together at Cape Girardeau, where many became ill.[93]

Having recovered from his illness, James left Cape Girardeau on horseback on November 22 and traveled east across Illinois to Golconda on the Ohio River, where he became ill once again.[94]

By December 2, 1820, James reached Smithland, Kentucky, where he spent the winter.[95] In the fall and winter of 1821 James resided in Philadelphia and completed his account of the expedition. His manuscript was turned over to Long, and on June 14, 1822, James left Philadelphia.[96]

James died in 1861 without having made another exploration of the magnitude of the one in 1820. The events that filled the remaining years of Edwin James's life are presented in detail by Benson.[97]

[88]JAMES [1], II, 261; JAMES [2] in THWAITES [1], XVI, 189.

[89]FULLER AND HAFEN, 281.

[90]FULLER AND HAFEN, 280.

[91]JAMES [1], II, 263; JAMES [2] in THWAITES [1], XVII, 12.

[92]Stephen W. Kearny had come to Fort Smith as inspector and paymaster. FULLER AND HAFEN, 280; JAMES [1], II, 264; JAMES [2] in THWAITES [1], XVII, 12.

[93]JAMES [1], II, 321; JAMES [2] in THWAITES [1], XVII, 84.

[94]JAMES [1], II, 328–29; JAMES [2] in THWAITES [1], XVII, 91.

[95]JAMES [3], December 2.

[96]JAMES [3], June 14.

[97]BENSON [2].

PART TWO
THE BOTANY

Dicliptera brachiata (Pursh) Spreng., Sys. 1:86.1825.
#354 *Justicia brachiata* Pursh, in Torr., Ann. Lyc. Nat. Hist. N.Y. 2:235.1827. "On the Arkansa?"
This plant could have been collected along the Canadian River from August 29, when they were in Cleveland County, Oklahoma, to its junction with the Arkansas, which they reached on September 10, or from there along the Arkansas to Fort Smith, which they reached on September 13.

Ruellia humilis Nutt. var. **longiflora** (Gray) Fern., Rhodora 47:56.1945. (Ruellia).
#354 "a" *Justicia* unnamed in Torr., Ann. Lyc. Nat. Hist. N.Y. 2:235.1827. Following some remarks on #354 (the *Dicliptera* above), Torrey added, "Besides this species there were specimens of another in the collection, which could not be determined for want of flowers." A detailed description followed. No locality was mentioned.
Justicia dubia Raf., Atl. Jour. 1:146.1832. Based on Torrey's description. [Not *J. dubia* Forsk., 1775].
When Gray[2] described *Ruellia ciliosa* var. *longiflora*, he listed several synonyms, including *R. humilis* and "*Justicia*, with char. & no name, Torr. in Ann. Lyc. N.Y. ii. 235."
When Fernald transferred the varietal epithet to *R. humilis* and cited Gray's name and reference, however, he added "as to descr., largely excl. synonyms." The synonym *R. humilis* would of course become Fernald's *R. humilis* var. *typica*. Whether the Torrey reference was excluded is not clear. At any rate, James's plant is clearly one of the varieties of *R. humilis* and was collected almost certainly in eastern Oklahoma in late August or early September.

Aceraceae

Acer glabrum Torr. (Rocky Mountain Maple).
#48 *Acer glabrum* Torr., Ann. Lyc. Nat. Hist. N.Y. 2:172.1827. "On the Rocky Mountains."

[1]The families are arranged alphabetically.
[2]GRAY [4], 326.

Type: NY. On the sheet is written "Rocky Mts. 1000 ft. elev. above the plain small shrub."

The type was collected on July 7 on Sheep Mountain, about seven miles southwest of Waterton, on the north side of South Platte Canyon, Jefferson County, Colorado. The plant may still be found there today.

James does not list this plant in his diary on July 7, but in the *Account* for that day "a small undescribed acer" is listed among the plants collected.[3]

Later on July 10 James listed *Acer rubrum* as occurring in the area of their midday rest.[4] They were then on Monument Creek, near the base of Elephant Rock, a mile or so east of Palmer Lake, El Paso County, Colorado. This, too, is surely *Acer glabrum*.

Acer negundo L., Sp. Pl. 1056. 1753. (Box Elder).

#49 Acer negundo L., in Torr., Ann. Lyc. Nat. Hist. N.Y. 2:172.1827. "On the Missouri, and westward to the valleys within the Rocky Mountains."

The expedition was in range of box elder during most of the trip. James first noted the plant on July 7 while exploring Sheep Mountain, about seven miles southwest of Waterton, on the north side of South Platte Canyon, Jefferson County, Colorado.[5] James again referred to the tree in his diary and the *Account* on July 25.[6] On this day James's group reached the Purgatoire in Otero County, Colorado, continued up this river to its junction with Chacuaco Creek, and followed up this creek a few miles into Las Animas County, Colorado.

Adoxaceae

Adoxa moschatellina L., Sp. Pl. 367. 1753. (Moschatel).

#3 Adoxa Moschatellina L., in Torr., Ann. Lyc. Nat. Hist. N.Y. 1:32.1824. "With the preceding ['On James' Peak, one of the highest of the Rocky Mountains, 10,000 feet above the level of the ocean, near the region of perpetual snow.']."

#165 Adoxa Moschatellina L., in Torr., Ann. Lyc. Nat. Hist. N.Y. 2:204.1827.

[3]JAMES [1], II, 8n.; JAMES [2] in THWAITES [1], XV, 294n.
[4]JAMES [1], II, 15n.; JAMES [2] in THWAITES [1], XV, 306n.; JAMES [3], July 10. All references are erroneously dated July 11.
[5]JAMES [1], II, 8; JAMES [2] in THWAITES [1], XV, 294.
[6]JAMES [1], II, 69; JAMES [2] in THWAITES [1], XVI, 66; JAMES [3], July 25.

The plant, then, was collected either on July 14 or 15 on Pikes Peak, El Paso County, Colorado. Dr. Torrey remarked that the plant "is now for the first time introduced as a native of the continent of America."

Alismataceae

Alisma plantago-aquatica L., Sp. Pl. 342. 1753. (Water Plantain). #444 *Alisma Plantago* L., in Torr., Ann. Lyc. Nat. Hist. N.Y. 2:251.1827. "Sources of the Platte."

On July 1 James noted this plant (as *Alisma plantago*) growing with other aquatics in stagnant pools near the Platte.[7] This collection was made a few miles east of Masters, Weld County, Colorado.

Sagittaria latifolia Willd., Sp. Pl. 4:409.1806. (Arrowhead). #445 *Sagittaria sagittifolia* L., in Torr., Ann. Lyc. Nat. Hist. N.Y. 2:251.1827. "Sources of the Platte."

On July 1 James noted this plant in stagnant pools near the Platte.[8] This collection was made a few miles east of Masters, Weld County, Colorado.

Amaranthaceae

Amaranthus albus L., Sp. Pl. ed. 2. 1404. 1763. (Pigweed).

In his diary, James mentioned this plant.[9] We find no verification of the identification, but there is no reason to doubt it. It would have been collected on June 27 in northeastern Colorado along the South Platte River between just west of Julesburg, Sedgwick County, to southeast of Crook, Logan County.

Froelichia floridana (Nutt.) Moq. var. **campestris** (Small) Fernald, Rhodora 43:336.1941. (Snake Cotton). #371 *Oplotheca floridana* Nutt., in Torr., Ann. Lyc. Nat. Hist. N.Y. 2:238.1827. "On the Canadian or Arkansa."

This plant is so usually collected in middle or late summer that along the Canadian River in Oklahoma in August seems the likely place that James collected it. Incidentally, the type of var. *campestris*, collected by B. F. Bush, is from Oklahoma.

[7]JAMES [1], I, 493; JAMES [2] in THWAITES [1], XV, 272; JAMES [3], July 1.
[8]JAMES [1], I, 493; JAMES [2] in THWAITES [1], XV, 272; JAMES [3], July 1.
[9]JAMES [3], June 27.

Anacardiaceae

Rhus glabra L., Sp. Pl. 265. 1753. (Smooth Sumac).

This plant was collected on May 29 along the Missouri River in the area of Engineer Cantonment, some five miles downstream from Fort Calhoun, Washington Couny, Nebraska. James mentioned this plant again in his diary on June 2. On this day the party remained at Engineer Cantonment.[10]

In his diary for September 11, James referred to "sumach."[11] This, too, could have been *Rhus glabra* or very possibly *Rhus copallina*. On this day the party traveled down the Arkansas from a few miles below the mouth of the Canadian to just west of Sallisaw, Sequoyah County, Oklahoma.

Toxicodendron radicans (L.) Kuntze subsp. **negundo** (Greene) Gillis, Rhodora 73:228.1971. (Poison Ivy).

Rhus radicans, as James referred in his diary to this collection, was found on June 2 "on the hills behind the cantonment."[12] Engineer Cantonment was some five miles downstream on the Missouri River from Fort Calhoun, Washington County, Nebraska.

Toxicodendron rydbergii (Small ex Rydb.) Greene, Leafl. Bot. Obser. Crit. 1:117.1905. (Poison Ivy).

#64 *Rhus toxicodendron* L., in Torr., Ann. Lyc. Nat. Hist. N.Y. 2:174.1827. "On the Rocky Mountains."

James first mentioned this plant in his diary on June 2, where he found it "on hills behind the cantonment."[13] Engineer Cantonment was some five miles downstream on the Missouri River from Fort Calhoun, Washington County, Nebraska.

James also recorded this plant in the diary and the *Account* for July 7.[14] This is doubtless the collection that Torrey referred to. On this day James ascended the South Platte as far as Sheep Mountain, about seven miles southwest of Waterton, Jefferson County, Colorado.

[10]JAMES [3], June 2.
[11]JAMES [3], September 11.
[12]JAMES [3], June 2.
[13]JAMES [3], June 2.
[14]JAMES [3], July 7; JAMES [1], II, 8n.; JAMES [2] in THWAITES [1], XV, 295n.

Annonaceae

Asimina triloba (L.) Dunal, Monog. Anon. 83. 1817. (Pawpaw).
#10 *Asimina triloba* Dunal, in Torr., Ann. Lyc. Nat. Hist. N.Y.
2:165.1827. "On the Arkansa, near Fort Smith."
The delicious fruit of the pawpaw tree was mentioned by James on
September 12.[15] Here at their midday halt, some five miles north-
northeast of Gans, Sequoyah County, Oklahoma, the fruits were
eaten.

Apocynaceae

Apocynum androsaemifolium L., Sp. Pl. ed. 2, 311. 1762.
(Dogbane).
James collected this plant on May 29, along the Missouri River in
the area of Engineer Cantonment, some five miles downstream from
Fort Calhoun, Washington County, Nebraska.[16]

Apocynum cannabinum L., Sp. Pl. 213. 1753. (Indian Hemp).
In his diary, James listed this plant on June 7 near the Elkhorn
River, a few miles southeast of Arlington, Washington, or Dodge
County, Nebraska.[17]

Araliaceae

Aralia nudicaulis L., Sp. Pl. 274. 1753. (Wild Sarsaparilla).
#181 *Aralia nudicaulis* L., in Torr. Ann. Lyc. Nat. Hist. N.Y.
2:208.1827. "Base of the Rocky Mountains."
James mentioned this plant in his diary on July 7, the day that some
of the party ascended the South Platte Canyon in Jefferson County,
Colorado, above the chasm near where they were encamped.[18]
Similarly, in the *Account,* James referred to this species for the same
location and date.[19]
This is one of the novelties in the Colorado flora, being an element
from the eastern United States woodlands. We found it as an
infrequent member of the canyon-bottom flora on the south side of

[15]JAMES [1], II, 170; JAMES [2] in THWAITES [1], XVI, 184.
[16]JAMES [3], May 29.
[17]JAMES [3], June 7.
[18]JAMES [3], July 7 (erroneously dated July 8).
[19]JAMES [1], II, 8; JAMES [2] in THWAITES [1], XV, 294.

the South Platte River in Douglas County, southeast of Sheep Mountain and about seven miles southwest of Waterton, Jefferson County, Colorado.

No James specimen was found at NY. Here there are half a dozen sheets, however, collected along the Front Range from 1874 to 1903.

Aralia racemosa L., Sp. Pl. 273. 1753. (Spikenard).

#182 *Aralia racemosa* L., in Torr., Ann. Lyc. Nat. Hist. N.Y. 2:272.1827. "With the preceding ['Base of the Rocky Mountains.']."

This Rocky Mountain location is again cited by Torrey and Gray for a James collection;[20] no James specimen of this, however, was found at NY. In the *Account* James listed this species from the same location as *A. nudicaulis* among the plants collected on July 7.[21] *A. racemosa* has also been reported from La Plata County, southwestern Colorado.[22] Other Rocky Mountain records include those from as far north as Sierra Grande in Union County, northern New Mexico (as *A. bicrenata* W. & S.)[23] and those from several counties in Arizona (as *A. arizonica* Eastw.). Both of these latter names have been placed in synonymy under *A. racemosa* by Smith.[24]

Panax quinquefolius L., Sp. Pl. 1058. 1753. (Ginseng).

James collected this plant on May 29,[25] along the Missouri River in the area of Engineer Cantonment, some five miles downstream from Fort Calhoun, Washington County, Nebraska.

Aristolochiaceae

Aristolochia tomentosa Sims, Bot. Mag. pl. 1369. 1811. (Dutchman's Pipe).

#394 *Aristolochia, n.sp.?* [Followed by a Latin description.] Torr., Ann. Lyc. Nat. Hist. N.Y. 2:242.1827. "On the Canadian."

Aristolochia coriacea Raf., Atl. Jour. 1:146.1832. Based on Torrey's #394.

Based on the presently known distribution of the species, the type

---

[20]TORREY AND GRAY [1], I, 646.
[21]JAMES [1], II, 8; JAMES [2] in THWAITES [1], XV, 294.
[22]WEBER [2], 97; O'KANE, WILKEN, AND HARTMAN, 72.
[23]WOOTON AND STANDLEY, 475.
[24]SMITH, 247.
[25]JAMES [3], May 29.

of *A. coriacea* would have been collected on September 8 or 9 in or near Muskogee County, Oklahoma.

Asclepiadaceae

Asclepias asperula (Dcne.) Woods. var. **decumbens** (Nutt.) Shinners, Field & Lab. 22:58.1954. (Antelope Horn).
#262 *Anantherix n.sp.* (as *Anatherix*) *Nutt. mss.*, in Torr., Ann. Lyc. Nat. Hist. N.Y. 2:219.1827. "Leaves linear-lanceolate, obtuse at the base, petiolate."
Anantherix (as *Anatherix*) *angustifolia* Raf., Atl. Jour. 146. 1832. Based on Torrey's #262.
Based on the known range of this variety, James could have collected the type of *Anantherix angustifolia* in late July to mid August as the party moved from Union County, New Mexico, through the Texas panhandle to Central Oklahoma.

Asclepias incarnata L., Sp. Pl. 215. 1753. (Swamp Milkweed).
#256 *Asclepias phytolaccoides* Lyon, in Torr., Ann. Lyc. Nat. Hist. N.Y. 2:218.1827. "On the Platte."
In his diary, James listed this plant under the date of June 20, stating that it grew in "marshy situations on the banks of the Platte."[26] On the previous day, while at the same campsite, this plant is listed in the *Account*.[27] The party camped near Gothenburg, Dawson County, Nebraska.

Asclepias lanuginosa Nutt., Gen. 1:168.1818. (Woolly Milkweed).
#258 *Asclepias Nuttalliana* Torr., Ann. Lyc. Nat. Hist. N.Y. 2:218.1827. "On the Canadian." Torrey erroneously believed that Nuttall's name was preempted by *A. lanuginosa* HBK., Nov. Gen. 3:193.1819.
James cited this species as having been collected "on the Canadian."[28] Presumably, this is where Torrey obtained his information. The Canadian River, however, is out of the range of this species. James's diary reads, "*Asclepias lanuginosa* of Nuttall occurs . . . 8 miles west of our cantonment."[29] This June 6 location is almost at Big

---

[26]JAMES [3], June 20 (erroneously dated June 19).
[27]JAMES [1], I, 461n.; JAMES [2] in THWAITES [1], XV, 233n.
[28]JAMES [4], 177.
[29]JAMES [3], June 6.

Papillion Creek, near Kenard, Washington County, Nebraska. Here the species is in good range.

Nuttall collected his type specimen on the dry hills along the Missouri River in southern South Dakota.

Asclepias latifolia (Torr.) Raf., Atl. Jour. 146. 1832. (Broad Leaved Milkweed).

#252 *Asclepias obtusifolia* β? *latifolia* Torr., Ann. Lyc. Nat. Hist. N.Y. 2:217–18.1827. "On the Canadian?" Type: NY.

Asclepias jamesii Torr., Mex. Bound. Surv. 162. 1859. (Based on Torrey's *A. obtusifolia* var. *latifolia*).

James described the type in his diary on July 15, apparently after having arrived back at the base camp on Fountain Creek after climbing Pikes Peak.[30] The camp was located a couple of miles south of Fountain, El Paso County, Colorado.

Asclepias pumila (Gray) Vail in Britton & Brown, Illustr. Fl. 3:12.1898. (Plains Milkweed).

In his diary for July 15, James described this *Asclepias* as being small with linear leaves and terminal umbels.[31]

At that time, James had apparently arrived back at the base camp on Fountain Creek after having climbed Pikes Peak. The camp was located a couple of miles south of Fountain, El Paso County, Colorado.

In the *Account* on July 21, James stated, "Along the base of the mountains and about this encampment, we had observed a small asclepias, not easily distinguished from A. *verticillata,* but rarely rising more than two or three inches from the ground."[32] This observation was made at their camp near Rocky Ford, Otero County, Colorado.

Woodson listed a Fendler specimen as the type.[33]

Asclepias speciosa Torr. (Showy Milkweed).

#260 *Asclepias speciosa* Torr., Ann. Lyc. Nat. Hist. N.Y. 2:218–19.1827. "On the Canadian?" Type: NY.

James referred to this plant in his diary, naming it for its large

[30]JAMES [3], July 15.
[31]JAMES [3], July 15.
[32]JAMES [1], II, 62; JAMES [2] in THWAITES [1], XVI, 57.
[33]WOODSON, 71.

flowers.[34] The description that follows leaves no doubt that this was the plant that became the type of *Asclepias speciosa.* The type was collected on June 14 as the party traveled south from the Loup River to the Platte through Merrick County, Nebraska. The plant may still be found in this same area today.

Asclepias subverticillata (Gray) Vail, Bull. Torr. Bot. Club 25:178.1898. (Poison Milkweed).
#254 Asclepias longifolia Michx., in Torr., Ann. Lyc. Nat. Hist. N.Y. 2:218.1827. "Upper part of the Arkansa."
In his diary for July 21, James described an *Asclepias* as a doubtful *Asclepias longifolia.*[35] He described the plant, which "resembles A. verticillata," as having leaves "linear very long in whorls of three."
On this same day in the *Account, A. longifolia,* a species of the southeastern United States, is listed by James among the plants occurring about their encampment near Rocky Ford, Otero County, Colorado.[36]
Based on similar leaf shape and size of the two species and distribution, *A. subverticillata* was chosen.

Asclepias sullivantii Engelm. ex Gray, Man. Bot. ed. 1, 366. 1848. (Milkweed).
#251 Asclepias obtusifolia Michx., in Torr., Ann. Lyc. Nat. Hist. N.Y. 2:217.1827. "Barren sandy soils along the Platte."
James referred to *A. obtusifolia* in the *Account* and in his diary on June 19.[37] *A. obtusifolia* is considered a synonym of *A. amplexicaulis,* which is in poor range of James's June 19 location.
Based on flower color and size and leaf shape, *A. sullivantii* seems most likely. This species is in good range near Gothenburg, Dawson County, Nebraska, James's June 19 location.

Asclepias syriaca L., Sp. Pl. 214. 1753. (Milkweed).
James mentioned this plant on June 19 as occurring in the sandy soil near their camp.[38] On this day the party camped near Gothenburg, Dawson County, Nebraska.

[34]JAMES [3], June 14 (included as part of the June 13 entry).
[35]JAMES [3], July 21.
[36]JAMES [1], II, 62; JAMES [2] in THWAITES [1], XVI, 57.
[37]JAMES [1], I, 461n.; JAMES [2] in THWAITES [1], XV, 233n.; JAMES [3], June 19.
[38]JAMES [1], I, 461n.; JAMES [2] in THWAITES [1], XV, 233n.; JAMES [3], June 19.

Asclepias tuberosa L. subsp. **terminalis** Woodson, Proc. Nat. Acad. Sci. 39:79.1953. (Butterfly-Weed).

#257 *Asclepias tuberosa* L., in Torr., Ann. Lyc. Nat. Hist. N.Y. 2:218.1827. "Sandy barrens along the Canadian and Arkansa."

James described this plant in his diary between July 10 and 12.[39] It appears that the plants were seen as the expedition traveled east across the plain from near Limekiln Valley toward Fountain Creek on July 12.

This plant is mentioned in the *Account* on July 12, the day the party camped on Fountain Creek, near the town of Fountain, El Paso County, Colorado.[40]

Woodson listed this subspecies from El Paso County.[41]

Asclepias verticillata L., Sp. Pl. 217. 1753. (Whorled Milkweed).

#253 *Asclepias verticillata* L., in Torr., Ann. Lyc. Nat. Hist. N.Y. 2:218.1827. "Upper part of the Arkansa."

James cited this milkweed in his diary on June 18.[42] Their camp on the Platte River a few miles west-southwest of Overton, Dawson County, Nebraska is in good range for this species.

Torrey's location on the Arkansas is either incorrect (*A. verticillata* not being known from Colorado) or his #253 is perhaps the similar *A. subverticillata* (Gray) Vail, first described in 1877 and that does occur along the Arkansas in Colorado.

Asclepias viridiflora Raf., Med. Repos. N.Y. 5:360.1808. (Green Antelope Horn).

#255 *Asclepias viridiflora* Raf., in Torr., Ann. Lyc. Nat. Hist. N.Y. 2:218.1827. "Upper part of the Arkansa."

In his diary for June 19, James described the leaves of this species as "nearly linear opposite."[43] This linear-leaved phase has been recognized as *Asclepias viridiflora* var. *linearis* (Gray) Fern.

On this same day in the *Account, A. viridiflora* is cited with the plants found about the sandhills near their camp.[44] They were camped west of Gothenburg, Dawson County, Nebraska.

---

[39]JAMES [3], July 12 (erroneously dated July 11 and including information for July 10, 11, and 12).

[40]JAMES [1], II, 21; JAMES [2] in THWAITES [1], XV, 312.

[41]WOODSON, 79.

[42]JAMES [3], June 18.

[43]JAMES [3], June 19.

[44]JAMES [1], I, 461n.; JAMES [2], XV, 233n.

Again in his diary for July 21, and on the same day in the *Account,* James cited this species.[45] The description in the diary gives no indication of leaf width.

At this time the party was camped on the Arkansas River, near Rocky Ford, Otero County, Colorado.

Asclepias viridis Walt., Fl. Carol. 107. 1788. (Spider Milkweed). #261 *Anantherix* n.sp. (as *Anatherix*) *Nutt. mss.,* in Torr., Ann. Lyc. Nat. Hist. N.Y. 2:219.1827. "Leaves ovate."

Anantherix (as *Anatherix*) *ovata* Raf., Atl. Jour. 146. 1832. Based on Torrey's #261.

Based on the known range of this species, James would have collected the type of *Anantherix ovata* along the Canadian River in Oklahoma in August.

Balsaminaceae

Impatiens capensis Meerb., Afb. Zeldz. Gewass. pl. 10. 1775. (Touch-Me-Not).

In his diary for September 8, James listed *Impatiens nolitangere,* an Old World species.[46] Based on distribution, it seems likely that James collected *I. capensis.*

The party traveled this day along the Canadian from a short distance east of Eufaula, McIntosh County, to four or five miles south of Porum, Muskogee County, Oklahoma.

Berberidaceae

Berberis repens Lindl., Bot. Reg. 14:pl.1176.1828. (Oregon Grape). #12 *Mahonia aquifolium* Nutt., in Torr., Ann. Lyc. Nat. Hist. N.Y. 2:165.1827. "On the Rocky Mountains."

No reference to this plant was found in James's diary; based on distribution, however, the collection would have been made in July in Colorado along the Front Range.

Betulaceae

Ostrya virginiana (Mill.) K. Koch, Dendrol. 2(2):6.1873. (Ironwood).

---

[45]JAMES [1], II, 62; JAMES [2] in THWAITES [1], XVI, 57 (as "A. viridifolia"); JAMES [3], July 21.
[46]JAMES [3], September 8.

#420 *Ostrya virginica* L., Michx. arb. iii. t.7, in Torr., Ann. Lyc. Nat. Hist. N.Y. 2:248.1827. "Near the Rocky Mountains."

James listed this plant as "Ostrya virginica" in his diary,[47] along with several others, as the expedition traveled the twenty miles from Dawson Butte, Douglas County, to the Air Force Academy, El Paso County, Colorado. The plant is listed in the *Account* as "Ostrya virginica L." from this same area.[48] The name, and nothing more, also appears in James's *Catalogue.*[49]

The plate in Michaux (Michaux f.) referred to by Torrey is the ironwood, *Carpinus ostrya,* i.e., *Ostrya virginiana.*

No James specimen of *Ostrya* was found at NY.

What was the plant? A *Prunus?* It seems unlikely that Torrey would have made such a mistake. Is the location wrong? Not likely, considering the reference in the diary. Did Torrey not see the specimen and simply copy the reference in the *Account?* Possibly. Or did James really see *Ostrya virginiana* in Colorado? That too is possible. *Corylus* is another possibility.

Bignoniaceae

Campsis radicans (L.) Seem., J. Bot. 5:362.1867. (Trumpet Vine). **#268** *Bignonia radicans* L., in Torr., Ann. Lyc. Nat. Hist. N.Y. 2:220.1827. "On the Arkansa?"

James mentioned *Bignonia radicans* in his diary on September 4.[50] One day later, bignonia is mentioned in the *Account.*[51]

On September 4 the party traveled along the Canadian mostly in Hughes County, Oklahoma, and camped a few miles northeast of Atwood.

Boraginaceae

Cryptantha celosioides (Eastw.) Payson, Ann. Mo. Bot. Gard. 14:299.1927.

#299 *Rochelia glomerata* (Nutt. ex Pursh) Torr., Ann. Lyc. Nat. Hist. N.Y. 2:226.1827. "Barren deserts near the sources of the Platte."

[47]JAMES [3], July 10 (erroneously dated July 11).
[48]JAMES [1], II, 15n.; JAMES [2] in THWAITES [1], XV, 306n. Both editions are erroneously dated July 11.
[49]JAMES [4], 189.
[50]JAMES [3], September 4.
[51]JAMES [1], II, 158; JAMES [2] in THWAITES [1], XVI, 170.

Payson cited Torrey's name as a synonym of *C. bradburiana*,[52] now also considered a synonym of *C. celosioides*.

James could have made his collection in late June through mid July, from the time he entered northeastern Colorado until he reached the Arkansas River near Pueblo, Pueblo County, Colorado.

Cryptantha cinerea (Greene) Cronq. var. **jamesii** Cronq., Inter-mountain Fl. 4:229.1984. (Here Cronquist is considering *jamesii* to be a new name rather than a transfer.)

#298 *Myosotis suffruticosa* Torr., Ann. Lyc. Nat. Hist. N.Y. 2:225–26.1827. "Barren deserts along the Platte." Type: NY [Not *Cryptantha suffruticosa* Piper, 1919].

This is the *Cryptantha jamesii* (Torr.) Payson, a name of much recent literature based on the illegitimate *Eritrichium jamesii* Torr.

In his diary for June 26, James described what he thought was "[o]ne of the Asperifoliae" as being a hispid plant with "seeds shining, naked."[53] The flowers were described as "large white in a terminal unilateral spike." In the marginal note on this page of the diary, the plant is referred to as a *Phacelia*. This had led some workers to list the June 25 date as the time of collection for the type of *Phacelia integrifolia (q.v.)*. In the *Account* for June 27, this plant is listed as one of the undescribed "asperifoliae."[54]

On June 26 the party traveled along the South Platte from near Ogallala, Keith County, Nebraska, to near Julesburg, Sedgwick County, Colorado.

Cryptantha crassisepala (T. & G.) Greene, Pittonia 1:112.1887, or

Cryptantha minima Rydb., Bull. Torr. Bot. Club 28:31.1901.

As the party traveled on July 30 southwest across the Don Carlos Hills, from Sierra Grande to Ute Creek, western Union County, New Mexico, James described a *Myosotis* with "[s]eeds rugose, Leaves obovate or spathulate. Stem much branched."[55] In the *Account* this plant is listed as merely a "myosotis."[56] The plant was likely one of the above species of *Cryptantha*.

---

[52]PAYSON, 307.
[53]JAMES [3], June 26 (erroneously dated June 25).
[54]JAMES [1], I, 484; JAMES [2] in THWAITES [1], XV, 258.
[55]JAMES [3], July 30.
[56]JAMES [1], II, 86; JAMES [2] in THWAITES [1], XVI, 86.

Cryptantha thyrsiflora (Greene) Payson, Ann. Mo. Bot. Gard. 14:283.1927.

#300 *Rochelia n.sp.* in Torr., Ann. Lyc. Nat. Hist. N.Y. 2:226.1827. "With the preceding ['Barren deserts near the sources of the Platte.'] Plant densely covered with long hispid hairs."

In his diary for July 4, James described a plant that was one to two feet high having "stem and calyx thickly beset with . . . bristly spines. Leaves spathulate linear 2–4 inches long."[57] James indicated that the plant might be *Myosotis glomerata* or a variety of it. One such variety, *Eritrichium glomeratum* var. *hispidissimum* Torr., was treated by Payson as a synonym of *C. thyrsiflora.*[58]

In the *Account,* James listed *Myosotis glomerata* among the plants collected about the July 4 campsite, which was on the South Platte River near Brighton, Adams County, Colorado.[59] For this campsite *Cryptantha thyrsiflora* is in good range.

Eritrichium nanum (Villars) Schrader, Comm. Recent. Soc. Reg. Sci. Gott. Cl. Phys. 4:186.1819. (Alpine Forget-Me-Not).

#5 *Myosotis nana* Villars?, in Torr, Ann. Lyc. Nat. Hist. N.Y. 1:33.1824. "With the preceding ['On James' Peak . . . near the region of perpetual snow.']."

#297 *Myosotis nana* Villars, in Torr., Ann. Lyc. Nat. Hist. N.Y. 2:225.1827. "Rocky Mountains."

This alpine or subalpine species would have been collected during James's climb of Pikes Peak, July 13–15, El Paso County, Colorado.

Heliotropium convolvulaceum (Nutt.) Gray, Mem. Amer. Acad. Arts, n.s., 6:403.1857. (Heliotrope).

On a sheet at NY are three plants of this heliotrope, with the notation "Euploca convolvulacea Nutt. in Trans. phil. soc. Philad. n.sp. V. p.189. Sandy plains of the Platte. Long's 1st. Exped. Dr. James."

In James's diary there is a description of what he thought was a new species.[60] The description clearly applies to *H. convolvulaceum.* A shorter but similar description is found in the *Account.*[61]

The collection was made on June 28, between Crook and Sterling, Logan County, Colorado.

[57]JAMES [3], July 4.
[58]PAYSON, 283.
[59]JAMES [1], I, 498n.; JAMES [2] in THWAITES [1], XV, 277n.
[60]JAMES [3], June 28.
[61]JAMES [1], I, 484; JAMES [2] in THWAITES [1], XV, 258.

Heliotropium curassavicum L. var. **obovatum** DC., Prodr. 9:538. 1845. (Seaside Heliotrope).

#289 *Heliotropium curassavicum* L., in Torr., Ann. Lyc. Nat. Hist. N.Y. 2:224.1827. "Saline soils on the Platte."

James, in his diary, described this plant as "one of the Asperifoliae?" so fully as to leave no doubt about its identity.[62] He adds: "In depressed and moist saline soils near the brink of the river." In the *Account* for June 27 this plant is listed as one of the undescribed "asperifoliae."[63]

At NY there is a specimen marked: "Saline soils on the Platte Dr. James."

Their travels of June 26 took them from near Ogallala, Keith County, through the southeast corner of Deuel County, Nebraska, and thence about two miles into Sedgwick County, Colorado.

Heliotropium tenellum (Nutt.) Torr., Mex. Bound. Surv. 2:138. 1859. (Heliotrope).

#295 *Lithospermum angustifolium* Michx., in Torr., Ann. Lyc. Nat. Hist. N.Y. 2:225.1827. "About Council Bluff on the Missouri. Obs. Plant 8–10 inches high, slender, with a few erect branches, strigosely hirsute; flowers minute, seeds turgidly ovate, smooth and polished."

From the information on the sheet at NY that contains the James specimen, which is not in fruit, the notation is made, apparently by Torrey, that the seeds described in the Ann. Lyc. are from Nuttall's specimen. Since the description "smooth and polished" does not fit the nutlets as described by Nuttall for *Lithospermum tenellum,* we believe Torrey must have had a different Nuttall specimen of the fertile phase of *Lithospermum incisum.*

In the Mex. Bound. Surv., however, Torrey stated the following:[64]

Heliotropium tenellum, *Torr. in Marcy Report, t.*14. Lithospermum tenellum, *Nutt. Fl. Arkans.in Trans. Amer. Phil. Soc. n. ser. 5, p.* 189. L. angustifolium, *Torr. in Ann. Lyc. N.York, 2,p.* 225, *non Michx.* (where the nutlets are incorrectly described as smooth and polished.).... Calyx very unequally 5-parted; ... Corolla white, 2½ lines long.... Nutlets subglobose, the upper part appressed-pubescent, below the middle (and often also above) reticulated, not verrucose as represented in the figure quoted above, without foveoles on the face.

[62]JAMES [3], June 26 (erroneously dated June 25).
[63]JAMES [1], I, 484; JAMES [2] in THWAITES [1], XV, 258.
[64]TORREY [3], 138.

Except for the plate and the entry under "Explanation of Plates" there are no other references to *H. tenellum* in the Marcy Report.[65] On a Marcy specimen at NY appears the following: "Capt. Marcy's Expedition Torr., Bot. Marcy's Rep. t.14. (omitted in the Catalogue by mistake)." This specimen has some mature fruits.

There is still a difficulty. *Heliotropium tenellum* does not occur in Nebraska. James would have collected this species between August 25 and September 13 in the eastern two-thirds of Oklahoma.

Lappula redowskii (Hornem.) Greene, Pittonia 4:97.1899. (Stickseed).

#296 Myosotis scorpioides L., in Torr., Ann. Lyc. Nat. Hist. N.Y. 2:225.1827. "Along the Platte."

It seems likely that the above names refer to the plants that in his diary James called *Myosotis scorpioides* and *Lycopsis arvensis* (both European introductions), even though only the *Lappula* has fruits with hooked bristles.[66]

James's June 12 collection was made as the party traveled along the Loup River and camped in Nance County some four miles north and a little east of Palmer, Merrick County, Nebraska. Later, on June 23, the collection (as *Lycopsis arvensis*) was made on the south side of the South Platte River, a few miles above its junction with the North Platte, Lincoln County, Nebraska.

In the *Account, Myosotis scorpioides* is said to have been "collected along the Platte on the 15th and 16th of June."[67]

Lithospermum canescens (Michx.) Lehm., Asperif. 2:305.1818. (Puccoon).

#293 Lithospermum canescens Lehm., in Torr., Ann. Lyc. Nat. Hist. N.Y. 2:225.1827. "Valley of the Loup Fork."

At NY there is a specimen, simply marked "Long's 1st Expedition Dr. James."

This species does occur in the Loup River Valley where the expedition traveled between June 9 and June 13 in Platte and Nance counties, Nebraska.

Lithospermum caroliniense (Walt.) MacM., Metasp. Minn. Valley 438. 1892. (Puccoon).

[65]TORREY [5], 304.
[66]JAMES [3], June 12 and June 23 (erroneously dated June 22).
[67]JAMES [1], I, 455n.; JAMES [2] in THWAITES [1], XV, 226n.

#294 *Lithospermum decumbens* Torr., not Vent., Ann. Lyc. Nat. Hist. N.Y. 2:225.1827. No location given.

It is difficult to determine whether Torrey was describing a new species (with a James specimen as the type) or transferring Nuttall's *Batschia decumbens* to *Lithospermum*.[68] Johnston interpreted it as a transfer and hence placed both names in synonymy with *L. incisum*.[69] When Nuttall described his *L. Torreyi* from the Flat Head River, Montana, he placed Torrey's *decumbens* in synonymy with it.[70] He also specifically excluded his *B. decumbens,* which is a synonym of *L. incisum*.

Cronquist treated the names similarly, placing both *L. Torreyi* and *L. decumbens* in synonymy under *L. ruderale*.[71]

Gray, however, put *L. decumbens* Torr. in synonymy under *L. hirtum* (i.e., *L. caroliniense*).[72] Torrey's description fits both *caroliniense* and *ruderale,* and perhaps fits the latter a little better. At no time, however, was the Long Expedition in good range for *L. ruderale*.

Concerning *L. ruderale,* Harrington states, "Our records from the western half of Colorado. . . . "[73] It probably does not occur in Nebraska; in Britton and Brown, however, appears the remark, "Western Nebraska (according to Williams);"[74] and thence westward.

Torrey's name was preoccupied a quarter century earlier for an Old World species. The problem is to determine what plant of James Torrey had. No James specimen was found at NY.

Because of the ranges of the two species, we are inclined to agree with Gray and consider it *L. caroliniense*.

Based on the flowering time of this species, James's collection was probably made in June in Nebraska.

Lithospermum incisum Lehm., Pl. Asperifol. 303. 1818.

#292 *Lithospermum incisum* Lehm., in Torr., Ann. Lyc. Nat. Hist. N.Y. 2:225.1827. "Valley of the Loup Fork."

This collection was made on June 9, either as the party traveled up Shell Creek (from northwest of Schuyler, Colfax County, to south-

[68]TORREY [2], 225.
[69]JOHNSTON [1], 25; JOHNSTON [2], 344.
[70]NUTTALL [2], 44.
[71]CRONQUIST [1], IV, 290.
[72]GRAY [4], 205.
[73]HARRINGTON, 462.
[74]BRITTON AND BROWN, III, 88.

east of Platte Center, Platte County) or at their evening's campsite on the Loup River just west of the mouth of Looking Glass Creek, approximately two miles east of Monroe, Platte County, Nebraska.

James referred to this plant as *Batschia longiflora,* an indication that his collection was the infertile phase of *L. incisum.*[75] No James specimen was found at NY.

Mertensia alpina (Torr.) G. Don, Gen. Hist. 4:372.1838. (Alpine Mertensia).

#290 *Pulmonaria alpina* Torr., Ann. Lyc. Nat. Hist. N.Y. 2:224.1827. "On the Rocky Mountains."

James would have collected the type (NY) of this alpine species on July 14 near the top of Pikes Peak, El Paso County, Colorado.

Mertensia ciliata (James ex Torr.) G. Don, Gen. Hist. 4:372.1838. (Tall Mertensia).

#291 *Pulmonaria ciliata* James ex Torr., Ann. Lyc. Nat. Hist. N.Y. 2:224–25.1827. "Crevices of rocks along streams, within the Rocky Mountains."

No reference to this plant has been found in James's diary or the *Account.* Based on the known range of this species, however, it seems likely that James made his type (NY) collection in July between Denver and Cañon City, Colorado.

Cactaceae

Coryphantha missouriensis (Sweet) Britton & Rose, in Britt. & Brown, Ill. Fl. ed. 2. 2:570.1913. (Nipple Cactus).

#157 *Cactus mammillaris* L., in Torr., Ann. Lyc. Nat. Hist. N.Y. 2:202.1827. "On the Platte and Canadian."

James also referred to this plant as *Cactus mammillaris.*[76]

His collection was made on June 13, the day they were camped on the south side of the Loup River near the Nance/Merrick county line, about three miles north and a little east of Palmer, Nebraska.

In his diary entry for July 15, apparently made after he arrived back at the base camp on Fountain Creek, El Paso County, James described

---

[75]JAMES [1], I, 433; JAMES [2] in THWAITES [1], XV, 200; JAMES [3], June 9.
[76]JAMES [1], I, 453; JAMES [2] in THWAITES [1], XV, 223 (both editions under June 14); JAMES [3], June 13.

a cactus "resembling C. mammilaris but much larger."[77] It is possible that he was once again encountering *Coryphantha missouriensis*. Another possibility would be *Pediocactus simpsonii*.

The camp was located a couple of miles south of Fountain, El Paso County, Colorado.

Coryphantha vivipara (Nutt.) Britton & Rose, in Britt. & Brown, Ill. Fl. ed. 2. 2:571.1913. (Pincushion Cactus).

#158 *Cactus viviparus* Nutt., in Torr., Ann. Lyc. Nat. Hist. N.Y. 2:202.1827. "On the Platte and Canadian."

This was the second cactus collected by James on June 13. He referred to this plant in his diary as *Cactus viviparus*.[78]

The collection was made on the south side of the Loup River near the Nance/Merrick county line, about three miles north and a little east of Palmer, Nebraska.

Echinocereus viridiflorus Engelm., in Wislizenus, Mem. Tour North. Mex. 91. 1848. (Hedgehog Cactus).

While camped near Rocky Ford, Otero County, Colorado (July 21–24), James mentioned *Cactus proliferus,* a pincushion type, among the plants about their encampment.[79]

Coryphantha vivipara and *Echinocereus viridiflorus* are the two pincushion cacti in range. Assuming James knew *C. vivipara* from his encounter on June 13 in Nebraska, it seems likely that he noted *E. viridiflorus* at Rocky Ford.

Opuntia davisii Engelm. & Bigel., Proc. Amer. Acad. 3:305.1856. (Jeff Davis Cholla).

This fruticose cactus is described in James's diary for August 5, where he stated that it had "very large strong spines, being thickly beset with them."[80]

In comparison with the other fruticose cactus (see *O. leptocaulis*) described this day, this species was said to be "smaller" and the trunk and branches "thicker."

In the *Account* entry for August 4[81] and in Torrey[82] this species is

---

[77]JAMES [3], July 15.
[78]JAMES [3], June 13.
[79]JAMES [3], July 22.
[80]JAMES [3], August 5.
[81]JAMES [1], II, 94; JAMES [2] in THWAITES [1], XVI, 95. In both editions, the entry for August 4 contains information for August 5 and 6.
[82]TORREY [2], 203.

mentioned only as one of two shrubby species of cacti encountered in their day's travel.

On August 5 the party continued down the Canadian River, most of the distance being in Quay County, New Mexico. Approximately the last three miles were in Oldham County, Texas.

Opuntia fragilis (Nutt.) Haworth, Suppl. Pl. Succ. 82. 1819. (Brittle Cactus).

#156 *Cactus fragilis* Nutt., in Torr., Ann. Lyc. Nat. Hist. N.Y. 2:202.1827. "On the Platte and Canadian."

This cactus is not listed in James's diary; on June 13 in the *Account,* however, it is noted on "the hills, at a little distance from the river."[83]

On this day they were camped on the south side of the Loup River near the Nance/Merrick county line, about three miles north and a little east of Palmer, Nebraska.

Opuntia imbricata (Haworth) DC., Prodr. 3:471.1828. (Candelabra Cactus).

#159 *Cactus Bleo* HBK., in Torr., Ann. Lyc. Nat. Hist. N.Y. 2:202–203.1827. "Along the base of the Rocky Mountains, and on the head waters of the Arkansa and Canadian."

Cactus cylindricus sensu James, Trans. Am. Phil. Soc. n.s. 2:182.1825.

According to Britton and Rose, Torrey's #159 (*Cactus bleo*) is *O. imbricata.*[84]

In his diary entry for July 12, James described this cactus as "fruticose much branched articulations nearly cylindric. Spines radiating flower brilliant purple. Rising to the height of 6 or 8 feet and having the trunk 6 inches in diameter."[85]

On the same day in the *Account,* a similar but more extensive description is given for this "great shrubby cactus" first observed near their encampment on Fountain Creek, a branch of the Arkansas, near the town of Fountain, El Paso County, Colorado.[86]

Opuntia leptocaulis DC., Mem. Mus. Hist. Nat. Paris 17:118.1828. (Pencil Cholla).

---

[83]JAMES [1], I, 449; JAMES [2] in THWAITES [1], XV, 219.

[84]BRITTON AND ROSE, I, 63.

[85]JAMES [3], July 12 (erroneously dated July 11 and including information for July 10, 11, and 12).

[86]JAMES [1], II, 19–20; JAMES [2] in THWAITES [1], XV, 310–11.

In his diary for August 5, James described this cactus as having "long solitary spines with a small yellow flower and red small edible fruits."[87]

The description in the *Account* on August 4[88] and that of Torrey[89] are remarkably similar to James's.

On August 5 the party continued down the Canadian River, most of the distance being in Quay County, New Mexico. Approximately the last three miles were in Oldham County, Texas. We observed this species on the sandy plains near their campsite. Again in mid August along the Canadian River in the eastern-Texas panhandle, James observed the "shrubby cactus."[90]

Opuntia macrorhiza Engelm., Bost. Journ. Nat. Hist. 6:206.1850. (Grassland Prickly Pear).

In his diary for June 16, James described a yellow-flowered cactus "which seems not to have been noticed by Nuttall."[91] A similar description occurs in the *Account* two days earlier.[92] If this cactus is not Nuttall's *Cactus ferox* (i.e., *O. polyacantha*), then it is likely *O. macrorhiza,* which too is in range. On June 16 the expedition was along the Platte River in Buffalo County, Nebraska.

In the *Account* on July 15, James stated that the group took a different route in their descent of Pikes Peak, hoping to have better footing, but were bothered by the "numbers of yuccas and prickly pears."[93] The cactus was likely *O. macrorhiza,* but it is also possible that they were encountering *O. polyacantha.*

Opuntia phaeacantha Engelm., in Gray, Mem. Amer. Acad. 4:52.1849. (New Mexican Prickly Pear).

#155 *Cactus ferox* Nutt., in Torr., Ann. Lyc. Nat. Hist. N.Y. 2:202.1827. As to fruit: "Fruit deep purple, as large as a hen's egg."

In the *Account* on August 4, James remarked, "The fruit of the C. *ferox,* which was also found here, was now ripe, being nearly as large as an egg, and of a deep purple colour."[94] It is apparently from this

[87]JAMES [3], August 5.
[88]JAMES [1], II, 94–95; JAMES [2] in THWAITES [1], XVI, 95–96. In both editions, the entry for August 4 contains information for August 5 and 6.
[89]TORREY [2], 203.
[90]JAMES [1], II, 120; JAMES [2] in THWAITES [1], XVI, 126.
[91]JAMES [3], June 16 (erroneously dated June 15).
[92]JAMES [1], I, 452; JAMES [2] in THWAITES [1], XV, 222–23.
[93]JAMES [1], II, 33; JAMES [2] in THWAITES [1], XVI, 23.
[94]JAMES [1], II, 95; JAMES [2] in THWAITES [1], XVI, 96.

entry that Torrey obtained his information on the size and color of the fruit. In this area near Logan, Quay County, New Mexico, this prickly pear has fruits as described. James continued to refer to it as *C. ferox*.

Opuntia polyacantha Haworth, Suppl. Pl. Succ. 82. 1819. (Plains Prickly Pear).

#155 *Cactus ferox* Nutt., in Torr., Ann. Lyc. Nat. Hist. N.Y. 2:202.1827. As to location: "On the arid plains of the Platte and Arkansa, and on the Rocky Mountains, at a great elevation."

Torrey and Gray cited a James specimen as *O. missouriensis* and the Ann. Lyc. reference.[95]

In the *Account* on June 23, James noted "cactus ferox" as the party traveled up the south side of the South Platte River in Lincoln County, Nebraska.[96]

In his diary James remarked, "Prickly pear is very abundant."[97] In the *Account* James stated, under the date of June 29, "The cactus ferox reigns sole monarch, and sole possessor, of thousands of acres of this dreary plain. It forms patches which neither a horse nor any other animal will attempt to pass over."[98] This species occurs in this area from near Sterling, Logan County, to Messex, Washington County, Colorado.

At their camp on the Arkansas River near Rocky Ford, Otero County, Colorado (July 21–24), he again mentioned *Cactus ferox* in the *Account*.[99] James listed only "Cactus proliferus," however, a pincushion type, for this same time in his diary.[100]

Campanulaceae

Campanula parryi A. Gray, Syn. Fl., ed. 2, 2(1):395.1886. (Harebell).

#245 *Campanula uniflora* L., in Torr., Ann. Lyc. Nat. Hist. N.Y. 2:216.1827. "Grassy plains about the head waters of the Arkansa, and on the Rocky Mountains."

James described this plant in his diary also as *C. uniflora*[101] and

[95]TORREY AND GRAY [1], I, 555.
[96]JAMES [1], I, 470; JAMES [2] in THWAITES [1], XV, 242.
[97]JAMES [3], June 29.
[98]JAMES [1], I, 488; JAMES [2] in THWAITES [1], XV, 263.
[99]JAMES [1], II, 63; JAMES [2] in THWAITES [1], XVI, 57.
[100]JAMES [3], July 22.
[101]JAMES [3], July 10 (erroneously dated July 11).

listed it in the *Account* on July 10.[102] This, however, is a plant of alpine tundras. James was near Elephant Rock at an elevation of about 7,000 feet, a mile or so east of Palmer Lake, El Paso County, Colorado. The only plant at that elevation that fits James's description is *Campanula parryi*. This collection by James was the first for what many years later became this species.

Campanula rotundifolia L., Sp. Pl. 163. 1753. (Common Harebell).
#246 *Campanula rotundifolia* L., in Torr., Ann. Lyc. Nat. Hist. N.Y. 2:216.1827. "Base of the Rocky Mountains."
James referred to this plant as *Campanula rotundifolia* in his diary[103] and as *C. decipiens* in the *Account*.[104] His collection was made on July 6 in Douglas County, Colorado, near the mouth of the canyon of the South Platte across the river from Waterton.

Triodanis perfoliata (L.) Nieuwl., Am. Midl. Nat. 3:192.1914. (Venus Looking-Glass).
James referred to this plant in his diary as *Campanula amplexicaulis*.[105]
His collection was made on June 13, the day they were camped on the south side of the Loup River near the Nance/Merrick county line, about three miles north and a little east of Palmer, Nebraska.

Cannabaceae

Humulus lupulus L. var. **neomexicanus** A. Nels. & Cockerell, Proc. Biol. Soc. Wash. 16:45.1903. (Common Hops).
#410 *Humulus Lupulus* L., in Torr., Ann. Lyc. Nat. Hist. N.Y. 2:246.1827. "On the Missouri, and about the base of the Rocky Mountains; indigenous."
Because James was on the Missouri River in early June and because hops do not flower until July, it is not known to what collection "On the Missouri" refers. The collection from the Rocky Mountains, however, is referred to on July 7 in the *Account*.[106] On that day James

---

[102]JAMES [1], II, 15n. (erroneously dated July 11); JAMES [2] in THWAITES [1], XV, 307 (erroneously dated July 12).
[103]JAMES [3], July 6.
[104]JAMES [1], II, 3n.; JAMES [2] in THWAITES [1], XV, 288n.
[105]JAMES [3], June 13.
[106]JAMES [1], II, 8; JAMES [2] in THWAITES [1], XV, 294.

ascended the South Platte above the chasm to a point about seven miles southwest of Waterton, Jefferson County, Colorado.

Capparidaceae

Cleome serrulata Pursh, Fl. Am. Sept. 441. 1814. (Rocky Mountain Bee Plant).
#22 *Peritoma serrulatum* DC., in Torr., Ann. Lyc. Nat. Hist. N.Y. 2:167.1827.
Cleome serrulata Pursh, in T. & G., Fl. No. Am. 1:121–22.1838. "Banks of the Missouri and Arkansas, *Nuttall!*, *Dr. James!* Aug."

James referred four times in his diary to this species:[107] first, on June 9, when along the Coquille (Shell Creek) in Colfax or Platte County, Nebraska; second, on June 26, as "Cleome tryphilla" rather than "Cleome serrulata," when traveling along the South Platte from Nebraska to near Julesburg, Sedgewick County, Colorado; next, on July 1, when just west of Fort Morgan, Morgan County, Colorado to near Kuner, Weld County, Colorado; and lastly, on July 22, when camped on the Arkansas River a short distance northwest of Rocky Ford, Otero County, Colorado.

The only mention in the *Account* of the *Cleome* (as *C. tryphilla*) is on June 23 "about the forks of the Platte."[108] On this day the party crossed to the south side of the South Platte a few miles west of the city of North Platte, Lincoln County, Nebraska, but the several plants that are mentioned were collected on June 23–26.

Cleomella angustifolia Torr., in Hook., Kew Jour. 2:255.1850. "Western Arkansas, *Dr. James*." (Cleomella).
#24 *Cleomella mexicana* DC. *sensu* Torr., Ann. Lyc. Nat. Hist. N.Y. 2:167.1827.

With his original description, Torrey cited both the Ann. Lyc. reference and a reference in the *Flora of North America*.[109] Based on a flowering time of middle to late summer and on the known distribution of the species, it seems likely that James collected the type in August in the Texas panhandle or in the western half of Oklahoma.

We have found no reference to this plant in James's diary.

---

[107]JAMES [3], June 9, June 26 (erroneously dated June 25), July 1, and July 22.
[108]JAMES [1], I, 468n.; JAMES [2] in THWAITES [1], XV, 241n.
[109]TORREY AND GRAY [1], I, 121.

Polanisia dodecandra (L.) DC. subsp. **trachysperma** (T. & G.) Iltis, Rhodora 68:47.1966. (Clammyweed).
#23 *Polanisia graveolens* Raf., in Torr., Ann. Lyc. Nat. Hist. N.Y. 2:167.1827.
James could have collected this plant in any state through which he traveled.

Polanisia jamesii (T. & G.) Iltis, Brittonia 10:54.1958. Type: NY. (James Crestpetal).
#25 *Cleome n.sp. Nutt. mss.*, in Torr., Ann. Lyc. Nat. Hist. N.Y. 2:168.1827. Here Torrey stated that Nuttall also had found this species "in the Arkansas Territory, in 1819." Nuttall's collection, however, was of *P. erosa*.
We have been unable to locate any description in James's diary that will fit this species. We are assuming that under *Cristatella jamesii,* Torrey and Gray's reference to its being from "[i]n sand, Arkansas" was because of the confusion with *P. erosa*.[110]
James's plant could have been collected in Nebraska, Colorado, the Texas panhandle, or western Oklahoma.

Caprifoliaceae

Sambucus canadensis L., Sp. Pl. 269. 1753. (American Elder).
#187 *Sambucus canadensis* L., in Torr., Ann. Lyc. Nat. Hist. N.Y. 2:208.1827. "Sources of the Canadian."
James's collection was made on June 8 during the party's travel from the previous night's campsite on Rawhide Creek, just north-west of Fremont, Dodge County, to the June 8 camp on Shell Creek, northwest of Schuyler, Colfax County, Nebraska.[111]
Torrey's citation may be in reference to this June 8 collection; the location given by Torrey, however, is much closer to that of a collection of the following species of *Sambucus*.

Sambucus coerulea Raf. var. **neomexicana** (Woot.) Rehd., Mitt. Deutsch. Dendrol. Ges. 1915:228.1915. (Blue Elder).
James collected this elder on July 25, near the Purgatoire River, Las Animas County, Colorado.[112]
We were able to find this *Sambucus* on the Purgatoire River and on

[110]TORREY AND GRAY [1], I, 124.
[111]JAMES [3], June 8.
[112]JAMES [1], II, 69; JAMES [2] in THWAITES [1], XVI, 66; JAMES [3], July 25.

Chacuaco Creek near their junction in Las Animas County, Colorado. Here plants ten feet high and twenty feet wide occur.

No James specimens were found at NY of *S. coerulea,* its variety, or of *S. canadensis.*

Symphoricarpos albus (L.) Blake, Rhodora 16:118.1914. (Snowberry).

#190 *Symphoria racemosa* Pursh, in Torr., Ann. Lyc. Nat. Hist. N.Y. 2:208.1827. "Prairies of the Missouri."

Assuming Torrey's identification to be correct, James would have collected this plant in July in Colorado.

We have found no reference to this plant in either the diary or the *Account.*

Symphoricarpos occidentalis Hook., Fl. Bor. Am. 1:285.1833. (Wolfberry).

#189 *Symphoria glomerata* Pursh, in Torr., Ann. Lyc. Nat. Hist. N.Y. 2:208.1827. "On the Missouri, from its mouth to the Loup Village."

Torrey and Gray cited a James collection as *Symphoricarpos vulgaris.*[113] Both *S. glomerata* and *S. vulgaris* are synonyms of *Symphoricarpos orbiculatus,* a species James likely saw on the Missouri, but not in flower. He again entered its range, during flowering time, in August in Oklahoma, where a collection of *S. orbiculatus* could have been made. No mention is made of it in the *Account* or diary in August.

In his diary, James remarked, "Symphoria glomerata? which is also common to the whole country west of the Missisipi is beginning to flower. Nuttall seems not to have described this plant with his usual accuracy, or my specimens are a variety or different species. . . . The flowers also are white with a faint and delicate tinge of red instead of 'greenish-red'."[114] A similar description is given on the same day in the *Account.*[115]

James's suspicions were correct. Thirteen years later the species, *S. occidentalis,* would be described from plants from the Pacific Northwest. James collected his plant from the south side of the Loup River, just after the party crossed the stream from the Pawnee Republic village, near the Nance/Merrick county line, three miles north and a half mile east of Palmer, Nebraska.

---

[113]TORREY AND GRAY [1], II, 4.
[114]JAMES [3], June 13.
[115]JAMES [1], I, 449; JAMES [2] in THWAITES [1], XV, 218–19.

In June of 1985 we found this species as "occasional" and in good flower at essentially the same location.
No James specimen of this was found at NY.

Viburnum rufidulum Raf., Alsog. Am. 56. 1838. (Southern Black Haw).
#188 *Viburnum Lentago* L., in Torr., Ann. Lyc. Nat. Hist. N.Y. 2:208.1827. "On the Canadian, near its junction with the Arkansa." Torrey added, "Two other undetermined species of *Viburnum* were found about the sources of the Canadian."
In his diary and the *Account* for the same day, James referred to "Viburnum Lentago."[116] On this day, a Sunday, the party remained in camp at the junction of Buggy Creek and the Canadian River, Grady County, Oklahoma. *Viburnum rufidulum* is the only species of the genus that occurs there. It seems likely that this is the location that Torrey referred to, because *Viburnum* is not mentioned subsequently in either the diary or the *Account* except on the next day, August 28, when James mentioned in his diary the beginning occurrence of "V. lantanoides."[117] If this plant were a *Viburnum,* it too would be *V. rufidulum.*
Torrey's comment about two other species of *Viburnum* from "about the sources of the Canadian" presumably refers to an entry in the *Account* for July 25.[118] On this day the party was approaching the Purgatoire River in Otero and Las Animas counties, Colorado, and the Account says that "one or two species of Viburnum" were seen.[119] *Viburnum* is not known from that area.

Caryophyllaceae

Arenaria obtusiloba (Rydb.) Fernald, Rhodora 21:14.1919. (Alpine Sandwort).
#37 *Arenaria obtusa* Torr., Ann. Lyc. Nat. Hist. N.Y. 2:170.1827. [Not All., Fl. Pedem. 2:114.1785]. "On the higher parts of the Rocky Mountains."
A. arctica var. γ T. & G., Fl. No. Am. 1:181.1838. "Rocky Mountains, on James' Peak, lat. 41°, *Dr. James!*"
Although no reference is given to this plant in James's diary, his

[116]JAMES [1], II, 145; JAMES [2] in THWAITES [1], XVI, 156; JAMES [3], August 27.
[117]JAMES [3], August 28.
[118]JAMES [1], II, 69; JAMES [2] in THWAITES [1], XVI, 66.
[119]JAMES [1], II, 69; JAMES [2] in THWAITES [1], XVI, 66 (as "biburium").

type (NY) collection was made on July 13–15 on Pikes Peak, El Paso County, Colorado, in the subalpine to alpine region in which the plant grows.

Arenaria rubella (Wahlenb.) Smith, English Bot. 4:276.1828. (Sandwort).

According to Torrey and Gray, James collected *Arenaria verna* on "James' Peak, Rocky Mountains, lat. 41°."[120] This species *sensu* American authors, not L., is now considered a synonym of *A. rubella*.

Cerastium arvense L., Sp. Pl. 438. 1753. (Chickweed).

James referred to this plant in his diary as *Cerastium arvense* and as a cerastium in the *Account*.[121] It seems very likely that James's identification is correct.

On this day (July 7) James ascended the South Platte above the chasm to a point about seven miles southwest of Waterton, Jefferson County, Colorado.

Paronychia jamesii T. & G., Fl. No. Am. 1:170.1838. "Rocky Mountains . . . *Dr. James!*" (Nailwort).

#174 *Paronychia dichotoma*? Nutt., in Torr., Ann. Lyc. Nat. Hist. N.Y. 2:206.1827. "On the Arkansa?"

On June 26, James collected a plant "resembling Sarothra gentianoides" as the party traveled from near Ogallala, Keith County, Nebraska to near Julesburg, Sedgwick County, Colorado.[122] This collection may have been the type collection of *Paronychia jamesii*. The species occurs, however, in all five of the states through which the expedition traveled during June through August.

According to Core, there is a James specimen of *P. jamesii* collected on the Long Expedition at NY.[123]

Paronychia pulvinata Gray, Proc. Acad. Sci. Phila. 1863:58.1864. (Alpine Nailwort).

A James specimen of this species is at NY.

This high-altitude species could have been collected by James only on Pikes Peak, El Paso County, Colorado, on July 13–15.

---

[120]TORREY AND GRAY [1], I, 181.

[121]JAMES [3], July 7 (erroneously dated July 8); JAMES [1], II, 8n.; JAMES [2] in THWAITES [1], XV, 295n.

[122]JAMES [3], June 26 (erroneously dated June 25).

[123]CORE, 392.

Silene acaulis L. var. **subacaulescens** (F.N. Williams) Fern. & St. John, Rhodora 23:120.1921. (Moss Campion).
#38 *Silene acaulis* L., in Torr., Ann. Lyc. Nat. Hist. N.Y. 2:170. 1827. "On the higher parts of the Rocky Mountains."
A James specimen from the Rocky Mountains is cited, as *S. acaulis,* in Torrey and Gray.[124]
James would have collected this alpine plant July 13–15 on Pikes Peak, El Paso County, Colorado.

Stellaria jamesiana Torr. (Tuber Starwort).
#34 *Stellaria jamesiana* Torr., Ann. Lyc. Nat. Hist. N.Y. 2:169. 1827. "Moist situations within the Rocky Mountains." Type: NY. Later as *Stellaria jamesii* in Torrey and Gray[125] and Robinson in Gray.[126]
"? *S. graminea,*" James Cat. 181. *fide* Robinson in Gray.[127]
No reference to this plant has been found in James's diary. Based on the habitat and distribution of the plant, James's collection was made in July along the front range between Jefferson and Fremont counties in Colorado.

Stellaria longipes Goldie, Edinb. Phil. Jour. 6:327.1822. (Long-Stalked Stitchwort).
#35 *Stellaria laeta* Richards., in Torr., Ann. Lyc. Nat. Hist. N.Y. 2:169.1827. "Rocky Mountains."
#36 *Stellaria Edwarsii* [sic] sensu Torr., Ann. Lyc. Nat. Hist. N.Y. 2:170.1827. "With the preceding ['Rocky Mountains']."
"? *Micropetalon gramineum,*" James Cat. 181. *fide* Robinson in Gray.[128]
Torrey and Gray cited two James specimens under two unnamed variants of *S. longipes.*[129]
S. laeta is frequently considered a synonym of *S. longipes,* but by some authors it is treated as a distinct taxon.
No reference to this species was found in the diary; based on distribution, however, it is likely that James made his collections in Colorado.

---

[124]TORREY AND GRAY [1], I, 189.
[125]TORREY AND GRAY [1], I, 183.
[126]GRAY [2], 237.
[127]GRAY [2], 237.
[128]GRAY [2], 233.
[129]TORREY AND GRAY [1], I, 185.

Celastraceae

Euonymus atropurpureus Jacq., Hort. Vindo. 2:55, pl. 120. 1772. (Burning-Bush).

#58 *Euonymus atropurpureus* L., in Torr., Ann. Lyc. Nat. Hist. N.Y. 2:173.1827. "On the steep banks of the Coquille."

James described this plant in his diary when the party was along the Loup River between Monroe, Platte County, and Merchiston, Nance County, Nebraska.[130] The location given for this particular plant, however, is the same as that for which Torrey recorded, "On the steep bank of the Coquille," which they had left the preceding day, June 9.

James described more fully the fruit of this species from a second collection, which he made on September 5 along the Canadian River between Atwood and Lamar, Hughes County, Oklahoma.[131]

Chenopodiaceae

Atriplex argentea Nutt., Gen. No. Am. Pl. 1:198.1818. (Saltbush).

#379 *Atriplex argentea* Nutt., in Torr., Ann. Lyc. Nat. Hist. N.Y. 2:240.1827. "On the Platte."

Watson cited both of the above references under *Atriplex argentea*.[132] We have found no reference to this plant in James's diary. If Torrey's location, "On the Platte," is correct, then, based on distribution, James would have collected the plant in Colorado. It is possible, however, that this species was one of "several species of Atriplex" that James noted on August 12 about their campsite on the Canadian River[133] about sixteen miles northeast of Borger, Texas, in Hutchinson County.

Atriplex canescens (Pursh) Nutt., Gen. No. Am. Pl. 1:197.1818. (Four-Winged Saltbush).

#378 *Atriplex canescens* Nutt., in Torr., Ann. Lyc. Nat. Hist. N.Y. 2:239.1827. "Near the Pawnee villages."

This name also occurs in James's *Catalogue*.[134] In Watson, James is

[130]JAMES [3], June 10.
[131]JAMES [3], September 5.
[132]WATSON [2], 115.
[133]JAMES [1], II, 115; JAMES [2] in THWAITES [1], XVI, 121.
[134]JAMES [4], 178.

cited as a collector, and reference is made to both the Torrey and James papers.[135]

This species is not known so far east in Nebraska as the Pawnee villages on the Loup River. James's collection was likely made in Colorado.

Atriplex torreyana Raf., Atl. Jour. 1:146.1832.

Rafinesque's name is based on the description by Torrey of an unnumbered and unnamed *Atriplex* immediately following his #379 *A. argentea*.[136] The description is, "A. fruticosa ? undique canescens; foliis lineari-oblongis, obtusiusculis, integerrimis; floribus glomeratis, subterminalibus; calycibus fructiferis latissimis, dentatis, pedicellatis. Allied to A. linifolia, Kunth?" It is our opinion that this description too fits within the variations of *A. canescens*. In works on the Chenopodiaceae, *A. torreyana* is not included and is an example of a Rafinesquian name that has gone unrecognized.

James's type collection of *A. torreyana* could have been made in any state through which the expedition traveled, beginning in western Nebraska.

It is possible that the type was one of "several species of Atriplex" that James noted on August 12 about their campsite on the Canadian River, about sixteen miles northeast of Borger, Texas, in Hutchinson County.[137]

Atriplex hastata L., Sp. Pl. 1:1053.1753. (Spear Orache).

Watson, under *A. patula* var. *hastata,* listed James as one of the collectors.[138] It is possible that this is the same plant that James described as a *Chenopodium* in his diary for June 18, when the party was camped on the Platte, six and a half miles west-southwest of Overton, Dawson County, Nebraska.[139]

Ceratoides lanata (Pursh) J. T. Howell, Wasmann J. Biol. 29:105. 1971. (Winter Fat).

This species was not included by Torrey.[140] James, however, included it as *Diotis lanata* Pursh,[141] and Watson, under *Eurotia*

---

[135]WATSON [2], 120.
[136]TORREY [2], 240.
[137]JAMES [1], II, 115; JAMES [2] in THWAITES [1], XVI, 121.
[138]WATSON [2], 107.
[139]JAMES [3], June 18.
[140]TORREY [2].
[141]JAMES [4], 189.

lanata (Pursh) Moq., cited the James reference and James as a collector.[142]

Based on studies of the ultrastructure of the wall of the pollen grains, Meeuse and Smit suggest that *Eurotia lanata* is congeneric with the Old World *Krascheninnikovia*, thus *K. lanata* (Pursh) Meeuse & Smit.[143]

This species could have been collected along their route in Colorado, New Mexico, or the Texas panhandle. Several chenopods were noted by James on August 12 about their campsite on the Canadian River, about sixteen miles northeast of Borger, Texas, in Hutchinson County.[144] Perhaps this species was one of them.

Chenopodium album L., Sp. Pl. 219. 1753. (Lamb's Quarters).

As indicated by Watson, #372 *Chenopodium subspicatum sensu* Torrey in Ann. Lyc. Nat. Hist. N.Y. 2:239.1827 is this species.[145] Torrey stated that the plant was from "[s]aline plains of the Canadian." There is nothing wrong with this locality in terms of present-day distribution, but it seems an unlikely locality for a European introduction in 1820. On the other hand, it could have been a Spanish introduction into New Mexico that later came down the Canadian.

A *Chenopodium* was mentioned by James in the *Account* on August 12, when the party camped near some marshes on the Canadian River, about sixteen miles northeast of Borger, Texas, in Hutchinson County.[146]

Chenopodium leptophyllum (Moq.) Wats., Proc. Am. Acad. Sci. 9:94.1874. (Narrowleaf Lamb's Quarters).

#376 *Kochia dioica* Nutt., in Torr., Ann. Lyc. Nat. Hist. N.Y. 2:239.1827. "On the Platte."

Watson cited Torrey's #376[147] and *Kochia dioica sensu* James[148] as *Chenopodium leptophyllum*.

Central U.S. plants of this species complex have been referred by various authors to *C. desiccatum* A. Nels. and *C. pratericola* Rydb., or the latter as *C. desiccatum* var. *leptophylloides* (Murr.) Wahl, Field & Lab. 23:22.1955.

[142]WATSON [2], 121.
[143]MEEUSE AND SMIT, 644.
[144]JAMES [1], II, 115; JAMES [2] in THWAITES [1], XVI, 121.
[145]WATSON [2], 96.
[146]JAMES [1], II, 115; JAMES [2] in THWAITES [1], XVI, 121.
[147]WATSON [2], 95.
[148]JAMES [4], 178.

"On the Platte" is possible, and based on flowering time (July to September), James's collection would have been made in Colorado. Several species of *Chenopodium* and *Kochia* were noted by James on August 12, however, along the Canadian River about sixteen miles northeast of Borger, Texas, in Hutchinson County.[149]

Chenopodium simplex (Torr.) Raf., Atl. Jour. 1:146.1832. (Maple-Leaved Goosefoot).
#373 *Chenopodium hybridum* β? *simplex* Torr., Ann. Lyc. Nat. Hist. N.Y. 2:239.1827. "Near Council Bluff, on the Missouri." The description reads, "caule simplici, 5-angulare; foliis ovatis, subcordatis, grosse repando-dentatis; spica simplici, terminali, nuda."
Watson listed Torrey's variety in synonymy under *C. hybridum* and cited James as a collector.[150]
James's type collection was likely made on May 29, in the area of Engineer Cantonment, some five miles downstream on the Missouri River from Fort Calhoun, Washington County, Nebraska. In his diary for this day, James commented that this species was "perhaps new."[151]
Again in his diary for Sunday, June 18, James mentioned this species.[152] At this time the party was camped about six miles west-southwest of Overton, Dawson County, Nebraska.
Different interpretations have been made on the taxonomy of this variable species. Aellen and Just believed that *C. hybridum sensu stricto* was not recorded from America.[153] They referred the American material to *C. gigantospermum* and its variety *standleyanum*. Wahl,[154] Steyermark,[155] and Correll and Johnston[156] referred the American material of *C. hybridum* to *C. gigantospermum*. Fernald[157] considered *gigantospermum* and *standleyanum*, as varieties of *C. hybridum*, to constitute the American representatives of the complex. It will be noted that the earliest epithet, either at the varietal or specific level for the American material, is *simplex*. Dorn[158] too came to this conclusion.

149JAMES [1], II, 115; JAMES [2] in THWAITES [1], XVI, 121.
150WATSON [2], 97.
151JAMES [3], May 29.
152JAMES [3], June 18.
153AELLEN AND JUST, 75.
154WAHL, 30.
155STEYERMARK [1], 610.
156CORRELL AND JOHNSTON, 536.
157FERNALD, 594.
158DORN, 162.

Corispermum hyssopifolium L., Sp. Pl. 4. 1753. (Bugseed).
#381 *Corispermum hyssopifolium* var. *americanum* Nutt., in Torr., Ann. Lyc. Nat. Hist. N.Y. 2:240.1827. "On the Missouri."
This plant is unlikely to have been collected so early as when they were on the Missouri. Based on flowering time, it is more likely to have been collected on the Canadian in Oklahoma.
This name is also listed in James, Am. Phil. Soc. 2:172.1825.

Cycloloma atriplicifolium (Spreng.) Coult., Mem. Torr. Bot. Club 5:143.1894. (Winged Pigweed).
#375 *Kochia dentata* Willd., in Torr., Ann. Lyc. Nat. Hist. N.Y. 2:239.1827. "On the Platte."
Cycloloma platyphyllum (Michx.) Moq., in Watson, Proc. Am. Acad. Sci. 9:92.1874, where the Ann. Lyc. Nat. Hist. N.Y. reference and a James specimen are cited.
This plant could have been collected in any of the five states through which the expedition traveled. James noted *Kochia* in the *Account* on August 12 near their campsite along the Canadian River, about sixteen miles northeast of Borger, Texas, in Hutchinson County.[159]

Monolepis nuttalliana (Schultes) Greene, Fl. Franc. 168. 1891. (Poverty Weed).
#380 *Blitum chenopodioides* Nutt. [(1818) not Lam. (1783)], in Torr., Ann. Lyc. Nat. Hist. N.Y. 2:240.1827. "Arid and saline soils on the Platte and Arkansa."
Based on distribution and flowering time, James could have collected this plant in any of the five states through which he traveled.

Sarcobatus vermiculatus (Hook.) Torr., in Emory, Notes Mil. Reconn. 150.1848. (Greasewood).
Fremontia vermicularis Torr., in Fremont Explor. 91. 1843. Torrey added that this is "undoubtedly the Batis? vermicularis of Hooker" (error for *vermiculata*) collected by Douglas. Torrey also added, "This remarkable plant, which I dedicate to Lieutenant Fremont, was first collected by Dr. James about the sources of the Canadian, (in Long's expedition) but was omitted in my account of his plants

---

[159]JAMES [1], II, 115; JAMES [2] in THWAITES [1], XVI, 121.

published in the Annals of the Lyceum of Natural History." Watson, too, listed James as a collector of this species.[160]

The known distribution of the plant indicates that James collected it in the latter half of July in southeastern Colorado in Pueblo, Otero, or Las Animas counties.

Suaeda calceoliformis (Hook.) Moq., Chenop. Monogr. Enum. 128. 1840. Based on a Drummond collection from Saskatchewan. (Sea-Blite).

Suaeda depressa of authors, not of (Pursh) Wats.

#377 *Salsola prostrata* Pursh, in Torr., Ann. Lyc. Nat. Hist. N.Y. 2:239.1827. "On the Platte."

McNeill et al. have shown that Pursh's *Salsola depressa,* Fl. Am. Sept. 197.1814, was based on Pallas's *Suaeda prostrata,* Ill. Pl. 55, pl.47.1803, a European plant, distinct from the American plant.[161]

Watson, under *Suaeda depressa,*[162] cited both Torrey's #377 and James's *Salsola salsa,*[163] where the collection is said to have come from "the upper part of the Canadian."

"On the Platte" is possible, and based on flowering time, James's collection would have been made in Colorado. *Salsola,* however, was noted by James on August 12, along the Canadian River, about sixteen miles northeast of Borger, Texas, in Hutchinson County.[164]

Suaeda nigra (Raf.) Macbride, Contr. Gray Herb. n.s. 56:50.1918.

#374 *Chenopodium maritimum sensu* Torr., Ann. Lyc. Nat. Hist. N.Y. 2:239.1827. Torrey questioned the identification and gave the following description, "C. caule ramoso, glabro; foliis linearibus, semi-cylindricis? succulentis, integerrimis, mucronatis; floribus axillaribus, pentandris." Type: "Upper part of the Canadian."

Chenopodium nigrum Raf., Atl. Jour. 146. 1832. Name based on Torrey's description.

Suaeda diffusa Wats., Proc. Am. Acad. Sci. 9:88.1874, where the Ann. Lyc. Nat. Hist. N.Y. reference and a James specimen are cited.

James's type specimen is likely the plant referred to in the *Account* as *Anabasis,* found near the campsite of August 12 along the Cana-

---

160WATSON [2], 86.
161MCNEILL, BASSETT, AND CROMPTON, 133–38.
162WATSON [2], 89.
163JAMES [4], 178.
164JAMES [1], II, 115; JAMES [2] in THWAITES [1], XVI, 121.

dian River in Hutchinson County, Texas, sixteen miles northeast of Borger.[165]

Hopkins and Blackwell considered both *Chenopodium nigrum* Raf. and *Suaeda diffusa* Wats. to be synonyms of *Suaeda torreyana* Wats., Proc. Am. Acad. Sci. 9:88.1874.[166] They considered *Chenopodium nigrum* Raf. to be a *nomen nudum,* but, as mentioned above, it was based on Torrey's description and hence is the oldest name for the complex.

Cistaceae

Helianthemum bicknellii Fern., Rhodora 21:36.1919. (Frostweed).

In his diary, James referred to this plant as "Cistus canadensis," which he collected on June 13 on the south side of the Loup River near the Nance/Merrick county line, about three miles north and a little east of Palmer, Nebraska.[167]

This collection appears as *H. canadense* in James's *Catalogue.*[168] Under this same name in the *Account,* James stated that this plant was collected "along the Platte on the 15th and 16th June."[169]

Commelinaceae

Commelina erecta L. var. **angustifolia** (Michx.) Fernald, Rhodora 42:439.1940. (Dayflower).

#447 *Commelina angustifolia* Michx.?, in Torr., Ann. Lyc. Nat. Hist. N.Y. 2:252.1827. "Sources of the Canadian."

James's diary for June 21 mentioned *Commelina erecta.*[170] On June 21 the party traveled up the Platte from near Gothenburg, Dawson County, Nebraska, to about six miles west of Maxwell, Lincoln County, Nebraska.

On July 3, 1985, we collected the var. *angustifolia* in the sandhills two miles northwest of Gothenburg.

Under the date of August 2 in the diary, James listed a *Commelina.*[171] His full description fits this variety well. This day the party traveled on Ute Creek between the mouth of Garcia Creek and

---

[165]JAMES [1], II, 115; JAMES [2] in THWAITES [1], XVI, 121.
[166]HOPKINS AND BLACKWELL, 163.
[167]JAMES [3], June 13.
[168]JAMES [4], 182.
[169]JAMES [1], I, 455n.; JAMES [2] in THWAITES [1], XV, 226n.
[170]JAMES [3], June 21 (erroneously dated June 20).
[171]JAMES [3], August 2 (an undated day in the diary).

their campsite about thirteen miles south of Bueyeros, Harding County, New Mexico. This locality is evidently the one to which Torrey referred.

Compositae

Agoseris glauca (Pursh) Raf., Herb. Raf. 39.1833.
#199 *Troximon glaucum* Nutt., in Torr., Ann. Lyc. Nat. Hist. N.Y. 2:209.1827. "Base of the Rocky Mountains."
In his diary, James referred to this plant as *Tragopogon*.[172] In the *Account* for the same day, the plant is called *Troximon glaucum*.[173]
James's collection was made on July 6 in Douglas County, Colorado, near the mouth of the canyon of the South Platte across the river from Waterton.

Ambrosia psilostachya DC., Prodr. 5:526.1836. (Western Ragweed).
#242 *Ambrosia hispida* Pursh, in Torr., Ann. Lyc. Nat. Hist. N.Y. 2:216.1827.
This plant could have been seen in flower by James from July on; it is not mentioned in the *Account,* however, until August 26.[174] The party was by then in either Canadian or Grady County, Oklahoma.

Arnica fulgens Pursh, Fl. Am. Sept. 527. 1814. (Orange Arnica).
#221 *Arnica montana* L., in Torr., Ann. Lyc. Nat. Hist. N.Y. 2:213.1827. "Near the Rocky Mountains."
It seems likely that this is the species James collected. If we are correct, the collection would have been made in early to mid July from Adams to Fremont counties, Colorado.

Artemisia filifolia Torr. (Sand Sagebrush).
Artemisia filifolia Torr., Ann. Lyc. Nat. Hist. N.Y. 2:211.1827. Following #210 (*A. ludoviciana*).
According to the flowering time and distribution, James could have collected the type (NY) in any of the five states through which he traveled. This species occurs abundantly in the Texas panhandle, which is perhaps the most likely collecting site.

---

[172]JAMES [3], July 6.
[173]JAMES [1], II, 3n.; JAMES [2] in THWAITES [1], XV, 288n.
[174]JAMES [1], II, 142; JAMES [2] in THWAITES [1], XVI, 152.

Artemisia ludoviciana Nutt., Gen. 2:143.1818. (Prairie Sagebrush). #210 *Artemisia ludoviciana* Nutt., in Torr., Ann. Lyc. Nat. Hist. N.Y. 2:211.1827. "Arid plains of the Platte."

Based on flowering time (late summer to fall) and distribution, James most likely collected this species in northeastern New Mexico, the Texas panhandle, or Oklahoma. In the *Account* on June 24, however, James listed *A. ludoviciana*[175] along with five other species.[176] These species were said to occupy "extensive tracts of land along the Platte" in Nebraska.

Aster falcatus Lindley subsp. **commutatus** (T. & G.) A. G. Jones, Rhodora 80:340.1978. Type: "Upper Missouri, *Dr. James!*" (NY, *fide* Jones).[177]

#216 *Aster biennis* Nutt., in Torr., Ann. Lyc. Nat. Hist. N.Y. 2:212.1827. "On the Missouri."

Aster multiflorus Ait. γ *commutatus* T. & G., Fl. No. Am. 2:125. 1841.

Based on flowering time and distribution, James would have collected the type in August or September in northeastern New Mexico or along the Canadian River in the Texas panhandle or the western half of Oklahoma.

Aster paludosus subsp. **hemisphaericus** (Alexander) Cronq., Bull. Torr. Bot. Club 74:145.1947. (Single-Stemmed Bog Aster).

#217 *Aster paludosus* Ait., in Torr., Ann. Lyc. Nat. Hist. N.Y. 2:212.1827. "On the Missouri."

James could have made his collection in the latter half of September along the Canadian or Arkansas rivers in far-eastern Oklahoma or in Arkansas.

Baccharis salicina T. & G., Fl. No. Am. 2:258.1842. (Willow Baccharis).

#211 *Baccharis* [followed by a Latin description] Torr., in Ann. Lyc. Nat. Hist. N.Y. 2:211.1827. "On the Canadian."

---

[175]JAMES [1], I, 475; JAMES [2] in THWAITES [1], XV, 249.

[176]The other species listed were *A. longifolia, A. serrata, A. columbiensis, A. cernua,* and *A. canadensis.* The species were also listed in the Ann. Lyc. (TORREY [2], following #210). The first two species listed above are out of range of the route of the expedition, while the latter three, as *A. cana, A. dracunculus,* and *A. campestris* subsp. *caudata,* respectively, occur along the route of the expedition but flower between August and September. *Artemisia biennis, A. carruthii,* and *A. frigida* are other species that the party could have encountered along their route.

[177]JONES, 341.

James's diary for July 22 contains a lengthy description of what James thought was a new species.[178] The description fits *B. salicina* reasonably well. In the *Account* on July 21 at the same campsite, James described this plant as simply "a syngenecious shrub, probably a vernonia."[179]

At this time the party was camped on the Arkansas River at Rocky Ford, Otero County, Colorado. James added that this plant was one of the undershrubs in the wooded area of their camp. Rocky Ford is a location given, incidentally, for this species in Rydberg.[180]

Berlandiera lyrata Benth., Pl. Hartweg. 17.1839. (Lyreleaf Green-eyes).

#241 *Silphium nuttallianum* Torr., in Ann. Lyc. Nat. Hist. N.Y. 2:216.1827. "S. (anonymous) Nutt. in Sill. jour. v. p. 103 [*sic*]." "First discovered in Florida by Mr. Ware, and described, but not named, by Nuttall." No locality for the James specimen is given.

Berlandiera incisa T. & G., Fl. No. Am. 2:282.1842. Here the Torrey name and reference are cited, with the following remark: "as to the plant collected by Dr. James; but not the Florida plant of Nuttall." "On the Arkansas or Platte, *Dr. James!*" Type: NY.

In Silliman's *Journal,* Nuttall reported on Ware's plants collected in October and November 1821, from east Florida.[181] Here Nuttall's usual practice was to italicize the specific epithet of the new species. On page 301, however, the entry reads, "Silphium* subacaule, scabriusculum" with no italics. This is doubtless why Torrey at the time considered the plant not to be named.

Based on its known distribution, James could have collected the type of *B. incisa* in southeastern Colorado, northeastern New Mexico, or along the Canadian River in the Texas panhandle in late July to early August.

Brickellia grandiflora (Hook.) Nutt., Trans. Am. Phil. Soc. n.s. 7:287.1840. (Tasselflower Brickellbush).

According to Torrey and Gray, James collected this plant on the "Upper Plains of the Platte?"[182]

Based on flowering time and distribution, James would have

[178]JAMES [3], July 22.
[179]JAMES [1], II, 62; JAMES [2] in THWAITES [1], XVI, 57.
[180]RYDBERG [1], 367.
[181]NUTTALL [3], 301.
[182]TORREY AND GRAY [1], II, 80.

collected this species along the Front Range in Colorado or in northeastern New Mexico in July or August.

Centaurea americana Nutt., J. Acad. Nat. Sci. Phila. 2:117.1821. (Basketflower).
#237 *Centaurea americana* Nutt., in Torr., Ann. Lyc. Nat. Hist. N.Y. 2:215.1827. "On the Canadian; abundant."
No mention of this plant is made in the diary; in the *Account* on August 20, however, James noted the occurrence of the "tall and graceful" *Centaurea*.[183] James referred to this plant as *C. speciosa*, with further descriptive comments in his footnote. The name is preempted, however, by *C. americana* should one interpret his comments as an attempt to describe a new species.
The plant was collected in southwestern Dewey County, Oklahoma.

Chrysopsis villosa (Pursh) Nutt. ex DC., Prodr. 5:327.1836. (Golden Aster).
#213 *Inula villosa* Nutt., in Torr., Ann. Lyc. Nat. Hist. N.Y. 2:212.1827. "With the preceding ['On the Platte.']."
If this species were collected "[w]ith the preceding," i.e., *Erigeron pumilus,* it would have been collected on June 20 near Gothenburg, Dawson County, Nebraska. *Chrysopsis villosa* occurs, however, throughout much of the route of the expedition.

Cirsium altissimum (L.) Spreng., Syst. Veg. 3:373.1826. (Roadside Thistle).
#203 *Carduus (Cnicus) altissimus* Willd., in Torr., Ann. Lyc. Nat. Hist. N.Y. 2:210.1827. "On the Missouri."
In his diary for August 26, James recorded the genus name *Cnicus* and stated that the stem was unarmed and the "[l]eaves flat sessile not decurrent alternate, white downey beneath naked and smooth above, margins slightly undulating sparingly beset with short slender spines. Flower large, purple."[184]
The location given by Torrey is wrong for any collection of this species by James, as the expedition was west of its range on the Missouri and Platte a month or more before this thistle starts to flower.
On August 26 the party traveled through southwestern Canadian

---

[183]JAMES [1], II, 135.
[184]JAMES [3], August 26.

County to the mouth of Buggy Creek in northwestern Grady County in central Oklahoma.

Cirsium undulatum (Nutt.) Spreng., Syst. Veg. 3:374.1826. (Wavy-leaf Thistle).

In his diary, James used the name *Cnicus undulatus*,[185] apparently from a misreading of Nuttall,[186] where *Cnicus* appears as a subgenus of *Carduus*. The combination used by James was not published until 1874.

The plant was collected on June 10 as the party traveled along the Loup River between Monroe, Platte County, and Merchiston, Nance County, Nebraska.

Conyza canadensis (L.) Cronq., Bull. Torr. Bot. Club 70:632. 1943. (Horseweed).

In his diary, James mentioned "Erigeron canadense" on July 22.[187] At that time the party was camped on the Arkansas River near Rocky Ford, Otero County, Colorado.

Crepis runcinata (James) T. & G., Fl. No. Am. 2:487.1843. (Hawksbeard).

Hieracium runcinatum James, Long Exped. (Phila. ed.) 1:453. 1823. "Hab. in depressed, grassy situations along the Platte."

#198 *Hieracium runcinatum* in Torr., Ann. Lyc. Nat. Hist. N.Y. 2:209.1827. Habitat identical to that given by James.

James described this plant in his diary and gave the name "Hieracium runcinatum Mihi."[188] The habitat is identical to that given with the original description.[189] The type was collected on June 15 along the Platte River from southeast of Grand Island to south of Gibbon in eastern Buffalo County, Nebraska.

Echinacea angustifolia DC., Prodr. 5:554.1836. (Blacksamson).

In the diary, James stated that *Rudbeckia purpurea,* whose rays were just beginning to expand, grew on "elevated grassy plains."[190] This species (as *Echinacea purpurea*) does not occur so far north as Nebraska. The collection was made on June 6 about eight to nine

[185]JAMES [3], June 10.
[186]NUTTALL [5], II, 130.
[187]JAMES [3], July 22.
[188]JAMES [3], June 15 (erroneously dated June 14).
[189]The description and habitat are repeated in the London edition of the *Account.* JAMES [7], II, 336.
[190]JAMES [3], June 6.

miles west of Engineer Cantonment near Big Papillion Creek, near Kenard, Washington County, Nebraska.

Eclipta alba (L.) Hassk., Pl. Jav. Rar. 528. 1848. (Yerba de Tajo). *#224 Eclipta procumbens* Michx., in Torr., Ann. Lyc. Nat. Hist. N.Y. 2:213.1827. "On the Missouri."

Based on distribution and flowering time, James most likely made his collection in late August or early September in the eastern half of Oklahoma along the Canadian or Arkansas River.

Elephantopus carolinianus Raeuschel, Nom. ed. 3. 256. 1797. (Leafy Elephantfoot).
#243 Elephantopus carolinianus L., in Torr., Ann. Lyc. Nat. Hist. N.Y. 2:216.1827.

Based on distribution, James would have collected this plant in late August or early September along the Canadian River in the eastern half of Oklahoma.

Engelmannia peristenia (Raf.) Goodm. & Laws., Rhodora 94: 381.1992. (Engelmann's Daisy).
Silphium peristenium Raf., Atl. Jour. 1:146.1832. "S[ilphium] anon T[orrey].239." Based on the following:
#239 Silphium n.sp. Nutt. mss., in Torr., Ann. Lyc. Nat. Hist. N.Y. 2:215.1827. "A singular species, with pinnatifid leaves, and the scales of the involucrum very narrow. Mr. Nuttall found the same on the Red River."
Engelmannia pinnatifida Nutt., Trans. Am. Phil. Soc. ser. 2, 7:343. 1840. "The plains of Red River."
Engelmannia pinnatifida T. & G., in Nutt., l.c. *fide* Torrey & Gray, Fl. No. Am. 2:283.1842. "Silphium, n.sp. (Nutt.) Torr. in ann. lyc. New York, 2. p.215. On the Canadian, *Dr. James!* Red River, Arkansas, *Nuttall!*"

In his diary for July 30, James listed a "Helianthus? Leaves pinnatifid" among the plants collected that day.[191] On the same day in the *Account* a "helianthus" is listed.[192] This collection may well be the type and would have been made as the party traveled southwest across the Don Carlos Hills, from Sierra Grande to Ute Creek, western Union County, New Mexico.

---

[191]JAMES [3], July 30.
[192]JAMES [6], II, 86; JAMES [7], II, 274.

Erigeron pumilus Nutt., Gen. No. Am. Pl. 2:147.1818. (Low Daisy).
#212 Erigeron pumilum Nutt., in Torr., Ann. Lyc. Nat. Hist. N.Y. 2:212.1827.
In his diary, James mentioned this plant on June 20.[193] It is listed from the same campsite in the *Account* on the previous day.[194]
The party camped near Gothenburg, Dawson County, Nebraska.

Eupatorium serotinum Michx., Fl. Bor. Am. 2:100.1803. (Late-Flowering Thoroughwort).
James listed "Eupatorium ageratoides" in his diary for August 22.[195] This plant is a synonym of *E. rugosum,* a white-flowered species that is out of range. It seems likely that what James found was *E. serotinum,* a white-flowered species in good range.
On this day the party traveled downstream in the eastern half of Dewey County, Oklahoma.

Gaillardia pinnatifida Torr. (Blanket Flower).
#231 Gaillardia pinnatifida Torr., Ann. Lyc. Nat. Hist. N.Y. 2:214–15.1827. "On the Canadian?"
The type (NY) could have been collected by James from late July to mid August in southern Colorado, northeastern New Mexico, or along the Canadian River in the Texas panhandle or extreme western Oklahoma.

Gaillardia pulchella Foug., in Mem. Acad. Sci. Paris 1786:5.1788. (Indian Blanket).
#230 Gaillardia bicolor Lam., in Torr., Ann. Lyc. Nat. Hist. N.Y. 2:214.1827.
Based chiefly on range, James most likely collected his specimen in August in northeastern New Mexico or along the Canadian River in the Texas panhandle or Oklahoma.

Grindelia squarrosa (Pursh) Dunal, in Mem. Mus. Par. 5:50.1819. (Gumweed).
#219 Grindelia squarrosa Brown, in Torr., Ann. Lyc. Nat. Hist. N.Y. 2:212.1827.
This species usually does not flower until July. It was most likely

[193]JAMES [3], June 20 (erroneously dated June 19).
[194]JAMES [1], I, 461n.; JAMES [2] in THWAITES [1], XV, 233n.
[195]JAMES [3], August 22.

collected by James along his route from a little north of Denver, Colorado, southward to the New Mexico line.

Gutierrezia texana (DC.) T. & G., Fl. No. Am. 2:194.1842. (Snakeweed).
#218 *Brachyris n.sp.* Nutt., in Torr., Ann. Lyc. Nat. Hist. N.Y. 2:212.1827. "Arkansa."
This species was most likely collected along the Canadian River in western Oklahoma in mid August. It is of interest that James would have collected this species, because it has been collected very infrequently in Oklahoma. Most collections here have been made in the south-central part of the state. Torrey's reference[196] and James as a collector are cited in Torrey and Gray.[197]
The nearest James came to a known collection site was on August 19, while he was camped on a branch of Quartermaster Creek near the Roger Mills/Dewey/Custer county line.

Haplopappus lyallii Gray, Proc. Acad. Phila. 1863:64.1864.
Aster jamesii O. Kuntze, Rev. Gen. 1:316.1891, is a nomenclatural synonym.
In the *Synoptical Flora,* Gray stated that a James specimen was the first one collected in Colorado.[198] Lyall's specimen (the type) from the Cascade Mountains would have been collected in 1860.
Because the plant grows at such high elevations, James would have collected his plant July 13–15 near the top of Pikes Peak, El Paso County, Colorado.

Haplopappus pluriflorus (T. & G.) Hall, Carnegie Inst. Wash. Publ. 389, p.237. 1928.
#207 *Chrysocoma graveolens* Nutt., in Torr., Ann. Lyc. Nat. Hist. N.Y. 2:211.1827. "Station not recorded."
Linosyris pluriflora T. & G., Fl. No. Am. 2:233.1842. Here the authors stated that this is the *Chrysocoma graveolens sensu* Torr. in the Ann. Lyc. Nat. Hist. 2:211. "Upper Missouri or Platte? *Dr. James!*"
According to Hall,[199] the type is at NY. Based on the known distribution of the *H. pluriflorus* complex, James could have collected the type along the Canadian River in the Texas panhandle or in

---

196TORREY [2], 212.
197TORREY AND GRAY [1], II, 194.
198GRAY [3], 131.
199HALL, 238.

Union, Harding, or Quay counties in northeastern New Mexico. Southeastern Colorado is only a very slight possibility.

We find no reference in the diary to a plant of this description.

Haplopappus pygmaeus (T. & G.) Gray, Am. Jour. Sci. II, 33:239. 1862.

Stenotus pygmaeus T. & G., Fl. No. Am., 2:237.1842. "Rocky Mountains, probably in about lat. 41°, *Dr. James!*"

The type (NY) of this alpine tundra species could have been collected by James only on the summit of Pikes Peak, El Paso County, Colorado, where he was on July 14.

Haplopappus spinulosus (Pursh) DC., Prodr. 5:347.1836.

#223 *Amellus? spinulosus* Pursh, in Torr., Ann. Lyc. Nat. Hist. N.Y. 2:213.1827. "On the Missouri, Platte, &c."

Based on distribution and flowering time, James could have collected his specimen in any of the five states through which he traveled.

Helianthus nuttallii T. & G., Fl. No. Am. 2:324.1842. (Nuttall's Sunflower).

In his diary for July 22, James noted a "large flowered Helianthus."[200] In the *Account* one day earlier, but at the same location, James referred to this sunflower as *Helianthus giganteus,* a species that is out of range.[201]

At their camp on the Arkansas River near Rocky Ford, Otero County, Colorado, it seems likely that James collected what would later become *H. nuttallii,* the species in range that most nearly resembles *H. giganteus.*

Helianthus petiolaris Nutt., J. Acad. Sci. Phil. 2:115.1821. (Plains Sunflower).

#238 *Helianthus altissimus* L., in Torr., Ann. Lyc. Nat. Hist. N.Y. 2:215.1827. "On the Platte."

On June 19 James collected a sunflower that in his diary he called *Helianthus tubaeformis,*[202] a synonym of *Helianthus annuus.* Although it is in range, this species does not flower until late July.

On this same day in the *Account,* James noted finding *Helianthus*

---

[200]JAMES [3], July 22.
[201]JAMES [1], II, 63; JAMES [2] in THWAITES [1], XVI, 57.
[202]JAMES [3], June 19.

giganteus, a species that does not flower until August and is out of range.[203] The name Torrey used, *H. altissimus,* is a synonym of *H. giganteus.*

With the two references by James to a sunflower from the Platte, it seems reasonably likely that Torrey's location is correct.

The only species of *Helianthus* along the Platte in Nebraska that flowers in June is *H. petiolaris.*

James's collection was made on June 19 on the sandhills near Gothenburg, Dawson County, Nebraska.

On July 21, James noted *H. petiolaris* in the *Account.*[204] At that time the party was camped on the Arkansas River, near Rocky Ford, Otero County, Colorado.

Hieracium gronovii L., Sp. Pl. 802. 1753. (Gronovius Hawkweed).

#197 *Hieracium marianum* Willd., in Torr., Ann. Lyc. Nat. Hist. N.Y. 2:209.1827. "On the Arkansa."

James mentioned *H. marianum* in his diary for September 12.[205] It is also mentioned in the *Account* as occurring near their camp of the afternoon of September 12.[206]

Under *H. venosum,* Cronquist stated that *H. marianum* "is thought to be a hybrid with another species, perhaps *H. scabrum* or *H. gronovii.*"[207] *Hieracium venosum* is far out of range, and the occurrence of *H. scabrum,* while reported in Oklahoma, is doubtful. Hence, it seems certain that James's plant was *H. gronovii.*

On this day the party camped on the Arkansas, south of Muldrow, Sequoyah County, Oklahoma.

Hymenopappus tenuifolius Pursh, Fl. Am. Sept. 742. 1814. (Woolly White Hymenopappus).

#209 *Hymenopappus tenuifolius* Pursh, in Torr., Ann. Lyc. Nat. Hist. N.Y. 2:211.1827. "Valley of the Loup Fork."

James's collection was made on June 10 along the Loup River between Monroe, Platte County, and Merchiston, Nance County, Nebraska.[208] In the *Account,* James listed this species among the plants collected on

---

[203]JAMES [1], I, 461n.; JAMES [2] in THWAITES [1], XV, 233n.

[204]JAMES [1], II, 63 (as *H. petiolaris*); JAMES [2] in THWAITES [1], XVI, 57 (as "an undescribed species" of *Helianthus*).

[205]JAMES [3], September 12.

[206]JAMES [1], II, 171; JAMES [2] in THWAITES [1], XVI, 185.

[207]CRONQUIST [2], 240.

[208]JAMES [3], June 10.

June 9.[209] In addition to this plant there are several other plants listed in the same footnote. According to the diary, some of these plants were collected before June 9, others after that date.

Lactuca ludoviciana (Nutt.) Riddell, Syn. Fl. W. St. 51. 1835. (Western Wild Lettuce).
#201 *Sonchus ludovicianus* Nutt., in Torr., Ann. Lyc. Nat. Hist. N.Y. 2:209.1827. "On the Platte."
The known distribution of this species and the long flowering period indicate that James would have collected it either on the Platte in Nebraska in June or on the Canadian in Oklahoma in August.

Leucelene ericoides (Torr.) Greene, Pittonia 3:148.1896. (White Aster).
#215 *Inula? ericoides* Torr., Ann. Lyc. Nat. Hist. N.Y. 2:212.1827. "On the Canadian?"
James could have collected the type (NY) in Colorado, New Mexico, the Texas panhandle, or western Oklahoma.
Shinners reported that James's type was "the transitional or summer form" and "may well have come from the Texas Panhandle, where it is very common."[210]
Nesom, who recently transferred this species to *Chaetopappa,* also stated that the type is probably from Texas.[211]
We find no reference in the diary to a plant of this description.

Liatris lancifolia (Greene) Kittell, in Tidestrom & Kittell, Fl. Ariz. & N. Mex. 370. 1941. (Gayfeather).
James's diary for August 9 listed "Liatris spicata L. About 4 feet high. Leaves linear smooth short lying close to the stem. Cal. 10 flowered spike thick, flowers large and beautiful."[212] The number of flowers per involucre and the range lead us to think that *L. lancifolia* is likely what James saw.
On August 9 the party traveled along the Canadian River from Oldham County into Potter County, Texas. Correll and Johnston remarked, "Rare in meadowlands and on open slopes in the Panhandle (Hemphill and Oldham cos.)," Texas.[213]

---

[209]JAMES [1], I, 433n.; JAMES [2] in THWAITES [1], XV, 200n.
[210]SHINNERS, 85.
[211]NESOM, 449.
[212]JAMES [3], August 9.
[213]CORRELL AND JOHNSTON, 1541.

Liatris punctata Hook., Fl. Bor. Am. 1:306.1833. (Dotted Gay-feather).

#204 *Liatris cylindrica* Michx., in Torr., Ann. Lyc. Nat. Hist. N.Y. 2:210.1827. "Sources of the Platte?"

Torrey's name was an obvious slip for "L. cylindracea." Gaiser,[214] following Torrey and Gray[215] and Gray,[216] stated that the James specimen (NY) is *L. punctata.* That the plant, which is rarely collected so early in the season, came from an area that in Torrey's time would have been called "Sources of the Platte" is evidenced by James's July 5 entries.[217] There he listed the name "Liatris graminifolia." On that day James made a side trip from the campsite on the South Platte, going up Clear Creek, just north of Denver in Adams County, Colorado.

Lygodesmia juncea (Pursh) D.Don, Edinb. New Phil. Jour. 6:311. 1829. (Skeletonweed).

#202 *Prenanthes juncea* Pursh, in Torr., Ann. Lyc. Nat. Hist. N.Y. 2:210.1827. "On the Platte and Missouri."

In his diary James included the following, "Prenanthes? juncea. Ought not this plant to be removed from the genus Prenanthes?"[218] The collection was made June 27 as James traveled up the South Platte in northeastern Colorado from just west of Julesburg, Sedgwick County, to southeast of Crook, Logan County.

Machaeranthera tanacetifolia (HBK.) Nees, Gen. & Sp. Aster. 225. 1832. (Tahoka Daisy).

In his diary for July 2 James described this plant in detail, questioning the name *Aster blandus* that he had applied to it.[219]

Aster tanacetifolius was described the same year that James made his collection.

James described this plant on a Sunday while they were camped near Kuner, Weld County, Colorado.

Microseris cuspidata (Pursh) Schultz-Bip., Pollichia 22–24:309. 1866. (Prairie False Dandelion).

---

[214]GAISER, 361–62.
[215]TORREY AND GRAY [1], II, 69.
[216]GRAY [3], 110.
[217]JAMES [1], I, 501n. (as "Liatris graminefolia"); JAMES [2] in THWAITES [1], XV, 281n.; JAMES [3], July 5.
[218]JAMES [3], June 27.
[219]JAMES [3], July 2.

#200 Troximon marginatum Nutt., in Torr., Ann. Lyc. Nat. Hist. N.Y. 2:209.1827. "On the Loup Fork, a branch of the Platte."

James's collection, which he referred to as *Troximon marginatum,* was made on June 9 on an elevated ridge that the expedition began to encounter about three miles southeast of Platte Center, Platte County, Nebraska.[220] Here this ridge divides Shell Creek from the Loup River.

Palafoxia sphacelata (Torr.) Cory, Rhodora 48:86.1946. (Rayed Palafoxia).

#229 Stevia sphacelata Nutt. mss., in Torr., Ann. Lyc. Nat. Hist. N.Y. 2:214.1827. "A plant with the habit of Stevia, but with a many-leaved involucrum, enclosing 25–30 flowers. It appears to be more nearly allied to Polypteris or Hymenopappus." No locality is given.

Palafoxia hookeriana T. & G. β *subradiata* T. & G., Fl. No. Am. 2:368.1842. This was based on *Stevia sphacelata* and cited are "Arkansas, *Dr. James!* Texas, *Mr. Callana!*"

The type, by James, is at NY.

Nuttall's manuscript name, Stevia sphacelata, refers to an 1819 collection of his from eastern Oklahoma. Nuttall's travels in 1819 did not get him into an area where *P. sphacelata* (Torr.) Cory is known.

In Nuttall's description of his *Stevia callosa,* he noted that the leaves terminate in "a yellowish sphacelous or callous point."[221] Much better evidence that his "sphacelata" became *callosa* is found in a footnote in Ammerman,[222] in which she states that a specimen of *callosa* at PH bears the label "Stevia sphacelata" in Nuttall's handwriting. Unlike several of the species of *Palafoxia,* these two species are readily distinct.

Palafoxia sphacelata has a long flowering period, and James could have collected the type from the time he entered Colorado in late June until after the middle of August in western Oklahoma. Turner and Morris suggested southeastern Colorado.[223]

Pectis angustifolia Torr. (Lemon-Scented Pectis).

#228 Pectis angustifolia Torr., Ann. Lyc. Nat. Hist. N.Y. 2:214. 1827. "On the Rocky Mountains."

No reference to this collection has been found in James's diary. The

---

[220]JAMES [1], I, 433n.; JAMES [2] in THWAITES [1], XV, 200n.; JAMES [3], June 9.
[221]NUTTALL [4], 121.
[222]AMMERMAN, 259n.
[223]TURNER AND MORRIS, 584.

type (NY) could have been collected in any of the five states through which James traveled with the exception of Oklahoma, where the plant is not known to occur along the route of the expedition.

Picradeniopsis oppositifolia (Nutt.) Rydb., in Britton Man. 1008. 1901, or

Picradeniopsis woodhousei (Gray) Rydb., Bull. Torr. Bot. Club 37:333.1910.
#222 *Trichophyllum oppositifolium* Nutt., in Torr., Ann. Lyc. Nat. Hist. N.Y. 2:213.1827. "On the Platte."
Within the route of the expedition the ranges of these two species overlap. Without seeing the actual collection, it would be difficult to determine which species James collected.
Whichever the species, the collection was surely made in Colorado, northeastern New Mexico, or the Texas panhandle.

Psilostrophe tagetina (Nutt.) Greene, Pittonia 2:176.1891. (Woolly Paperflower).
Gray stated, "In establishing the genus [*Riddellia*], Mr. Nuttall omitted to state that his plant was derived from the collection of Dr. James, through Dr. Torrey."[224]
The habitat for *Riddellia tagetinae* was given by Nuttall as the "southern range of the Rocky Mountains, towards the sources of the Platte."[225]
Based on the range of the species as given by Brown, James would have collected the type (isotype, NY) in the first half of August along the Canadian River in Quay County, New Mexico, or the Texas panhandle.[226] Nuttall's itineraries were never within the range of this species.

Ratibida columnifera (Nutt.) Woot. & Standl., Contr. U.S. Nat. Herb. 19:706.1915. (Prairie Coneflower).
James mentioned this plant in his diary as *Rudbeckia columnifera*. The entry was made on July 2, a Sunday, while they were camped near Kuner, Weld County, Colorado.[227] On this same day, this plant is mentioned in the *Account* as *Rudbeckia columnaris*.[228]

[224]GRAY [6], 94.
[225]NUTTALL [1], 371.
[226]BROWN, 188.
[227]JAMES [3], July 2.
[228]JAMES [1], I, 494; JAMES [2] in THWAITES [1], XV, 273.

Ratibida tagetes (James) Barnh., Bull. Torr. Bot. Club 24:410. 1897. (Short-Ray Prairie Coneflower).
Rudbeckia tagetes James, in Long Exped. (Phila. ed.) 2:68. 1823.[229]
#232 *Rudbeckia columnaris* Nutt., in Torr., Ann. Lyc. Nat. Hist. N.Y. 2:215.1827. "Sources of the Arkansa." Curiously, Torrey made no reference to James's name here.

The first reference to this species appears in the diary on July 24, where it is described as a new species of *Rudbeckia*.[230]

It was some time before this species was widely accepted as such. Torrey and Gray cited[231] both *Rudbeckia columnaris* of Torrey[232] and *R. tagetes* James as synonyms of *Lepachys columnaris* var. *pulcherrima*. They also listed James's collection from the "Upper Arkansas," adding, "The specimens of Dr. James belong to a dwarf, much branched and leafy plant, with short peduncles."

A decade later the following appeared:
Lepachys columnaris var. *tagetes* (James) Gray, Pl. Wright. pt. 1:106.1852, with the comment, "It holds its characters very well, and has not yet occurred with large rays, nor with an elongated disk; so that it is perhaps a distinct species."

Still later came:
Lepachys tagetes (James) Torr., Pac. R.R. Rept. 4:103.1857, with this conclusion, "This appears to hold its characters, and to claim a place as a distinct species."

James's type specimen, which according to Richards is at NY,[233] was collected on July 24, the day the expedition separated into two groups. Long's group, which included James, forded the Arkansas and headed southeastward toward "Pike's First Fork," that is, the Purgatoire River. Four and a half miles south-southeast of the town of Rocky Ford, likely near Timpas Creek, Otero County, Colorado, James made his collection.

Rudbeckia laciniata L. var. **ampla** (A. Nels.) Cronq., Univ. Wash. Publ. Biol. 17(5):280.1955. (Tall Coneflower).

The name "Rudbeckia laciniata" appears in James's diary for July 14.[234] That is the day James climbed Pikes Peak, El Paso County, Colorado.

---

[229]The name and description are repeated in the London edition of the *Account*. JAMES [7], II, 353.
[230]JAMES [3], July 24.
[231]TORREY AND GRAY [1], II, 315.
[232]TORREY [2], 215.
[233]RICHARDS, 385.
[234]JAMES [3], July 14 (erroneously dated July 15).

Senecio canus Hook., Fl. Bor. Am. 1:333.1834. (Gray Ragwort).
#220 *Cineraria integrifolia* Willd., in Torr., Ann. Lyc. Nat. Hist.
N.Y. 2:212.1827. "On the Missouri."

This interpretation is in agreement with Torrey and Gray.[235]

James likely made his collection during the first half of July along the front range in Colorado from Adams County to El Paso County.

Senecio douglasii DC. var. **longilobus** (Benth.) Benson, Am. Jour. Bot. 30:631.1943. (Threadleaf Groundsel).

Senecio filifolius Nutt., Trans. Am. Phil. Soc. II. 7:414.1841. [Not Berg., 1767]. "The banks of the Missouri towards the Rocky Mountains. . . . (I have seen but a single small specimen.)"

According to Torrey and Gray, Nuttall's *S. filifolius* was "described from an imperfect specimen in *herb. Torr.*"[236] That specimen was a James collection (NY). Gray wrote on this sheet of *S. filifolius* Nutt. from the Torrey Herbarium at NY that Nuttall "described it evidently from the sight of this specimen and leaves it to be inferred that he collected it himself." Nuttall could not have collected the type specimen, as evidenced by the range of the species, which does not include any portion of the route of Nuttall's travels.

The type, according to Barkley, is a Nuttall specimen at BM.[237] The sheet carries a description and an asterisk by Nuttall, but the specimen was collected by James in late July or early August in southeastern Colorado, northeastern New Mexico, or along the Canadian River in the Texas panhandle.

Torrey and Gray cited *S. filifolius* Nutt. in synonymy under their illegitimate *S. filifolius* α *jamesii*.[238]

Stephanomeria minor (Hook.) Nutt., Trans. Am. Phil. Soc., ser. 2, 7:427.1841. (Wire Lettuce).

#202(2) *Prenanthes* ? *tenuifolia* Torr., Ann. Lyc. Nat. Hist. N.Y. 2:210.1827. "Near the Rocky Mountains." [Not *P. tenuifolia* L., Sp. Pl. 797.1753].

Stephanomeria tenuifolia (Torr.) Hall, Univ. Calif. Publ. Bot. 3:256.1907, based on a preempted name.

The type sheet of *Prenanthes tenuifolia* Torr. at NY includes the following information: "Long's 1st Exp. July 30 Dr. James." If this date

[235]TORREY AND GRAY [1], II, 443.
[236]TORREY AND GRAY [1], II, 444.
[237]BARKLEY, 117.
[238]TORREY AND GRAY [1], II, 444.

is correct, the plant was collected while Long's party traveled south-west from Sierra Grande across the Don Carlos Hills to Ute Creek, Western Union County, New Mexico.

Stephanomeria pauciflora (Torr.) A. Nels., Man. Bot. Rocky Mts. 588. 1909. (Wire Lettuce).
#202(1) *Prenanthes* ? *pauciflora* Torr., Ann. Lyc. Nat. Hist. N.Y. 2:210.1827. "Near the Rocky Mountains."
Jamesia pauciflora (Torr.) Nees, in Neuwied, Reise No. Am. 2:442.1844.
The Philadelphia edition of the *Account,* entry for July 7, lists the plant as "*Prenanthes runcinatum*" with no description;[239] for the same day in the London edition of the *Account,* however, *Prenanthes runcinata* is described as "leaves runcinate pinnatifid, ⅔ inches long, five lines wide."[240] Clearly, the "⅔ inches" should be "2–3 inches," as it is in the diary.[241]

The name *Prenanthes runcinata,* however, was published earlier for a European plant by Lagasca in 1816.[242] Lagasca's *Sonchus reflexus* is listed there under *P. runcinata* as a synonym. *Sonchus reflexus* was published earlier by Lagasca but is a *nomen nudum.*[243]

We do not know whether Torrey knew of the Lagasca name.[244] At any rate, he described *Prenanthes pauciflora* with a description similar to that given by James.

Stephanomeria runcinata Nutt. is based on a Nuttall plant from Big Sandy Creek, a branch of the Green River in Sweetwater County, Wyoming.[245] Whether this plant is involved in the problem is not clear. Rydberg listed it in synonymy under *pauciflora* [*Ptiloria pauciflora* (Torr.) Raf.].[246] In 1923 he placed a question mark before the synonym.[247] Blake did so as well.[248] Cronquist, however, accepted it as distinct from *S. pauciflora.*[249]

Torrey and Gray called the taxon "*S. runcinata* (Nutt.! l.c.),"[250] the reference being to Nuttall's 1841 original description of his species from Big Sandy Creek. It is difficult to know what they intended. Listed as

[239]JAMES [6], II, 8n.
[240]JAMES [7], II, 344–45.
[241]JAMES [3], July 7 (erroneously dated July 8).
[242]LAGASCA [1], 24.
[243]LAGASCA [2], 15.
[244]TORREY [2], 210.
[245]NUTTALL [1], 428.
[246]RYDBERG [1], 403.
[247]RYDBERG [2], 1018.
[248]TIDESTROM, 623.
[249]CRONQUIST [3], 315–16.
[250]TORREY AND GRAY [1], II, 472.

synonyms are *Prenanthes runcinatum* James (1823), *P.* ? *pauciflora* Torr. (1827), and *S. runcinata* and *S. heterophylla* of Nuttall (1841).

It seems very unlikely that Torrey and Gray intended to accept Nuttall's 1841 *S. runcinata* when Torrey's 1827 epithet "*pauciflora*" was available. They may have thought erroneously that Nuttall transferred James's 1823 epithet, "*runcinata,*"[251] to *Stephanomeria*.

Over eighty years were to pass before Torrey's epithet, "*pauciflora*" would be transferred to *Stephanomeria*. Likely this was largely because most authors—correctly, at the time—used the name *Ptiloria;* Rafinesque, whose genus it was, had transferred both of Torrey's species of *Prenanthes* to it in 1832.[252] The name *Stephanomeria* has been conserved over the older *Ptiloria*.

James's type (NY) collection was made in Jefferson County, Colorado, on July 7 during an excursion into the mountains from the mouth of South Platte Canyon.

Tetraneuris acaulis (Pursh) Greene var. **acaulis**, Pittonia 3:265. 1898. (Stemless Tetraneuris).

#226 Actinea acaulis Spreng., in Torr., Ann. Lyc. Nat. Hist. N.Y. 2:213.1827. "On the Platte?"

No reference to this plant was found in James's diary; Torrey and Gray, however, cited the Ann. Lyc. reference and James as a collector of *Actinella acaulis*.[253] Based on distribution and most frequent flowering time, James likely made this collection in June or July in Colorado or late July in northeastern New Mexico; this variety, however, is also known in the other three states through which James traveled.

Tetraneuris acaulis (Pursh) Greene var. **caespitosa** A. Nels., Bot. Gaz. 28:127.1899.

#227 Actinea integrifolia sensu Torr., Ann. Lyc. Nat. Hist. N.Y. 2:213.1827. [Not Kunth]. "On the highest parts of the Rocky Mountains."

We find no reference to this plant in James's diary; Torrey and Gray, however, cited the Ann. Lyc. reference and James as a collector of the synonym, *Actinella lanata* Nutt., not Pursh (1814).[254] This variety is frequently found in alpine regions such as Pikes Peak, El Paso County, Colorado, where James was on July 13–15. Other collections,

---

[251]JAMES [7], II, 344–45.
[252]RAFINESQUE [1], 145.
[253]TORREY AND GRAY [1], II, 381–82.
[254]TORREY AND GRAY [1], II, 382.

including the type of this variety, have been made in Upper Sonoran to Montane zones. Rydberg noted that James was the first to collect it.[255]

Tetraneuris glabra (Nutt.) Greene, Pittonia 3:268.1898.
Torrey and Gray cited James as a collector under *Actinella glabra.*[256] Based on what is currently considered the known range of this species, James would have made his collection in southeastern Colorado, northeastern New Mexico, the Texas panhandle, or western Oklahoma.
Curiously, Nuttall stated, "Hab. Missouri, (near the Shawnee villages.)."[257] This is at least 350 miles east of the "known" range of this species.

Thelesperma megapotamicum (Spreng.) Kuntze, Rev. Gen. Pl. 3:182.1898. (Greenthread).
#234 Bidens gracilis Torr., Ann. Lyc. Nat. Hist. N.Y. 2:215.1827. "On the Canadian?"
Thelesperma gracile (Torr.) Gray, Hooker's Jour. Bot. Kew Gard. Misc. 1:252.1849.
James's diary entry is so detailed and accurate as to make it worth comment.[258] His syngenesious plant is of the order Aequalis, that is, with perfect flowers. It appeared to be one of the Flosculosae, that is, with all the florets tubular. The involucral bracts were united ("calyx one-leaved") and "calyculate at the base. . . . The chaffy scales of the receptacle lanceolate membranaceous and acute. Pappus of two retrorsely aculeate leaves. Stem nearly simple. Leaves opposite pinnatifid, divisions linear."
The type (NY) was collected June 20 on the sandhills near Gothenburg, Dawson County, Nebraska.
This species still occurs on these hills.

Townsendia grandiflora Nutt., Trans. Am. Phil. Soc. n.s. 7:306. 1840. (Easter Daisy).
According to Torrey and Gray, James collected this plant on the "plains of the Upper Platte."[259]

---

[255]RYDBERG [4], 445.
[256]TORREY AND GRAY [1], II, 382.
[257]NUTTALL [1], 379.
[258]JAMES [3], June 20 (erroneously dated June 19).
[259]TORREY AND GRAY [1], II, 186.

Based on flowering time and distribution, James would have collected his specimen in July along the Front Range from near Denver to Cañon City, Fremont County, Colorado.

Verbesina virginica L., Sp. Pl. 901. 1753. (Frostweed).
#225 *Verbesina virginica* L., in Torr., Ann. Lyc. Nat. Hist. N.Y. 2:213.1827. "With the preceding ['On the Missouri.']."
Based on distribution and flowering time, James would have made his collection in late August or early September along the Canadian River in the eastern half of Oklahoma.

Vernonia marginata (Torr.) Raf., Atl. Jour. 1:146.1832. (Plains Ironweed).
#205 *Vernonia altissima* β? *marginata* Torr., Ann. Lyc. Nat. Hist. N.Y. 2:210.1827. "On the Arkansa?"
Vernonia jamesii T. & G., Fl. No. Am. 2:58.1841. Based on *V. altissima* var. *marginata* Torr.
No reference to this collection has been found in James's diary. Based on flowering time and presently known distribution, the type (NY) was likely collected in northeastern New Mexico or in the Texas panhandle in late July to mid August.

Xanthium strumarium L., Sp. Pl. 987. 1753. (Cocklebur).
#244 *Xanthium Strumarium* L., in Torr., Ann. Lyc. Nat. Hist. N.Y. 2:216.1827. "Near the Rocky Mountains."
This plant, with ripened fruits, is mentioned in the *Account* on August 7,[260] while the party was traveling along the Canadian River in Oldham County, Texas.

Zinnia grandiflora Nutt., Trans. Am. Phil. Soc. n.s. 7:348.1840. (Plains Zinnia).
Torres indicated that the type may be at BM.[261] The specimen at NY is very likely a fragment of it. With his original description, Nuttall stated, "The only specimen I have (presented me by my friend, Dr. Torrey,) is scarcely more than five inches high." Nuttall never mentioned James, but indicated the specimen was collected in "the Rocky Mountains, towards Mexico." The writing on the sheet of the fragment at NY reads that James

---

[260]JAMES [1], II, 98; JAMES [2] in THWAITES [1], XVI, 100.
[261]TORRES, 10.

collected it from the Rocky Mountains and that it came "from Dr. Torrey." The phrase, "from Dr. Torrey," surely was taken from Nuttall. James collected the type in late July to mid August in southeastern Colorado, northeastern New Mexico, or along the Canadian River in the Texas panhandle or in extreme-western Oklahoma.

Convolvulaceae

Cuscuta umbellata HBK., Nov. Gen. & Sp. Pl. 3:95.1818 (Dodder). #287 *Cuscuta umbellata* Kunth, in Torr., Ann. Lyc. Nat. Hist. N.Y. 2:223.1827. "Very abundant about the sources of the Canadian; parasitic on Portulaca oleracea."
In his diary for August 1, James described a *Cuscuta* that appears to be this species, which was "[p]arasitic on Portulaca oleracea."[262]
Yuncker cited a James specimen from "Foot of Rocky Mountains" that could be this collection.[263]
James's collection was made near the August 1 campsite, near the confluence of Garcia Creek and Ute Creek, about six miles east and a little north of Yates, Harding County, New Mexico.

Evolvulus nuttallianus Roemer & Schultes, Syst. Veg. 6:198. 1820. (Hairy Evolvulus).
#285 *Evolvulus Nuttallianus* Roem. & Schult., in Torr., Ann. Lyc. Nat. Hist. N.Y. 2:223.1827. "About the forks of the Platte."
James mentioned this plant in the diary under the date of June 23 as *E. argenteus*.[264] In the *Account* it is listed as *E. nuttallianus*.[265]
The plant was collected on June 23 on the south side of the South Platte River, a few miles above its junction with the North Platte, Lincoln County, Nebraska.

Ipomoea leptophylla Torr., in Fremont Explor. 90. 1843. (Bush Morning-Glory).
Torrey stated that Fremont's collection was made from "Forks of the Platte to Laramie river, July 4–Sept. 3." Torrey added, "Imperfect specimens of this plant were collected about the sources of the Canadian, by Dr. James, in Long's expedition, but they were not described in my account of his plants. The root, according to Dr.

[262]JAMES [3], August 1.
[263]YUNCKER, 42.
[264]JAMES [3], June 23 (erroneously dated June 22).
[265]JAMES [1], I, 468n.; JAMES [2] in THWAITES [1], XV, 241n.

James, is annual, producing numerous thick prostrate, but not twining, stems, which are two feet or more in length."

James, in his diary for June 28,[266] described a plant that he believed to be new: "Pent. Mon. Lactescent. Leaves and stem somewhat resembling Asclepias incarnata. . . . Root fusiform descending. Stem recurved, branches scattered leaves linear lanceolate short petioled. Flowers bright purple, of the size of those of Datura Stramonium." James augments the description, in a handwriting such as he used when sitting at a table instead of around a campfire, as follows: "This splendid plant has usually a stem about 3 feet in length but rises less than one foot from the ground it being invariably recurved. The leaves are numerous and rather crowded, about 4 or 6 inches in length and near an inch in width. Seeds about 4, very large." A leaf width this great is a bit disturbing, but less so than the comment in the *Account,* under the date of June 27,[267] where an annual is described as follows: "Another plant very conspicuously ornamental to these barren deserts, is a lactescent annual, belonging to the family of the convolvulacae with a bright purple corrolla, as large as that of the common Stramonium." From the *Account,* then, must be where Torrey got his information, surely incorrect, when he stated under #284 *Convolvulus:* "Dr. James states that he observed an annual lactescent species, with a flower as large as that of Stramonium."[268] If Torrey did get the information from the *Account,* however, it is difficult to understand why he did not notice the date, June 27, which is a full month before James reached "the sources of the Canadian," the locality given by Torrey in the original description.

Much later, Gray, under *Ipomoea leptophylla,* remarked, "[A] striking and showy species, first collected, in Long's Expedition, by *Dr.E.James,* who singularly mistook it for an annual. Torr. in Ann. Lyc. N.Y. ii.223 (*Convolvulus.*)"[269]

If James obtained his plant on June 28, as he indicated in his diary, rather than on June 27 as is indicated in the *Account,* it was collected from just east of Crook to a couple of miles west of Sterling, Logan County, Colorado.

Cornaceae

Cornus drummondii Mey., Cornus Arten 20. 1845. (Rough-Leaved Dogwood).

[266]JAMES [3], June 28.
[267]JAMES [1], I, 484; JAMES [2] in THWAITES [1], XV, 258–59.
[268]TORREY [2], 223.
[269]GRAY [4], 213.

#184 *Cornus alba* L'Herit., in Torr., Ann. Lyc. Nat. Hist. N.Y. 2:208.1827. "On the Canadian."

In his diary and in the *Account* for August 21, James remarked that black bears fed abundantly on the berries of *Cornus alba* and *Cornus circinata*.[270] Why James mentioned two species of *Cornus* we do not know. *Cornus drummondii* is the only species of the genus that he would have encountered as he traveled along the Canadian in Dewey County, Oklahoma.

James also mentioned *Cornus alba* in his diary for September 3.[271] On this day the party was in Hughes County, Oklahoma. Again, *C. drummondii* is the species most likely to have been seen there.

The earliest reference to *Cornus* by James is in his diary for June 13,[272] when he was in Nance County, Nebraska. Again he spoke of it as *Cornus alba*. In addition to *C. drummondii*, *C. stolonifera* and *C. obliqua* occur in the region.

Under Torrey's entry, #185 *Cornus circinata* L'Herit., Ann. Lyc. Nat. Hist. N.Y. 2:208.1827, he added: "With the preceding ['Cornus alba. . . . On the Canadian.']."

For James to have collected a second species of *Cornus* on the Canadian, the collection would have been made in eastern Oklahoma, where *C. obliqua* Raf., along with *C. florida,* occurs.

Cornus florida L., Sp. Pl. 117. 1753. (Flowering Dogwood)

#186 *Cornus florida* L., in Torr., Ann. Lyc. Nat. Hist. N.Y. 2:208. 1827. "On the Arkansa, near the confluence of the Canadian."

The only mention of this plant by James is in the diary for September 11.[273] Among the several plants listed is "dog-wood." That, we think, can safely be interpreted as "flowering dog-wood," not only because of Torrey's name and location but also because of James's earlier references to the genus (species with cymose inflorescences) as "Cornus."

On September 11 the party was in Sequoyah County, Oklahoma.

Cornus obliqua Raf., West. Rev. 1:229.1819.

#185 *Cornus circinata* L'Herit., in Torr., Ann. Lyc. Nat. Hist. N.Y. 2:208.1827. "With the preceding ['On the Canadian.']."

See discussion under *Cornus drummondii*.

[270]JAMES [1], II, 136; JAMES [2] in THWAITES [1], XVI, 146; JAMES [3], August 21.
[271]JAMES [3], September 3.
[272]JAMES [3], June 13.
[273]JAMES [3], September 11.

Crassulaceae

Sedum integrifolium (Raf.) A. Nels., in Coulter and Nelson, New Manual of Botany of the Central Rocky Mountains, p.233. 1909. (Kings Crown).

#173 *Sedum Rhodiola sensu* Torr., Ann. Lyc. Nat. Hist. N.Y. 2:206.1827. "On the Rocky Mountains."

Rhodiola integrifolia Raf., Atl. Jour. 1:146.1832. Based on Torrey's #173.

Sedum frigidum Rydb., Bull. Torr. Bot. Club 28:282–83.1901. A James specimen from Colorado was cited here.

James would have encountered this high-altitude species on Pikes Peak, July 13–15, El Paso County, Colorado.

The type of *R. integrifolia* Raf. is at NY according to Clausen.[274]

Sedum lanceolatum Torr. (Stonecrop).

#172 *S. lanceolatum* Torr., Ann. Lyc. Nat. Hist. N.Y. 2:205–206.1827. "Near the Rocky Mountains."

#170 *Sedum stenopetalum* Pursh, in Torr., Ann. Lyc. Nat. Hist. N.Y. 2:205.1827. "On the Rocky Mountains."

Sedum stenopetalum, as presently understood, does not occur so far east as any point on James's itinerary. We think that Torrey may have had one of the variations of *S. lanceolatum.*

In the *Account* for July 14, James noted a plant that he called *S. stenopetalum* during his ascent of Pikes Peak, El Paso County, Colorado.[275]

James could have collected the type (NY) of *S. lanceolatum* in early July along his route from the chasm of the Platte, Jefferson County, south to Manitou Springs and Pikes Peak, El Paso County, Colorado.

Sedum pulchellum Michx., Fl. Bor. Am. 1:277.1803. (Rockmoss).

#171 *Sedum n.sp. Nutt.,* in Torr., Ann. Lyc. Nat. Hist. N.Y. 2:205. 1827. "Near the Rocky Mountains. Leaves roundish, flat, entire, scattered; cymes terminal, trichotomous."

Sedum nuttallianum Raf., Atl. Jour. 1:146.1832. Based on Torrey's #171.

Sedum nuttallii Torrey & James ex Eaton, Man. Bot. No. Am. ed.6. 334. 1833. Based on Torrey's #171.

Sedum torreyi G. Don, Gen. System of Gardening 3:121.1834. Based on Torrey's #171.

---

[274]CLAUSEN, 510.
[275]JAMES [1], II, 26–27; JAMES [2] in THWAITES [1], XVI, 15.

Given the distribution of the plant presently called *S. nuttallianum* along James's route (central Oklahoma eastward) and the known flowering time (April to late July), it seems very doubtful that James collected that plant. He did not reach central Oklahoma until late August.

The description given by Torrey for his #171 fits very well *S. pulchellum*. The species is also known from central and eastern Oklahoma, and its known flowering time in Oklahoma is May to September. *S. pulchellum* could have been collected in May in Missouri; such a plant, however, is not cited in James's diary.

At the New York Botanical Garden there is a specimen of James's annotated as *S. pulchellum,* but no specimen of his has been found for *S. nuttallianum.*

We would suggest that Torrey's #171 was *S. pulchellum. S. nuttallianum* Raf., along with other names based on Torrey's #171, would be synonyms. The type of *S. nuttallianum* Raf. is the James specimen, Torrey's #171, (NY).

Nuttall's *S. sparsiflorum* Nutt. ex T. & G. would then become the proper name for the plant presently called *S. nuttallianum.* Nuttall's specimen in this case is the type.

Based on these arguments, the James specimen cited by Torrey and Gray as *S. sparsiflorum* would be *S. pulchellum.*[276]

Cruciferae

Descurainia pinnata (Walt.) Britt., Mem. Torr. Bot. Club 5:173. 1894. (Tansy Mustard).
#18 *Sisymbrium canescens* Nutt., in Torr., Ann. Lyc. Nat. Hist. N.Y. 2:166.1827.
We find no reference to this plant in the diary. James could have made his collection in any of the five states he visited.

Dimorphocarpa candicans (Raf.) Rollins, Cruciferae Continental No. Am. 361. 1993. (Spectacle Pod).
Iberis candicans Raf., Atl. Jour. 1:146.1832. Based on Torrey's #17.
#17 *Iberis n.sp.?* Torr., Ann. Lyc. Nat. Hist. N.Y. 2:166.1827, followed by a Latin description.
We have not located this plant in James's diary; based on the known distribution, however, the type would have been collected in August

[276]TORREY AND GRAY [1], I, 559.

along Ute Creek, Harding County, New Mexico, or along the Canadian River in the Texas panhandle or extreme western Oklahoma.

Erysimum asperum (Nutt.) DC., Syst. Veg. 2:505.1821. (Western Wallflower).

#20 *Erysimum asperum* DC., in Torr., Ann. Lyc. Nat. Hist. N.Y. 2:166.1827. "On the Platte. . . . Plant very bitter, particularly the root. It is used as a medicine by the Indians."

In his diary, James mentioned this plant, as *Cheiranthus asper,* on June 13.[277] He remarked that it was very bitter. At that time they were in camp on the south side of the Loup River about three miles north and a little east of Palmer, Merrick County, Nebraska.

Curiously, in the *Account* this plant is said to have been collected "along the Platte on the 15th and 16th June."[278]

Erysimum spp.

On June 18, while camped some six and a half miles west-southwest of Overton, Dawson County, Nebraska, James collected what he called *Erysimum parviflorum* and *E. barbarea.*[279]

Erysimum parviflorum is now a synonym of *E. inconspicuum,* which has been collected but rarely in Nebraska. The small-flowered *E. cheiranthoides* is possibly what James collected.

Erysimum barbarea, that is, *Barbarea vulgaris,* is an introduction. It is possible that the plant that James had was *Rorippa palustris.*

Lepidium virginicum L., Sp. Pl. 645. 1753. (Peppergrass).

This June 7 collection was referred to by James as *L. virginicum,* very likely correctly.[280]

James's collection was made "in the open country about the Elk Horn" River, a few miles southeast of Arlington, Washington or Dodge County, Nebraska.[281]

In the *Account* for June 29, James again referred to *L. virginicum* as the party traveled from near Sterling, Logan County, to Messex, Washington County, Colorado.[282] In this location it seems more likely that James encountered *L. densiflorum* Schrad.

---

[277]JAMES [3], June 13.
[278]JAMES [1], I, 455n.; JAMES [2] in THWAITES [1], XV, 226n.
[279]JAMES [3], June 18.
[280]JAMES [3], June 7; JAMES [4], 185.
[281]JAMES [3], June 7.
[282]JAMES [1], I, 488; JAMES [2] in THWAITES [1], XV, 264.

Lesquerella ludoviciana (Nutt.) Wats., Proc. Am. Acad. Sci. 23:252.1888. (Bladderpod).

#19 *Vesicaria ludoviciana* DC., in Torr., Ann. Lyc. Nat. Hist. N.Y. 2:166.1827.

In his diary and in the *Account,* James mentioned "Coronopus dydima."[283] The leaves of this species are pinnatifid, whereas in *L. ludoviciana* the leaves are entire or nearly so. In Nuttall's *Genera,*[284] however, which James frequently referred to, the leaves of the genus *Coronopus* are said to be entire or pinnatifid, with no comment about which kind *C. didyma* had. The conspicuously twinned fruit is mainly what caused us to choose *Lesquerella,* rather than, for example, a *Lepidium.*

Under "*Vesicaria ludoviciana*" Torrey and Gray included "[r]ocky hills of the Missouri and Platte, *Nuttall, Dr. James!*"[285]

James's plant was collected June 23, on the south side of the South Platte River, a few miles above its junction with the North Platte River, Lincoln County, Nebraska.

Stanleya pinnata (Pursh) Britt. var. **integrifolia** (James) Rollins, Lloydia 2:118.1939. (Prince's Plume).

Stanleya integrifolia James, Long Exped. (Phila. ed.) 2:17.1823. Type: NY.

#21 *Stanleya integrifolia* James, in Torr., Ann. Lyc. Nat. Hist. N.Y. 2:166.1827. "Sandstone ridges, at the base of Rocky Mountains."

James described this plant in his diary for July 10.[286] From the *Account* it is clear that James collected the type (NY) as the party traveled down Monument Creek from Elephant Rock,[287] near Palmer Lake, to their campsite on the grounds of the Air Force Academy, El Paso County, Colorado.

Cucurbitaceae

Cucurbita foetidissima HBK., Nov. Gen. & Sp. Pl. 2:123.1817. (Buffalo Gourd).

Cucumis? perennis James, Long Exped. (Phila. ed.) 2:20.1823.

---

[283]JAMES [1], I, 468n.; JAMES [2] in THWAITES [1], XV, 241n.; JAMES [3], June 23 (erroneously dated June 22).

[284]NUTTALL [5], II, 64.

[285]TORREY AND GRAY [1], I, 101.

[286]JAMES [3], July 10 (erroneously dated July 11).

[287]JAMES [6], II, 17n. (erroneously dated July 11); JAMES [7], II, 345 (text, II, 206, is erroneously dated July 12).

#396 *Cucumis? perennis* James, in Torr., Ann. Lyc. Nat. Hist. N.Y. 2:242–43.1827. *Cucurbita foetidissima* Kunth? "On the arid and sandy wastes along the base of the Rocky Mountains, from the confluence of the Arkansa and Boiling-spring Fork, to the sources of the Red River."

James described this plant in the diary between July 10 and 12.[288] Given the habitat he described, it appears that the plants were seen as the expedition traveled east across the plain from near Limekiln Valley toward Fountain Creek on July 12.

In the *Account* for July 12, James described the type.[289] The party was camped on Fountain Creek, near the town of Fountain, El Paso County, Colorado, where the plant continues to grow today.

Echinocystis lobata (Michx.) T. & G., Fl. No. Am. 1:542.1840. (Wild Cucumber).

In his diary, James described a plant under "Monoecia Monadelphia."[290] His description excellently fits the above species, which would have been in flower and in good range.

The plant was collected near the campsite at the confluence of Garcia Creek and Ute Creek, about six miles east and a little north of Yates, Harding County, New Mexico.

Cupressaceae

Juniperus communis L., Sp. Pl. 1040. 1753. (Dwarf Juniper).

#432 *Juniperus communis* L., in Torr., Ann. Lyc. Nat. Hist. N.Y. 2:250.1827. "On the Rocky Mountains."

This plant is mentioned in James's diary[291] and the *Account*[292] on July 7, the day that a few of the party ascended the South Platte River above the mouth of the chasm to Sheep Mountain, about seven miles southwest of Waterton, Jefferson County, Colorado.

The species is mentioned again as "common juniper" in the *Account,* on July 15, on the slopes of Pikes Peak.[293]

Juniperus scopulorum Sarg., Silva N. Am. 14:93, pl. 739. 1902. (Rocky Mountain Juniper).

---

[288]JAMES [3], July 12 (erroneously dated July 11 and including information for July 10, 11, and 12).
[289]JAMES [6], II, 20n., 21n.; JAMES [7], II, 346.
[290]JAMES [3], August 1.
[291]JAMES [3], July 7 (erroneously dated July 8).
[292]JAMES [1], II, 8n.; JAMES [2] in THWAITES [1], XV, 294n.
[293]JAMES [1], II, 34; JAMES [2] in THWAITES [1], XVI, 25.

#433 Juniperus virginiana L., in Torr., Ann. Lyc. Nat. Hist. N.Y. 2:250.1827. "Sources of the Arkansa and Platte to the Rocky Mountains." James first mentioned "Juniperus virginiana" on July 7.[294] On that day James and a few others ascended the South Platte River above the mouth of the chasm to Sheep Mountain, about seven miles southwest of Waterton, Jefferson County, Colorado.

The species is again mentioned in the diary[295] and in the *Account*[296] (as "red cedar") as occurring on the slopes of Pikes Peak. A third reference to cedar appears in the diary on July 25.[297] Near Jack Canyon, in southeastern Otero County, Colorado, James mentioned the "small but beautifully shaped cedars" that occur on the declivities and plains. The cedars are still there on the plains; they are *J. scopulorum*. The *Account* for the day refers to "a few cedars, attached . . . in the crevices of the rock."[298]

Cyperaceae

Carex nebraskensis Dewey, Am. Jour. Sci. II. 18:102.1854. (Nebraska Sedge).
Carex jamesii Torr., Ann. Lyc. Nat. Hist. N.Y. 3:398.1836. [Not of Schwein., 1824]. "Rocky Mountains, *Dr. James!* collected in Long's first expedition." James's type (NY) would have been collected in June or July in Nebraska or Colorado.

Cyperus aristatus Rottb., Desc. & Icon. 23. 1773. (Umbrella Sedge).
#452 Cyperus inflexus Muhl., in Torr., Ann. Lyc. Nat. Hist. N.Y. 2:252.1827. "Upper part of the Arkansa and Platte."
In his diary, James recorded this plant from both of the rivers mentioned by Torrey and also from the Canadian River.[299] The first entry is on July 4. James thought that the plant was a new species, described it, and gave it a manuscript name. At the time the party was a few miles south of Brighton, Adams County, Colorado. On July 22 (July 21 in the *Account*),[300] James simply listed "Cyperus uncinatus."

[294]JAMES [1], II, 8n.; JAMES [2] in THWAITES [1], XV, 294n. (as "I. virginiana"); JAMES [3], July 7 (erroneously dated July 8).
[295]JAMES [3], July 14 (erroneously dated July 15).
[296]JAMES [1], II, 27, 34; JAMES [2] in THWAITES [1], XVI, 16, 25.
[297]JAMES [3], July 25.
[298]JAMES [1], II, 69; JAMES [2] in THWAITES [1], XVI, 66.
[299]JAMES [3], July 4, 22, and August 23.
[300]JAMES [1], II, 63; JAMES [2] in THWAITES [1], XVI, 58.

At this time the expedition was camped on the Arkansas River at the crossing known as Rocky Ford. That is about three and a half miles north and a little west of the town of Rocky Ford, Otero County, Colorado. On August 23 James again mentioned the plant. That day the party was traveling down the Canadian River in southeastern Dewey County, the adjacent corner of Custer County, and into Blaine County, Oklahoma.

Fuirena simplex Vahl var. **aristulata** (Torr.) Kral, Sida 7(4): 336.1978. (Umbrella Grass). Based on
Fuirena squarrosa Michx. є *aristulata* Torr., Ann. Lyc. Nat. Hist. N.Y. 3:291–92.1836. "Hab. Arkansas? Collected by Dr. James in Long's Expedition to the Rocky Mountains."
#455 *Fuirena squarrosa* Michx., in Torr., Ann. Lyc. Nat. Hist. N.Y. 2:252.1827. "On the Arkansa?"

Based on the flowering time of this species, James could have made the type (NY) collection of this variety from mid August to mid September along the Canadian River in the Texas panhandle or in Oklahoma. The species is not known along the Arkansas River in Colorado, and it has not been recorded for that portion of the Arkansas River in eastern Oklahoma where James traveled.

Ebenaceae

Diospyros virginiana L., Sp. Pl. 1057. 1753. (Persimmon).
#250 *Diospyros virginiana* L., in Torr., Ann. Lyc. Nat. Hist. N.Y. 2:217.1827. "On the Canadian, near its junction with the Arkansa."

James noted the occurrence of persimmon on August 27.[301] On that day, a Sunday, the party remained in camp at the junction of Buggy Creek and the Canadian, Grady County, Oklahoma. With the exception of one disjunct and likely introduction of persimmon in far-western Oklahoma, this area marks its westernmost distribution along the Canadian.

James mentioned persimmon again in his diary for September 3.[302] At that time they were on the Canadian about five miles northwest of Allen, near the junction of Seminole, Hughes, and Pontotoc counties, Oklahoma. One day earlier, September 2, while

[301]JAMES [1], II, 145; JAMES [2] in THWAITES [1], XVI, 156; JAMES [3], August 27.
[302]JAMES [3], September 3.

the party was six or eight miles upstream, "dyospiros" is mentioned in the *Account*.[303]

The mention in the *Account* of *Diospyros* near the campsite of August 5 and 6 (along the Canadian River at the western edge of the Texas panhandle)[304] is an apparent error, as this tree is not known, except as a possible waif, west of Oklahoma.

Elaeagnaceae

Shepherdia argentea (Pursh) Nutt., Gen. No. Am. Pl. 2:240.1818. (Buffaloberry).

#393 *Shepherdia argentea* Nutt., in Torr., Ann. Lyc. Nat. Hist. N.Y. 2:242.1827. "On the Platte."

Based on the known range, this shrub was almost certainly collected along the Platte in June in Nebraska.

Equisetaceae

Equisetum hyemale L., Sp. Pl. 1062. 1753. (Scouring Rush).

James reported the occurrence of this species near their campsite of June 6, near Big Papillion Creek, close to Kenard, Washington County, Nebraska.[305]

James mentioned this horsetail again on July 15, during his ascent of Pikes Peak, El Paso County, Colorado.[306]

In both locations there are other species in range.

Ericaceae

Arctostaphylos uva-ursi (L.) Spreng., Syst. Veg. 2:287.1825. (Kinnikinick).

#248 *Arbutus Uva ursi* L., in Torr., Ann. Lyc. Nat. Hist. N.Y. 2:217.1827.

Among the plants James listed for July 7 was *Arbutus uva-ursi*.[307] James's collection was made as he ascended the South Platte from the

---

[303]JAMES [1], II, 155; JAMES [2] in THWAITES [1], XVI, 168.

[304]JAMES [1], II, 96; JAMES [2] in THWAITES [1], XVI, 98.

[305]JAMES [3], June 6.

[306]JAMES [1], II, 35; JAMES [2] in THWAITES [1], XVI, 26.

[307]JAMES [1], II, 8n.; JAMES [2] in THWAITES [1], XV, 294n.; JAMES [3], July 7 (erroneously dated July 8).

chasm to a point about seven miles southwest of Waterton, Jefferson County, Colorado.

Pyrola secunda L., Sp. Pl. 396. 1753. (One-Sided Wintergreen).
James collected this plant on July 10 in the area of their midday rest on Monument Creek, near the base of Elephant Rock, a mile or so east of Palmer Lake, El Paso County, Colorado.[308]

Euphorbiaceae

Acalypha sp. (Copperleaf).
James listed "Acalypha virginica" in his diary for August 27.[309]
"Acalypha" is also listed in the *Account* for this date.[310]
In terms of known distribution, that could have been any of three species: *A. monococca, A. ostryaefolia,* or *A. virginica.* The first two of these were described after 1820.
On that day, a Sunday, the party remained in camp at the junction of Buggy Creek and the Canadian River, about three and a half miles northeast of Minco, Grady County, Oklahoma.

Argythamnia mercurialina (Nutt.) Muell. Arg., Linnaea 34:148. 1865. (Wild Mercury).
#403 *Ditaxis?,* in Torr., Ann. Lyc. Nat. Hist. N.Y. 2:244.1827. "On the Canadian." Torrey added that "I have specimens of the same plant from Mr. Nuttall, which he collected on the Arkansa. They are labelled, 'A new genus allied to Mercurialis.'"
Nuttall stated that the type was collected on "prairies of Red river, near the confluence of the Kiamesha."[311] In 1819 this area was included in Arkansas Territory. Today, Nuttall's type locality is in Choctaw County, Oklahoma, at the southeastern limits of the plant's range in the state.
At NY there is a collection made by James of this plant, mounted on a sheet with an isotype of Nuttall's *Aphora mercurialina.* Based on the expedition's itinerary and the distribution of this species, James would have collected his plant along the Canadian in August in the Texas panhandle or in western Oklahoma.

---

[308]JAMES [1], II, 15n.; JAMES [2] in THWAITES [1], XV, 306n.; JAMES [3], July 10. All references are erroneously dated July 11.
[309]JAMES [3], August 27.
[310]JAMES [1], II, 145; JAMES [2] in THWAITES [1], XVI, 155.
[311]NUTTALL [6], 174.

Cnidoscolus texanus (Muell. Arg.) Small, Fl. Southeast. U.S. p.1333. 1903. (Bull Nettle).
#408 *Jatropha stimulosa* Michx., in Torr., Ann. Lyc. Nat. Hist. N.Y. 2:245.1827. "On the Canadian."
When James first encountered this species on August 28[312] (August 27 according to the *Account*)[313] he was apparently uncertain of its identity, although he included a detailed description. The next morning he found what he believed to be the "tubular funnel shaped corolla" of this plant and stated that the plant belonged to *Jatropha*.
On August 28 the party traveled downstream on the Canadian from near Minco, Grady County, to three or four miles northeast of Newcastle near the McClain/Cleveland county line, Oklahoma.

Croton glandulosus L. var. **septentrionalis** Muell. Arg., in DC., Prodr. 15(2):686.1866. (Tropic Croton).
#406 *Croton glandulosum* L., in Torr., Ann. Lyc. Nat. Hist. N.Y. 2:245.1827. "With the preceding ['Sources of the Canadian.']."
Based on distribution and flowering time, James could have collected this specimen in August or September along the Canadian River in the Texas panhandle or Oklahoma.
In the *Account* "a new croton" is listed for August 6, while the party was camped on the Canadian River approximately three miles east of the New Mexico/Texas line in Oldham County, Texas.[314] That could be this croton. Where the information in the *Account* came from, when it is not mentioned in James's diary, is a puzzle.

Croton monanthogynus Michx., Fl. Bor. Am. 2:215.1803. (Prairie Tea).
#405 *Croton ellipticum* Nutt., in Torr., Ann. Lyc. Nat. Hist. N.Y. 2:245.1827. "Sources of the Canadian."
Torrey later stated that his *C. ellipticum* is *C. monanthogynus*.[315] Based on its known distribution, the James collection was almost surely made in the latter half of August or early September in the eastern half of Oklahoma.

Euphorbia corollata L., Sp. Pl. 459. 1753. (Flowering Spurge).
#401 *Euphorbia corollata* L., in Torr., Ann. Lyc. Nat. Hist. N.Y. 2:245.1827. "On the Canadian."

[312]JAMES [3], August 28.
[313]JAMES [1], II, 145–46; JAMES [2] in THWAITES [1], XVI, 156.
[314]JAMES [1], II, 96; JAMES [2] in THWAITES [1], XVI, 98.
[315]TORREY [5], 295.

The only other mention of this plant is by James in his diary for August 29.[316] There he described a plant as "Stem nearly simple erect. Leaves small linear scattered. Fls. in a terminal level topped corymb." He did not indicate that he thought that it was new but did give it a name (followed by a question mark) that described the inflorescence.

On August 29 the party traveled about twenty miles, mostly on the prairie, and camped on the Canadian about three miles north of Lexington, Cleveland County, Oklahoma.

Euphorbia hexagona Nutt. ex Spreng., Syst. 3:791.1826. (Green Spurge).

#398 *Euphorbia hexagona* Nutt., in Torr., Ann. Lyc. Nat. Hist. N.Y. 2:244.1827. "Sources of the Canadian."

James, in his diary for July 26, remarked on what he thought was a new species of *Euphorbia* and included the following: "very slender, much branched. Leaves opposite, nearly linear."[317] The species is perhaps one of the "two or three Euphorbias" mentioned that day in the *Account*.[318]

The party camped that day in Bachicha Canyon, about eight miles north-northeast of the junction of State Highway 389 and U.S. Highway 160, in southern Las Animas County, Colorado.

Euphorbia maculata L., Sp. Pl. 455. 1753. (Spotted Spurge).

James mentioned this plant in his diary on June 13.[319] We are using the name in the sense that it was used in James's time. It is frequently referred to in recent literature as *E. supina* Raf.

The plant was found as the party traveled past the Pawnee villages along the Loup River, Nance County, Nebraska.

Euphorbia marginata Pursh, Fl. Am. Sept. 607. 1814. (Snow-on-the-Mountain).

#397 *Euphorbia marginata* Pursh, in Torr., Ann. Lyc. Nat. Hist. N.Y. 2:244.1827. "Sources of the Platte. Annual. A beautiful species, now cultivated in many of the gardens about New-York, from seeds collected by Dr. James."

James cited this species in his diary for June 29, remarking, "The

[316]JAMES [3], August 29.
[317]JAMES [3], July 26.
[318]JAMES [1], II, 73; JAMES [2] in THWAITES [1], XVI, 71.
[319]JAMES [3], June 13.

large colored leaves of the involucrum give this plant a showy appearance."[320]

On this same day in the *Account* reference is made to *E. variegata*, a synonym of *E. marginata*.[321]

On June 29 James traveled from near Sterling, Logan County, to Messex, Washington County, Colorado.

Euphorbia missurica Raf., Atl. Jour. 1:146.1832. (Prairie Spurge). Based on

#400 *Euphorbia portulacoides* Willd.?, in Torr., Ann. Lyc. Nat. Hist. N.Y. 2:244.1827. "On the Missouri, near Franklin." Followed by a description.

Wheeler designated a Nuttall specimen (NY) as the type,[322] even though Rafinesque based *E. missurica* on a James specimen. That specimen, mounted on the same sheet with the Nuttall specimen at NY, was said by Wheeler to be "a sterile seedling."[323] Torrey included descriptive characters of the inflorescence, which would indicate that the specimen was not always without an inflorescence.[324]

James could well have collected his specimen "near Franklin," Howard County, Missouri, but, based on the long flowering time and broad distribution, he could have encountered this species in any of the five states through which the expedition traveled after leaving Engineer Cantonment. The label for the James collection reads "Franklin M.T. [Missouri Territory] May." No *Euphorbia* is listed from Franklin in James's diary.

Euphorbia montana Engelm. var. **robusta** Engelm., in Torr., Bot. Mex. Bound. Surv. 2(1):192.1859. "[O]n the upper Platte; *James, Nuttall, Fremont*." (Rocky Mountain Spurge).

Of the three collectors cited by Engelmann, James would have been the first to collect this variety. The James and Fremont specimens at NY are labeled as syntypes.

James would have collected his specimen along the Front Range in Colorado in July.

This taxon is frequently referred to as *E. robusta* (Engelm.) Small.

[320]JAMES [3], June 29.
[321]JAMES [1], I, 488; JAMES [2] in THWAITES [1], XV, 263–64.
[322]WHEELER, 133.
[323]WHEELER, 134.
[324]TORREY [2], 244.

Euphorbia strictior Holz., Contr. U.S. Nat. Herb. 1:214, pl.18. 1892. (Panhandle Spurge).

James's diary for August 4 contains this entry: "Euphorbia ——? Slender erect branching above, smooth. Leaves sessile linear lanceolate acute entire nerveless, alternate. Flowers (sub)solitary in a terminal leafy panicle. Fem. long pedicelled."[325] James's description fits so well *E. strictior* that there seems little doubt about the identification.

On August 4 James and his party traveled a few miles down Ute Creek then turned southeast, following an Indian trace, to the Canadian River, all in Harding County, New Mexico.

The type, incidentally, was collected by M. A. Carleton in August 1891, in Oldham County, Texas, a county that James would enter the next day.

Stillingia sylvatica L. var. **salicifolia** Torr. (Queen's Delight).

#404 *Stillingia sylvatica* L. β *salicifolia* Torr., Ann. Lyc. Nat. Hist. N.Y. 2:245.1827. "On the Canadian?"

James briefly described this plant in his diary for August 5.[326] Most of the day the party, following the Canadian River, was in Quay County, New Mexico. The last two or three miles, however, were in Oldham County, Texas. The type (NY) could have been collected in either county.

The reference in the *Account* on August 4 to *Jatropha stimulosa* was surely to *Stillingia* rather than to *Cnidoscolus texanus* (*q.v.*),[327] as the latter species does not occur so far west on the Canadian River.

Tragia ramosa Torr. (Noseburn).

#407 *Tragia ramosa* Torr., Ann. Lyc. Nat. Hist. N.Y. 2:245.1827. "Sources of the Canadian?"

Tragia ramosa has been considered a synonym of *T. nepetifolia* Cav. and as a variety of the latter. Miller and Webster considered *T. ramosa* to be a distinct species and suggested that the type (NY) came from southeastern Colorado.[328] That could well be correct. Northeastern New Mexico, along the Canadian in the Texas panhandle, or in western Oklahoma are also likely type localities.

[325]JAMES [3], August 4.
[326]JAMES [3], August 5.
[327]JAMES [1], II, 95; JAMES [2] in THWAITES [1], XVI, 96.
[328]MILLER AND WEBSTER, 281.

Fagaceae

Quercus alba L., Sp. Pl. 996. 1753. (White Oak).
#415 *Quercus alba* L., in Torr., Ann. Lyc. Nat. Hist. N.Y. 2:247. 1827. "On the Canadian."
James could have seen this species on the Arkansas River in Sequoyah County, Oklahoma, or near Ft. Smith, Arkansas. Possibly he encountered it on the Canadian River, but only at its junction with the Arkansas.

Quercus gambelii Nutt., Proc. Acad. Nat. Sci. Phila. 4:22.1848. (Gambel Oak).
In his diary for July 7, James mentioned an oak as "Quercus ilicifolia."[329] In the *Account* on this day it is called "Quercus banisteri Mx."[330] Gambel oak is the only one known in the area where James collected on July 7 — the day that he ascended the South Platte above the chasm, about seven miles southwest of Waterton, Jefferson County, Colorado.

Quercus marilandica Muenchh., Hausvat. 5:253.1770. (Blackjack Oak).
On August 25 James entered into his diary "Quercus nigra," the name applied to the blackjack in his time.[331]
On that day the party traveled down the Canadian River in Caddo and Canadian counties, Oklahoma.

Quercus muehlenbergii Engelm., Trans. Acad. Sci. St. Louis 3:391.1877. (Chinkapin Oak).
In the *Account* on September 1 James described the mountainous regions to the south and east, which he could see from the top of the hills near the Canadian River.[332] One of the trees he noted was *Castanea pumila*. He would not have seen the chestnut at all and must have mistaken chinkapin oak for it.
By September 1 the party had ascended some hills near Konawa, Seminole County, Oklahoma.

Quercus phellos L., Sp. Pl. 944. 1753. (Willow Oak).

[329]JAMES [3], July 7.
[330]JAMES [1], II, 8n.; JAMES [2] in THWAITES [1], XV, 294n.
[331]JAMES [3], August 25.
[332]JAMES [1], II, 153; JAMES [2] in THWAITES [1], XVI, 165.

#417 *Quercus phellos* Willd., in Torr., Ann. Lyc. Nat. Hist. N.Y. 2:247.1827. "On the Arkansa, &c."

James could have encountered this oak from September 10 to September 13 along the Arkansas River in Sequoyah County, Oklahoma, or later in September in Arkansas.

During the time James was in Sequoyah County, he mentioned "woods of oak" in the *Account*.[333]

Quercus stellata Wangenh., Beytr. Teutsch. Holzg. Forstwiss. Anpflanz. Nordam. Holz. 78, pl.6. 1787. (Post Oak).

#416 *Quercus stellata* Willd., in Torr., Ann. Lyc. Nat. Hist. N.Y. 2:247.1827. "With the preceding ['Quercus alba. . . . On the Canadian.']."

James mentioned post oak and white oak in his diary as well as in the *Account* under the date of August 24.[334] On that day the party continued down the Canadian River in Dewey County, Oklahoma.

James mentioned the "upland white oak" in the *Account* on August 30.[335] On that day the party traveled from near Lexington, Cleveland County, to about four miles southwest of Asher, Pottawatomie County, Oklahoma.

James would not have encountered *Q. alba* in these locations. Here his references to white oak are likely to a variation of *Q. stellata* that is very variable in Oklahoma, and hybrids occur.

Quercus undulata Torr. (Wavyleaf Oak).

#418 *Quercus undulata* Torr., Ann. Lyc. Nat. Hist. N.Y. 2:248, pl.4. 1827. "Sources of the Canadian, and the Rocky Mountains." Type: NY.

Oaks are mentioned in James's diary for August 1,[336] while he mentioned them in the *Account* under the date of August 2 as being "met with in this district."[337] Tucker, in his excellent article on this oak, thought that August 1 was likely because Long's party spent that day in camp and James would have had time to botanize.[338] August 1 was spent at the junction of Garcia Creek and Ute Creek, about six miles east and a little north of Yates, Harding County, New Mexico. If

---

[333]JAMES [1], II, 169; JAMES [2] in THWAITES [1], XVI, 183.
[334]JAMES [1], II, 141; JAMES [2] in THWAITES [1], XVI, 151; JAMES [3], August 24.
[335]JAMES [1], II, 151; JAMES [2] in THWAITES [1], XVI, 162.
[336]JAMES [3], August 1.
[337]JAMES [1], II, 92; JAMES [2] in THWAITES [1], XVI, 92.
[338]TUCKER [1], 333.

the specimen were collected on August 2, the party would have been a few miles farther down Ute Creek in Harding County. Tucker concluded that "what has been regarded as a 'species'— *Quercus undulata*—is in fact a variable complex derived from hybridization." Incidentally, Tucker thought that Torrey's illustration (plate 4, mentioned above) is likely *Q. havardii.*

Frankeniaceae

Frankenia jamesii Torr., in Gray, Proc. Am. Acad. 8:622.1873. (Frankenia).
The known distribution of *Frankenia* and the route of the expedition overlap only in the Arkansas Valley of Colorado. James first intersected the Arkansas west of Pueblo near Turkey Creek, where Long's party camped on July 16–18. On July 17 and 18, James and Bell made a trip up the Arkansas Valley to Cañon City, during which time James "found a few new plants which I have not time to examine."[339] On July 21–23 the party camped at Rocky Ford before James's portion of the expedition left the river and headed south.

That James collected *Frankenia jamesii* along the Arkansas somewhere between Cañon City, Fremont County, and Rocky Ford, Otero County, there is no doubt. Whalen, however, has designated *Wright 626,* "'[c]ollected in the Expedition from Western Texas to El Paso, New Mexico, May–Oct 1849,'" as the lectotype.[340] Based on the distribution of this species and the route of Charles Wright in 1849, it is likely that his collection was made in Hudspeth County, Texas.

Frankenia jamesii still occurs frequently on the bluffs on the north side of the Arkansas west of Pueblo along Turkey Creek, as we discovered in late June 1983.

We have examined specimens of *Frankenia* from Cañon City and the area west of Pueblo. The species is reported also from Rocky Ford.[341] There is the possibility that the plant that James referred to as "Hypericum corymbosum" in his diary for July 22 could be the original collection of *Frankenia jamesii.*[342] If that is true, then James's collection would have been from Rocky Ford, Otero County, Colorado.

---

[339]JAMES [3], July 18.
[340]WHALEN, 68.
[341]RYDBERG [1], 231; WHALEN, 70.
[342]JAMES [3], July 22.

Gentianaceae

Centaurium calycosum (Buckl.) Fernald, Rhodora 10:54.1908. (Centaury).

The above name is merely a guess at what plant James had when he entered in his diary on August 1, "Centaurella aestivalis Ph.? In rocky declivities."[343] At the time the party was camped at the junction of Garcia and Ute creeks, six miles east and a little north of Yates, Harding County, New Mexico.

Eustoma grandiflorum (Raf.) Shinners, S.W. Nat. 2:41.1957. (Prairie Gentian).

#266 *Lisianthus glaucifolius* Jacq., in Torr., Ann. Lyc. Nat. Hist. N.Y. 2:219.1827. "Sources of the Canadian."

James described this species as a "Gentiana?" in his diary for August 3, noting that the flowers were "larger than those of G. crinita."[344] Following James's description is the notation "Fig no 82," which refers to the sketch of the plant made by Peale.[345] The sketch is also dated August 3, 1820, and is numbered 82. Peale's sketch has been reproduced by Benson.[346]

James made his collection "about the grassy margins of springs and brooks in the declivities of gravelly hills." As the party did not encounter any water until reaching their evening's campsite, it seems likely that the *Eustoma* was collected then. The campsite was in Harding County, about fifteen miles northwest of Logan, New Mexico.

It is not until August 6 in the *Account* that James noted finding "a gentian, with a flower much larger than G. crinita."[347]

Frasera speciosa Dougl. ex Griseb., in Hook., Fl. Bor. Am. 2:66. 1838. (Green Gentian).

#265 *Frasera carolinensis* Walt., in Torr., Ann. Lyc. Nat. Hist. N.Y. 2:219.1827. "Sources of the Arkansa."

The only other reference that we have found to this collection by James is in his *Catalogue,* in which he listed "Frasera Waltheri. Near the Rocky Mountains, on the Arkansaw."[348]

[343]JAMES [3], August 1.
[344]JAMES [3], August 3.
[345]The original sketch is now part of the Titian R. Peale Sketches, American Philosophical Society, Philadelphia.
[346]BENSON [3], 266.
[347]JAMES [1], II, 96; JAMES [2] in THWAITES [1], XVI, 98.
[348]JAMES [4], 175.

The party reached the Arkansas drainage at Elephant Rock on July 10. That would have been James's first opportunity to be both on the Arkansas and at the proper elevation for *Frasera*. We observed *Frasera* about twelve miles north of Elephant Rock near the top of Dawson Butte, Douglas County, Colorado. That location, however, is on the Platte River drainage.

James remained in fair range of this species for about the next week as he continued to the Arkansas River and up to Cañon City.

Geraniaceae

Geranium intermedium James, Long Exped. (London ed.) 2:190. 1823. (Wild Geranium).

#56 *Geranium caespitosum* James, in Long's Exped. ii.p.3, in Torr., Ann. Lyc. Nat. Hist. N.Y. 2:173.1827. "There are no specimens of this plant in the collection. Found on the sandstone ledges at the base of the Rocky Mountains."

In his diary for July 6, James gave the following: "Geranium columbianum ? [doubtless a slip for "columbinum"] Caespitose, pubescent. Stem sparingly branched above. Radical leaves reniform, deeply 5–7 cleft. Between G. mac. and G. robertianum."[349]

At the time, James was camped near the mouth of the chasm of the South Platte River, and that afternoon he collected the type along the hogbacks on the south side of the river, Douglas County, Colorado. That is about a mile southwest of Waterton, Jefferson County, Colorado.

In the Philadelphia edition of the *Account* there appears the following: "About the sandstone ledges we collected a geranium intermediate between crane's bill and herb robert."[350] The description, in a footnote on the same page, reads almost the same as the diary entry. The first few words are "*G. caespitose,* sub-erect, pubescent, sparingly branched above. Radical leaves reniform deeply 5–7 cleft."

In the London edition of the *Account* the description of the new species reads, "*G. intermedium,* I.—Cespitose, sub-erect, pubescent," etc.[351] [The "I" is an error for James's initial].

Because James's collection of the *Geranium* never reached Torrey, and because the exact location of the collecting site was not known, it

[349]JAMES [3], July 6.
[350]JAMES [6], II, 3, 3n.
[351]JAMES [7], II, 344.

is not surprising that Torrey and Gray listed *G. caespitosum* under "Doubtful species."[352] Another decade later, however, Gray, in *Plantae Fendlerianae,* proposed typifying James's name with a Fendler collection from near Santa Fe, New Mexico.[353] That solution was followed by many botanists, but as more collections were made and the type locality of James's plant became known, it became usual to refer to the plants from the Santa Fe area as *G. atropurpureum* Heller[354] and the appropriate plants from the north half of Colorado as *G. caespitosum* (*sensu* Torrey non Gray). An exception is in the revision by Jones and Jones.[355] Here *G. caespitosum* is accepted in the Grayian sense.

In company with Dr. William A. Weber of the University of Colorado, whose knowledge of botany and the botanical history of Colorado was most valuable to us, we spent an afternoon in late June 1981, unsuccessfully exploring the hogbacks near the chasm of the South Platte in search of *Geranium* at the type locality.

In the early 1920s, however, Mr. Geo. E. Osterhout made collections of *Geranium* at the type locality and concluded that they were conspecific with *G. parryi.* We have examined at RM these Osterhout specimens, and they are indeed glandular to the base, as in *G. parryi.* Osterhout stated that the plant known as *G. parryi* "is the only *Geranium* found in the immediate vicinity."[356] He further suggested that the correct name is *G. intermedium* James, in Long Exped., London edition, but on the mistaken impression that the Philadelphia edition did not appear until 1825, two years after the London edition.

It seems evident that the London edition appeared in 1823. That it appeared before the Philadelphia edition, however, is highly unlikely. In *The Papers of John C. Calhoun*[357] is the following note dated December 21, 1822, concerning the Philadelphia edition. The note, from Major Long to Secretary of War Calhoun, reads, "I embrace the earliest opportunity to transmit a Copy of the 'Account of the Expedition' and will forward eleven others as soon as the work shall have been published, which will complete the dozen ordered in your instructions of Nov. [17,] 1821." On January 3, 1823, Long wrote to Calhoun, "I transmit by this day[']s mail, six copies of the 'Account' of the late Expedition [to the Rocky Mountains] under my command,

[352]TORREY AND GRAY [1], I, 207.
[353]GRAY [6], 25.
[354]HELLER, 195.
[355]JONES AND JONES, 47.
[356]OSTERHOUT [2], 83.
[357]HEMPHILL, 391, 404.

being the residue of the Dozen Copies which you have instructed me to furnish to the War Department."

Arguments could be made in favor of either name, G. *caespitosum* or G. *intermedium*. It is true that, in the Philadelphia edition, the word "caespitose," is in italics, and Torrey simply attempted to correct it by adding the proper Latin termination. On the other hand, it is notable that James, in his diary and in both editions of the *Account*, referred to the plant as being intermediate between two other species. One could then interpret the Philadelphia edition as having the specific epithet omitted, and the name, *intermedium*, that James seemingly intended appeared in the London edition four years before Torrey published the name *caespitosum* in the Ann. Lyc.

Gramineae

Agrostis hyemalis (Walt.) BSP., Prel. Cat. N.Y. 68. 1888. (Ticklegrass).

James listed the synonym name, *Trichodium laxiflorum,* in his diary for June 11.[358] The name also appears in a footnote in the *Account* on June 9.[359] Seven species are mentioned in the footnote; all are mentioned in the diary either a few days before or a few days after June 9.

Quite possibly, but a little less likely, the plant is the variety *tenuis* (Tuckerm.) Gleason.[360]

Accepting June 11 as correct, this grass was collected near the village of the Grand Pawnee on the Loup River, about seven miles southwest of Fullerton, Nance County, Nebraska.

Alopecurus aequalis Sobol., Fl. Petrop. 16. 1799. (Short-Awn Foxtail).

In his diary for Sunday, July 2, James listed "Alopecurus geniculatus. In running water."[361] This species has been reported so infrequently in Colorado that it seems more likely that James collected the common *aequalis*. On that day the party remained in camp on the South Platte near Kuner, Weld County, Colorado.

Andropogon gerardii Vitm., Summa Pl. 6:16.1792. (Big Bluestem).

#473 *Andropogon furcatum* Muhl., in Torr., Ann. Lyc. Nat. Hist. N.Y. 2:254.1827. "Upper part of the Arkansa."

[358]JAMES [3], June 11.
[359]JAMES [1], I, 433n.; JAMES [2] in THWAITES [1], XV, 200n.
[360]GLEASON [1], 21.
[361]JAMES [3], July 2.

In his diary for July 22, James mentioned *Andropogon furcatum*.[362] The species is mentioned in the *Account* one day earlier at the same location.[363] At that time the party was camped on the Arkansas River near Rocky Ford, Otero County, Colorado.

Andropogon saccharoides Sw. var. **torreyanus** (Steud.) Hack., in DC., Monogr. Phan. 6:495.1889. (Silver Bluestem).
#5 *Andropogon glaucum* Torr., Ann. Lyc. Nat. Hist. N.Y. 1:153–54.1824. [Not of Retz., 1789]. "On the Canadian River." Type: NY.
#474 *Andropogon glaucum* Torr., Ann. Lyc. Nat. Hist. N.Y. 2:254. 1827. "Canadian."
Andropogon torreyanus Steud., Nom. Bot. ed.2. 1:93.1840. Based on *A. glaucum* Torr.
Andropogon jamesii Torr., in Marcy, Expl. Red River (Senate Exec. Doc. 54) 302. 1853. Based on *A. glaucum* Torr.
This grass could have been collected in southeastern Colorado in late July, in northeastern New Mexico in late July or early August, or in the Texas panhandle or Oklahoma in August.

Aristida adscensionis L., Sp. Pl. 82. 1753. (Sixweeks Threeawn).
#7 *Aristida fasciculata* Torr., Ann. Lyc. Nat. Hist. N.Y. 1:154.1824. "In forests of the Canadian River."
#462 *A. fasciculata* Torr., in Torr., Ann. Lyc. Nat. Hist. N.Y. 2:253.1827. "On the Canadian."
Assuming the Canadian River location to be correct, James's type was almost surely collected in the Texas panhandle. We find no mention of it, however, in either the diary or the *Account*.

Aristida purpurea Nutt. var. **longiseta** (Steud.) Vasey, in Wheeler, Rpt. U.S. Surv. W. 100th. Merid. 6:286.1878. (Fendler Threeawn).
#461 *Aristida pallens* Nutt., in Torr., Ann. Lyc. Nat. Hist. N.Y. 2:253.1827. "About the Forks of the Platte."
In his diary, James wrote: "Aristida gracilis? Hab. on elevated barren soils forming small tufts which have a purple color and a very elegant appearance."[364] We are assuming that this is the plant to which Torrey referred. In view of James's description and the distribution, we think it likely that it is the variety given above.

[362]JAMES [3], July 22.
[363]JAMES [1], II, 63; JAMES [2] in THWAITES [1], XVI, 57.
[364]JAMES [3], June 25 (erroneously dated June 24).

In the *Account* the plant is listed as *A. pallens*.[365] The plants collected on June 23–26 are listed together there in one footnote. James's plant would have been collected on June 25, while the party spent that Sunday camped on the South Platte River about two miles west of Ogallala, Keith County, Nebraska.

Arundinaria gigantea (Walt.) Muhl., Cat. Pl. 14. 1813. (Giant Cane).
#458 *Miegia macrosperma* Pers., in Torr., Ann. Lyc. Nat. Hist. N.Y. 2:253.1827. "On the Arkansa and Canadian."
In his diary for September 11, James listed "cane" as part of the "undergrowth both on the Canadian and the Arkansaw."[366] On this day the party traveled from a few miles downstream of the junction of the Canadian and Arkansas rivers to just west of Sallisaw, Sequoyah County, Oklahoma.

Beckmannia syzigachne (Steud.) Fernald., Rhodora 30:27.1928. (Sloughgrass).
#463 *Beckmannia eruciformis* Jacq., in Torr., Ann. Lyc. Nat. Hist. N.Y. 2:254.1827. "On the Platte."
James described this grass in his diary for July 2, a Sunday, on which the party remained in camp on the South Platte near Kuner, Weld County, Colorado.[367]

Bouteloua curtipendula (Michx.) Torr., in Emory, Notes Mil. Reconn. 154. 1848. (Sideoats Grama).
#475 *Atheropogon apludoides* Muhl., in Torr., Ann. Lyc. Nat. Hist. N.Y. 2:254.1827. "On the Platte."
James mentioned this grass as *Chloris curtipendula* in his diary for June 14.[368] At the time they were traveling south from the Loup River to the Platte through Merrick County, Nebraska.
In the *Account,* this grass (as *Atheropogon apludoides*) is said to have been collected "along the Platte on the 15th and 16th June."[369]

Bouteloua gracilis (HBK.) Lag. ex. Steud., Nom. Bot. ed. 2.1:219. 1840. (Blue Grama).

[365]JAMES [1], 468n.; JAMES [2] in THWAITES [1], XV, 241n.
[366]JAMES [3], September 11.
[367]JAMES [3], July 2.
[368]JAMES [3], June 14 (erroneously included as part of June 13).
[369]JAMES [1], I, 455n.; JAMES [2] in THWAITES [1], XV, 226n.

#476 *Atheropogon? oligostachyum* Nutt., in Torr., Ann. Lyc. Nat. Hist. N.Y. 2:254.1827. "On the Platte."

James, in his diary, referred to this plant as *Atheropogon oligostachyum*.[370] The plant was collected on June 15 along the Platte River, either in Hall County or adjacent eastern Buffalo County, Nebraska.

In the *Account* this plant is listed with those collected on June 9.[371] In addition to this plant there are several other plants listed in the same footnote. According to the diary, some of these plants were collected before June 9, others after that date.

Buchloe dactyloides (Nutt.) Engelm., Trans. Acad. Sci. St. Louis 1:432, pl.12,14, figs.1–17. 1859. (Buffalo Grass).

#468 *Sesleria dactyloides* Nutt., in Torr., Ann. Lyc. Nat. Hist. N.Y. 2:254.1827. "On the Platte."

Based on the known distribution and the long flowering time, the grass could have been collected in any of the five states through which the expedition passed.

Cenchrus incertus M. A. Curtis, Boston J. Nat. Hist. 1:135.1837. (Sandbur) or

Cenchrus longispinus (Hack.) Fern., Rhodora 45:388.1943.

#456 *Cenchrus echinatus* L., in Torr., Ann. Lyc. Nat. Hist. N.Y. 2:253.1827. "Sources of the Canadian."

James described a grass he thought was *Cenchrus echinatus* in his diary for August 7.[372] This species is out of range for their location on August 7. His description is not definitive enough to limit it to only one of the above species. On the same day in the *Account* James mentioned "cenchrus tribuloides," a species also out of range.[373]

Cenchrus incertus and *C. longispinus* both occur along the Canadian River in Oldham County, Texas, where the party traveled this day.

Distichlis spicata (L.) Greene, Cal. Acad. Sci. Bull. 2:415.1887. (Saltgrass).

#469 *Uniola spicata* L., in Torr., Ann. Lyc. Nat. Hist. N.Y. 2:254. 1827. "Missouri."

---

[370]JAMES [3], June 15 (erroneously dated June 14).
[371]JAMES [1], I, 433n.; JAMES [2] in THWAITES [1], XV, 200n.
[372]JAMES [3], August 7.
[373]JAMES [1], II, 98; JAMES [2] in THWAITES [1], XVI, 100.

This collection of D. *spicata* by James is not referred to in his diary or the *Account,* and its known distribution along the route of the expedition is extremely limited. This species is known inland from an isolated salt marsh in Saline County, central Missouri, where Steyermark collected it in 1938.[374]

James passed very near this location in early May when he made collections along the Missouri River near Franklin in adjacent Howard County. Steyermark noted that isolated salt marshes also occur in adjacent Cooper and Howard counties.[375]

Distichlis stricta (Torr.) Rydb., Bull. Torr. Bot. Club 32:602.1905. (Inland Saltgrass).

#8 *Uniola* ? *stricta* Torr., Ann. Lyc. Nat. Hist. N.Y. 1:155.1824. "On the shores of the Canadian River." Type: NY.

#470 *Uniola stricta* Torr., in Torr., Ann. Lyc. Nat. Hist. N.Y. 2:254.1827. "On the Canadian."

No reference in the diary or the *Account* to this collection by James has been found. If Torrey's location is correct, then James would have collected this grass in the Texas panhandle or western Oklahoma. This grass, however, occurs in all of the five states through which James traveled.

Echinochloa crusgalli (L.) Beauv., Ess. Agrost. 53, 161. 1812. (Barnyard Grass).

In his diary, James mentioned "Panicum crus-galli" for July 22.[376] At the time the party was camped on the Arkansas River at Rocky Ford, Otero County, Colorado.

Many references state that this species was introduced from the Old World. If that is so, it is interesting that it would have been introduced so early this far up the Arkansas.

Elymus glaucus Buckl., Proc. Acad. Philad. 1862:99.1863. (Blue Wild Rye).

#477 *Elymus striatus* Willd., in Torr., Ann. Lyc. Nat. Hist. N.Y. 2:254.1827. "Upper part of the Arkansa."

In his diary for July 22, James mentioned *Elymus striatus*.[377] The

---

[374]STEYERMARK [2], 24.
[375]STEYERMARK [2], 23.
[376]JAMES [3], July 22.
[377]JAMES [3], July 22.

species is mentioned in the *Account* one day earlier at the same location.[378]

Elymus striatus, in the sense of many American authors, is considered a synonym of *E. villosus.* In the sense of Willdenow it is considered a synonym of *E. virginicus.* It is not clear in which sense Torrey used it, and it does not much matter, as both species are so infrequent in Colorado. There are three or four other species (all described many years after Torrey's paper) that James's plant could be, but *Elymus glaucus,* based on distribution, seems the most likely.

On July 22 the party was camped on the Arkansas River, near Rocky Ford, Otero County, Colorado.

Erioneuron pilosum (Buckl.) Nash, in Small, Fl. Southeast. U.S. p.144. 1903. (Sharp-Scaled Erioneuron).

James, in his diary for July 27, included a description of what he thought was a new species of grass.[379] The description is excellent for this species. Buckley's description, based on a collection of his from central Texas, was published over forty years later.

This grass is also known as *Tridens pilosus* (Buckl.) Hitchc.

James stated that the plant occurred "on dry gravelly hills." It was collected between Bachicha Canyon and their camp of July 27, about eight miles northeast of Branson, Las Animas County, Colorado.

Hilaria jamesii (Torr.) Benth., Linn. Soc. Jour. Bot. 19:62.1881. (Galleta).

#1 *Pleuraphis Jamesii* Torr., Ann. Lyc. Nat. Hist. N.Y. 1:148–50, pl.10. 1824. "On the high plains of the Trap Formation at the sources of the Canadian River. July." Type: NY.

#480 *Pleuraphis Jamesii* Torr., in Torr., Ann. Lyc. Nat. Hist. N. Y. 2:254.1827. "Sources of the Canadian."

The "spike-bearing" grass that James described in his diary for July 24 as "having the spikelets involucured with a tuft of down" became the type of *Hilaria jamesii.*[380]

On July 24, James's party crossed the Arkansas River and headed southeast across Timpas Creek toward the Purgatoire River. To judge by the sequence of the diary entries, it appears that this collection could have been made three to six miles farther southeast of where

[378]JAMES [1], II, 63; JAMES [2] in THWAITES [1], XVI, 58.
[379]JAMES [3], July 27.
[380]JAMES [3], July 24.

they crossed Timpas Creek, perhaps during their midday halt in southcentral Otero County, Colorado.

Hordeum jubatum L., Sp. Pl. 85. 1753. (Foxtail Barley).
#478 *Hordeum jubatum* Ait., in Torr., Ann. Lyc. Nat. Hist. N.Y. 2:254.1827. "On the Missouri and Platte."
In James's diary for June 12, a grass was described as having "leaves short scattered culms mostly geniculate at the base."[381] The grass is called *Elymus*, with a specific epithet referring to the nature of the culm bases. Geniculate culms are not frequent in *Elymus*, but they are in *Hordeum jubatum*. It seems very likely that this plant is the basis for *Hordeum jubatum*, both in Torrey and in James's *Catalogue*.[382]
Hordeum jubatum is also cited in the *Account* on June 9.[383] In addition to this plant there are several other plants listed in the same footnote which, according to the diary, were collected either before or after June 9.
On June 12 the party traveled along the Loup River and camped in Nance County, some four miles north and a little east of Palmer, Merrick County, Nebraska.

Hordeum pusillum Nutt., Gen. No. Am. Pl. 1:87.1818. (Little Barley).
#479 *Hordeum pusillum* Nutt., in Torr., Ann. Lyc. Nat. Hist. N.Y. 2:254.1827. "On the Missouri."
Based on the flowering time of this grass, it is likely that James made his collection in Nebraska in June.

Koeleria pyramidata (Lam.) Beauv., Ess. Agrost. 84, 166 and 175. 1812. (Junegrass).
#466 *Koeleria nitida* Nutt., in Torr., Ann. Lyc. Nat. Hist. N.Y. 2:253.1827. "On the Missouri."
There is little doubt but that this grass was collected in Nebraska in June.

Muhlenbergia racemosa (Michx.) BSP., Prel. Cat. N.Y. 67. 1888. (Marsh Muhly).
#460 *Polypogon racemosus* Nutt., in Torr., Ann. Lyc. Nat. Hist. N.Y. 2:253.1827. "On the Missouri."

[381]JAMES [3], June 12.
[382]JAMES [4], 173.
[383]JAMES [1], I, 433n.; JAMES [2] in THWAITES [1], XV, 200n.

If Torrey's location is correct, this late-blooming grass would have been collected in late September near Cape Girardeau, Missouri. Otherwise it would likely have been collected in August along the Canadian in Oklahoma.

Muhlenbergia torreyi (Kunth) Hitchc. ex Bush, Am. Midl. Nat. 6:84.1919. (Ring Muhly). This name is based on *Agrostis torreyi* Kunth (1830), which was based on *Agrostis caespitosa* Torr., a preempted name.

#4 *Agrostis caespitosa* Torr., Ann. Lyc. Nat. Hist. N.Y. 1:152.1824. [Not of Salisb., 1796]. "On the plains of the Missouri and Platt rivers."

On July 19 in the *Account,* James noted "a small caespitose" *Agrostis.*[384] This may well be the type (NY) locality for *Agrostis caespitosa* Torr.

At the time the party was eight or ten miles downstream on the Arkansas River from Turkey Creek, near Pueblo, Pueblo County, Colorado.

Munroa squarrosa (Nutt.) Torr., Rpts. Expls. R.R. Route Miss. to Pacif. 4(5):158.1857. (False Buffalo Grass).

#481 *Crypsis? squarrosa* Nutt., in Torr., Ann. Lyc. Nat. Hist. N.Y. 2:254.1827. "Near the Rocky Mountains."

Based on the known distribution and the long flowering time, the False Buffalo Grass could have been collected in any of the five states through which the expedition passed.

Oryzopsis hymenoides (Roem. & Schult.) Ricker, in Piper, Contr. U.S. Nat. Herb. 11:109.1906. (Indian Ricegrass).

#464 *Eriocoma cuspidata* Nutt., in Torr., Ann. Lyc. Nat. Hist. N.Y. 2:253.1827. "On the Platte."

No other reference to James's collection has been found. The plant was almost certainly collected in late June or in July in Colorado.

Schedonnardus paniculatus (Nutt.) Trel., in Branner & Coville, Rpt. Geol. Surv. Ark. 1888:236.1891. (Tumblegrass).

#471 *Lepturus paniculatus* Nutt., in Torr., Ann. Lyc. Nat. Hist. N.Y. 2:254.1827. "Platte."

No reference in the diary or the *Account* to this grass has been found. It has a long flowering period and could have been collected in

---

[384]JAMES [1], II, 51; JAMES [2] in THWAITES [1], XVI, 44.

any of the five states through which James traveled. Along the Platte River, as Torrey stated, could well be correct.

Sitanion hystrix var. **brevifolium** (J. G. Smith) C. L. Hitchc., Univ. Wash. Publ. Biol. 17(1):701.1969. (Squirreltail).
#472 *Aegilops hystrix* Nutt., in Torr., Ann. Lyc. Nat. Hist. N.Y. 2:254.1827. "On the Missouri and Platte."
James referred to a plant in his diary for July 22 as *Asprella hystrix,* a synonym of *Hystrix patula*.[385] That is a species of the eastern United States. Based on the aspect and the flowering time, it could well have been *Sitanion hystrix* or, as Torrey referred to it, *Aegilops hystrix*. It is also possible that the specimen Torrey examined was another collected earlier on the Platte in northeastern Colorado or adjacent Nebraska.
The grass referred to in the diary for July 22 was collected about their camp on the Arkansas River near Rocky Ford, Otero County, Colorado.

Sorghastrum nutans (L.) Nash, in Small, Fl. Southeast. U.S. p.66. 1903. (Indian Grass).
In his diary for July 22, James mentioned *Andropogon ciliatum*.[386] This species is mentioned in the *Account* one day earlier at the same location.[387] *Andropogon ciliatum* is considered to be a synonym of *Sorghastrum nutans*.
At this time the party was camped on the Arkansas River near Rocky Ford, Otero County, Colorado.

Spartina pectinata Link, Jahrb. Gewaechsk. 1:92.1820. (Prairie Cordgrass).
#457 *Spartina cynosuroides* Willd., in Torr., Ann. Lyc. Nat. Hist. N.Y. 2:253.1827. "On the Platte."
No reference in the diary or the *Account* to this collection by James has been found.
Spartina cynosuroides is a coastal species of the eastern and southeastern United States. Of the two species in range, *pectinata* and *gracilis,* the former seems the more similar to *S. cynosuroides* as Torrey identified it.

385JAMES [3], July 22.
386JAMES [3], July 22.
387JAMES [1], II, 63; JAMES [2] in THWAITES [1], XVI, 58.

Spartina pectinata occurs in all five states through which the expedition traveled.

Sporobolus airoides (Torr.) Torr., Rpts. Expls. R.R. Route Miss. to Pacif. 7:21.1858. (Alkali Sacaton).
#3 *Agrostis airoides* Torr., Ann. Lyc. Nat. Hist. N.Y. 1:151–52.1824. "On the branches of the Arkansas, near the Rocky Mountains." Type: NY.

No reference in the diary or the *Account* to this collection by James has been found. If Torrey's location is correct, the type would have been collected from July 10 at Elephant Rock, El Paso County, to July 27 at the head of Bachicha Canyon, Las Animas County, Colorado.

Sporobolus cryptandrus (Torr.) Gray, Man. 576. 1848. (Sand Dropseed).
#2 *Agrostis cryptandra* Torr., Ann. Lyc. Nat. Hist. N.Y. 1:151.1824. "On the Canadian river." Type: NY.
#459 *Agrostis cryptandra* Torr., Ann. Lyc. Nat. Hist. N.Y. 2:253. 1827.

No reference in the diary or the *Account* to this collection by James has been found. The type could have been collected in any of the five states through which James traveled. If Torrey's location is correct, the type would have been collected in August along the Canadian River in the Texas panhandle or western Oklahoma.

Stipa sp.
#465 *Stipa barbata* Michx., in Torr., Ann. Lyc. Nat. Hist. N.Y. 2:253.1827. "Sources of the Platte and Canadian."
Stipa barbata Michx. is considered to be a synonym of *S. avenacea* L., a species that does not occur so far west as James's route. If indeed the plant were collected on both the Platte and the Canadian, it was what was later described as *S. comata*. James mentioned *S. barbata* and *S. juncea* (a synonym of *S. comata*) on July 5, the day on which he took a side trip up Clear Creek, just north of Denver in Adams County, Colorado.[388] Along the route of the expedition, however, there are several possible species.

Tridens flavus (L.) Hitchc., Rhodora 8:210.1906. (Redtop).
#467 *Tricuspis seslerioides* Torr., in Torr., Ann. Lyc. Nat. Hist. N.Y. 2:253.1827. "Sources of the Platte."

[388]JAMES [1], I, 500; JAMES [2] in THWAITES [1], XV, 280.

James mentioned "Poa quinquefida" while at the camp on July 4 at the north end of Henderson Island, South Platte River, about four miles south of Brighton, Adams County, Colorado.[389] Both names used by Torrey and by James are synonyms of *Tridens flavus*. The species, however, is not known from Colorado. We are assuming that James misidentified his plant. But it seems unlikely that Torrey would have misidentified *Tridens flavus*. Instead we think he had the locality wrong. James was in range for the *Tridens* while along the Canadian in Texas or Oklahoma. What grass James referred to on July 4 we cannot guess.

Trisetum spicatum (L.) Richt., Pl. Eur. 1:59.1890.
#6 *Trisetum airoides* Beauv., in Torr., Ann. Lyc. Nat. Hist. N.Y. 1:154.1824. "On the Rocky Mountains."
This grass of high altitudes was doubtless collected by James on his trip to Pikes Peak, El Paso County, Colorado, July 13–15.

Uniola latifolia Michx., Fl. Bor. Am. 1:70.1803. (Broad-Leaved Spikegrass).
In his diary for August 26, James provided a full description of this species, including "Cal. 3-valved," referring, of course, to the two glumes and the sterile lemma.[390]
On August 26 the party traveled through southwestern Canadian County to the mouth of Buggy Creek in northwestern Grady County, central Oklahoma.
On Sunday, June 11, while the party was at the village of the Grand Pawnee, James entered the names *Digitaria filiformis* and *D. villosa*. We do not know what he had. *Chloris verticillata? Schedonnardus?* Both of the Digitarias are out of range. The introduced *D. sanguinalis*, which is in range, at least now, does not flower until midsummer.
James mentioned a third species of *Digitaria, D. paspalodes*.[391] That is *Paspalum distichum* L. It, too, is out of range.
If this species of *Paspalum* were mistaken for a *Digitaria*, perhaps the other two Digitarias could be referred to the one or two June-flowering Paspalums that occur in Nebraska.

---

[389]JAMES [1], I, 498n.; JAMES [2] in THWAITES [1], XV, 277n.; JAMES [3], July 4.
[390]JAMES [3], August 26.
[391]JAMES [4], 174.

Haloragaceae

Myriophyllum exalbescens Fern., Rhodora 21:120.1919.
#451 *Myriophyllum verticillatum* L., in Torr., Ann. Lyc. Nat. Hist.
N.Y. 2:252.1827. "Ponds near the Platte."
The plant was collected by James "in stagnant water near the Platte"
on June 16 in Buffalo County, Nebraska.
In his diary, James described the plant as aquatic and referred to it
as "Myriophyllum demersum?"[392] On that same day in the *Account*
James noted seeing "an interesting species of Myriophillum."[393]
James could have collected *M. verticillatum,* but based on present
known distribution, it seems more likely that he collected what
became *M. exalbescens.*

Hippocastanaceae

Aesculus glabra Willd. var. **arguta** (Buckl.) Robins., in Gray, Syn.
Fl. No. Am. 1¹:447.1897. (Texas Buckeye).
On August 25 James entered in his diary "Aesculus flava" and
added that "several other trees begin to occur."[394]
The farthest west that we have been able to find *Aesculus* on the
Canadian is about a half a mile east of Bridgeport, Caddo County,
Oklahoma. That is just a few miles east of the site of Long's camp of
the previous night (August 24).
James did not mention the tree in the *Account* until August 27 and
September 1.[395]

Hydrangeaceae

Jamesia americana Torr. & Gray, Fl. No. Am. 1:593–94.1840.
"Along the Platte or the Canadian River, near the Rocky Mountains?
Dr. James!" (Waxflower).
Torrey and Gray also remarked that "the particular locality is not
recorded." Based on its known distribution and James's route, the
type would have been collected in July as the party traveled through
Adams County, south along the Front Range into Fremont County,
Colorado.

---

[392]JAMES [3], June 16 (erroneously dated June 15).
[393]JAMES [1], I, 455; JAMES [2] in THWAITES [1], XV, 226.
[394]JAMES [3], August 25.
[395]JAMES [1], II, 145, 152; JAMES [2] in THWAITES [1], XVI, 156, 164.

We find no description of this plant in either the diary or the *Account.*

Hydrophyllaceae

Ellisia nyctelea (L.) L., Sp. Pl. ed. 2. 1662. 1763. (Waterpod).
#283 *Ellisia Nyctelea* L., in Torr., Ann. Lyc. Nat. Hist. N.Y.
2:222.1827. "On the Missouri."
This plant was probably collected en route from St. Louis, Missouri, to Engineer Cantonment in Nebraska; the species, however, does occur sporadically along the South Platte in Nebraska and in northeastern Colorado.

Hydrolea ovata Nutt. ex Choisy, Mem. Soc. Phys. Geneve 6:109.
1833. (Hairy Hydrolea).
#288 *Hydrolea spinosa* L., in Torr., Ann. Lyc. Nat. Hist. N.Y.
2:223.1827. "On the Canadian?"
Torrey stated that the leaves were ovate-oblong instead of lanceolate and that Nuttall considered it to be a distinct species.
James would have made his collection in mid September in eastern Oklahoma or in Arkansas.

Phacelia integrifolia Torr. (Crenate-Leaved Phacelia).
#281 *Phacelia integrifolia* Torr., Ann. Lyc. Nat. Hist. N.Y. 2:222,
pl.3. 1827. "Banks of the Platte."
On the type sheet (NY) is written, "See James' Notes, 1–p.69. On the Platte. June 25." On this day (actually June 26) the party traveled along the South Platte from near Ogallala, Keith County, Nebraska, to near Julesburg, Sedgwick County, Colorado. *Phacelia integrifolia* does not occur anywhere on the Platte.
The *Phacelia* in the marginal note on page 69 of James's diary proved to be *Cryptantha cinerea* var. *jamesii* (*q.v.*).
James most likely collected the type of *Phacelia integrifolia* in mid August along the Canadian in western Oklahoma or possibly in early August along Ute Creek in Harding or Quay counties, New Mexico.

Iridaceae

Sisyrinchium campestre Bickn., Bull. Torr. Bot. Club 26:341.
1899. (Prairie Blue-Eyed Grass).
#435 *Sisyrinchium mucronatum* Michx., in Torr., Ann. Lyc. Nat.
Hist. N.Y. 2:250.1827. "On the Missouri and Platte."

This is doubtless the "beautiful triandrous plant with aggregate purple flowers" that James mentioned in his diary for June 7.[396] At the time the party was near the Elkhorn River, a few miles southeast of Arlington, Washington or Dodge counties, Nebraska.

Juglandaceae

Carya illinoensis (Wangenh.) K. Koch, Dendrol. 1:593.1869. (Pecan).

On September 2 James noted pecan among the trees of the "dense forests of the river valley" as the party traveled in Seminole County or Pontotoc County, Oklahoma.[397]

Juglans nigra L., Sp. Pl. 997. 1753. (Black Walnut).

#422 *Juglans nigra* L., in Torr., Ann. Lyc. Nat. Hist. N.Y. 2:248. 1827. "On the Canadian."

In his diary James mentioned "black walnut" on August 19, as the party traveled along the banks of the Canadian River in Roger Mills County, Oklahoma.[398]

Two days earlier, however, James had mentioned black walnut in the *Account* when the party was upstream in adjacent Hemphill County, Texas.[399]

In the *Account* for August 24, black walnut is mentioned among the trees observed.[400] At that time the party was traveling downstream primarily through southwestern Blaine County, Oklahoma, to a point near Bridgeport.

Again on September 2 James mentioned this tree among those forming the "dense forests of the river valley."[401] The party was traveling in Seminole County or Pontotoc County, Oklahoma.

Krameriaceae

Krameria lanceolata Torr. (Ratany).

#33 *Krameria lanceolata* Torr., Ann. Lyc. Nat. Hist. N.Y. 2:168–69.1827. "On the Canadian?" Type: NY.

[396]JAMES [3], June 7.
[397]JAMES [I], II, 155; JAMES [2] in THWAITES [1], XVI, 168.
[398]JAMES [3], August 19.
[399]JAMES [1], II, 127; JAMES [2] in THWAITES [1], XVI, 135.
[400]JAMES [1], II, 141; JAMES [2] in THWAITES [1], XVI, 151.
[401]JAMES [1], II, 155; JAMES [2] in THWAITES [1], XVI, 168.

The plant is abundant along the Canadian River in the Texas panhandle and in the western half of Oklahoma. James was in this area beginning in early August. The primary flowering time, however, is May to July. The plant also occurs in southeastern Colorado and northeastern New Mexico. James was in these areas in late July. Torrey and Gray cited a James specimen from the "sandy soil on the upper part of the Arkansas or the Canadian."[402]

Labiatae

Dracocephalum parviflorum Nutt., Gen. No. Am. Pl. 2:35.1818. (Dragonhead).
#336 *Dracocephalum parviflorum* Nutt., in Torr., Ann. Lyc. Nat. Hist. N.Y. 2:231.1827. "Upper part of the Platte."
In his diary, James described a mint with a bilabiate calyx whose segments were acute.[403] It seems very likely that he was describing *Dracocephalum*. The collection was made on June 30 likely near Brush, Morgan County, Colorado.

Hedeoma hispida Pursh, Fl. Am. Sept. 414. 1814. (Rough False Pennyroyal).
#346 *Hedeoma hirta* Nutt., in Torr., Ann. Lyc. Nat. Hist. N.Y. 2:233.1827. "About the Pawnee Villages."
In his diary for June 12, James listed *Hedeoma hirta* and included a brief description.[404] He also included the name in his *Catalogue*, with the remark "about the Paunee Villages."[405]
Hedeoma hirta is also cited in the *Account* on June 9.[406] In addition to this plant there are several others listed in the same footnote. According to the diary, some of these plants were collected before June 9, others after that date.
On June 12 the party traveled up the Loup River from just west of the first Pawnee village to the third village, all in Nance County, Nebraska.

Lycopus asper Greene, Pittonia 3:339.1898. (Rough Bugleweed).
#348 *Lycopus virginicus* L., in Torr., Ann. Lyc. Nat. Hist. N.Y. 2:233.1827.

---

[402]TORREY AND GRAY [1], I, 134.
[403]JAMES [3], June 30.
[404]JAMES [3], June 12.
[405]JAMES [4], 173.
[406]JAMES [1], I, 400n.; JAMES [2] in THWAITES [1], XV, 200n.

James referred to his collection as *Lycopus europeus*.[407] The plant was collected on July 5 when James and three others made a side trip up "cannon-ball river" (Clear Creek), just north of Denver in Adams County, Colorado.

We are calling the plant *L. asper* because Torrey's *L. virginicus,* which as now understood is out of range, resembles *L. asper* more than it does *L. americanus,* the only other species in range.

Monarda fistulosa L. var. **menthifolia** (Graham) Fernald, Rhodora 3:15.1901. (Wild Bergamot).

#342 *Monarda fistulosa* L., in Torr., Ann. Lyc. Nat. Hist. N.Y. 2:232.1827. "On the Missouri, near Franklin."

In his diary for July 5 James included the following: "Monarda. About 3 feet high nearly simple stems not proliferous."[408] On that day James made a side trip from camp on the South Platte up Clear Creek, just north of Denver in Adams County, Colorado.

Torrey's location is either incorrect or his reference is to another collection in the state of Missouri, where var. *fistulosa* and var. *mollis* are common.

Monarda pectinata Nutt., Jour. Acad. Nat. Sci. Philad. ser. 2. 1:182.1847. (Plains Beebalm).

In his diary James included "Monarda? rugosa. Heads proliferous, very aromatic."[409] The plant was collected on June 23 on the south side of the South Platte River, just a few miles above its junction with the North Platte, Lincoln County, Nebraska.

Monarda punctata L. var. **villicaulis** (Pennell) Shinners, Field & Lab. 21:90.1953. (Spotted Beebalm).

#340 *Monarda punctata* L., in Torr., Ann. Lyc. Nat. Hist. N.Y. 2:232.1827. "On the Missouri?"

In his diary for August 29 James listed *Monarda punctata* with the following remarks: "Heads proliferous. Bracts canescent above. Flowers yellow, conspicuously marked with brown spots."[410] We are presuming that this is the collection to which Torrey referred. In the *Account* "monarda" is referred to only on August 27.[411]

---

[407]JAMES [1], I, 50ln.; JAMES [2] in THWAITES [1], XV, 28ln.; JAMES [3], July 5.
[408]JAMES [3], July 5.
[409]JAMES [3], June 23 (erroneously dated June 22).
[410]JAMES [3], August 29.
[411]JAMES [1], II, 146; JAMES [2] in THWAITES [1], XVI, 156.

On August 29 the party traveled about twenty miles, mostly on the prairie, and camped on the Canadian about three miles north of Lexington, Cleveland County, Oklahoma.

Salvia azurea Lam. var. **grandiflora** Benth., in DC., Prodr. 12:302. 1848. (Blue Sage).
#334 *Salvia elongata* Kunth, in Torr., Ann. Lyc. Nat. Hist. N.Y. 2:231.1827.
James likely collected this plant along the Canadian River in mid August in the Texas panhandle or along the Canadian or Arkansas rivers from mid August to mid September in Oklahoma.

Salvia reflexa Hornem., Pl. Hort. Hafn. 1:34.1807. (Lance-Leaved Sage).
#333 *Salvia trichostemoides* Pursh, in Torr., Ann. Lyc. Nat. Hist. N.Y. 2:231.1827. "On the Missouri."
The only plant that we find mentioned in the diary while James was along the Missouri River that is at all similar to the *Salvia* is one that he referred to very doubtfully as "Ajuga chamaepitys." He was then but a few days out of St. Louis, in Montgomery County, Missouri.
Much later, James described a plant in his diary that best fits *S. reflexa*.[412] On that day the party was traveling down the Canadian River in Roberts County, Texas.
Pursh's name is considered to be a synonym of *S. reflexa*.

Scutellaria galericulata L., Sp. Pl. 599. 1753. (Marsh Skullcap).
This species was mentioned by James in the diary and the *Account*.[413] The party was then along the Platte River near Gothenburg, Dawson County, Nebraska, in good range for this species.

Scutellaria parvula Michx. var. **missouriensis** (Torr.) Goodm. & Laws., Rhodora 94:381.1992. (Small Skullcap). Based on
#338 *S. ambigua* Nutt. β *missouriensis* Torr., Ann. Lyc. Nat. Hist. N.Y. 2:232.1827. "Council Bluff, on the Missouri."
This is known in recent literature as *S. parvula* var. *leonardi* (Epling) Fernald, Rhodora 47:172.1945.
The type could have been collected at Engineer Cantonment, where James stayed from May 27 until June 6. "Council Bluff" was

[412]JAMES [1], August 14.
[413]JAMES [1], I, 461n.; JAMES [2] in THWAITES [1], XV, 233n.; JAMES [3], June 20 (erroneously dated June 19).

commonly used to indicate the general area where it, Ft. Lisa, Camp Missouri, and Engineer Cantonment lay, all within about a seven-mile stretch of the Missouri River in Washington County, Nebraska.

Based on flowering time and distribution, however, James could have collected the type of this variety anywhere from near Cincinnati on the Ohio River down to its mouth, thence up the Mississippi to its junction with the Missouri River, and then up that river to Engineer Cantonment.

Scutellaria resinosa Torr. (Resinous Skullcap).

#339 Scutellaria resinosa Torr., Ann. Lyc. Nat. Hist. N.Y. 2:232. 1827. "On the Canadian."

This plant was described by James in his diary under the date of August 16.[414] The type (NY) was collected as the party came down the Canadian River in Hemphill County, Texas.

Stachys tenuifolia Willd., Sp. Pl. 3:100.1801. (Slenderleaf Betony).

In his diary James mentioned "Stachys hyssopifolia. Leaves crenate."[415] That species is out of range, and we are guessing that he had *S. tenuifolia* or, nearly as likely, *S. palustris* L.

On June 19 the party was near Gothenburg, Dawson County, Nebraska.

Teucrium canadense L. var. **occidentale** (Gray) McCl. & Epl., Brittonia 5:499.1946. (American Germander).

In the entry for July 1, James described in his diary a *Teucrium* that he thought might be a new species.[416] His lengthy description leaves no doubt as to the identity of the plant.

On that day the party traveled across the plain from just west of Fort Morgan, Morgan County, and finally northwest up the river to near Kuner, Weld County, Colorado.

Teucrium laciniatum Torr. (Cutleaf Germander).

#335 Teucrium laciniatum Torr., Ann. Lyc. Nat. Hist. N.Y. 2:231. 1827. "On the Rocky Mountains."

Under the date of July 30 in the diary, James described this new species so fully as to leave no doubt as to its identity.[417] The type

---

[414]JAMES [3], August 16.
[415]JAMES [3], June 20 (erroneously dated June 19).
[416]JAMES [3], July 1.
[417]JAMES [3], July 30.

(NY) was collected as the party traveled across the Don Carlos Hills from Sierra Grande to Ute Creek, western Union County, New Mexico.

Lauraceae

Sassafras albidum (Nutt.) Nees, Syst. Laur. 490. 1836. (Sassafras). #392 *Laurus Sassafras* L., in Torr., Ann. Lyc. Nat. Hist. N.Y. 2:242.1827. "On the Arkansa, near the junction of the Canadian."
Long's party would have come within the known range of this tree on September 7 in McIntosh County or Pittsburg County, Oklahoma, and would have stayed in range for the remaining few days of the expedition's travels, ending at Fort Smith on September 13.

Leguminosae

Acacia hirta Nutt. ex Torr. & Gray, Fl. No. Am. 1:404.1840. (Prairie Acacia).
#108 *Mimosa? seu Acaciae sp.?* Torr., Ann. Lyc. Nat. Hist. N.Y. 2:192.1827. "With the preceding ['On the Canadian?']." Torrey provided both a Latin and an English description, mentioning that the stamens are "more than 100 in each flower."
Torrey and Gray made no mention of this entry in the Ann. Lyc. by Torrey, but among the several specimens that they cite is "On the Canadian, *Dr. James!*" Based on James's itinerary and the known distribution of the plant, it would most likely have been collected along the Canadian River in Oklahoma during the latter half of August or a few days earlier in the Texas panhandle. This is the only species of *Acacia* that James would have encountered along the entire route of the expedition.
It seems impossible that Rafinesque would have failed to name this plant, but we have been unable to find such a name in the literature.

Amorpha canescens Pursh, Fl. Am. Sept. 467. 1814. (Leadplant).
#89 *Amorpha canescens* Nutt., in Torr., Ann. Lyc. Nat. Hist. N.Y. 2:178.1827. "On the Missouri, and on the Platte to its sources."
In his diary James mentioned this plant under the date of June 20.[418] On the previous day, while at the same campsite, he mentioned the plant in the *Account*.[419]

---

[418]JAMES [3], June 20 (erroneously dated June 19).
[419]JAMES [1], I, 46ln.; JAMES [2] in THWAITES [1], XV, 233n.

The party camped near Gothenburg, Dawson County, Nebraska.

Amorpha fruticosa L., Sp. Pl. 713. 1753. (False Indigo).
#88 *Amorpha fruticosa* L., in Torr., Ann. Lyc. Nat. Hist. N.Y. 2:178.1827. "On the Missouri and Platte, to the Rocky Mountains."

In his diary for June 18, James commented about the amorpha that grew on the islands in the Platte.[420] On that day they were camped west-southwest of Overton, Dawson County, Nebraska.

In the *Account, Amorpha fruticosa* is listed as occurring on these islands.[421]

More than a month later James listed *Amorpha fruticosa* as occurring about their campsite of July 21–23, which was on the Arkansas River about three miles north and a little west of Rocky Ford, Otero County, Colorado.[422]

Again on August 5 James listed *Amorpha nana* in his diary.[423] Most of that day the party followed the Canadian River in Quay County, New Mexico, with the exception of the last two or three miles of travel, which were in Oldham County, Texas. *Amorpha nana* is not known to occur in this area, so it is likely that James found *A. fruticosa*, perhaps in stunted form.

In the *Account*, reference is made only to "an amorpha."[424]

Astragalus adsurgens Pall. var. **robustior** Hook., Fl. Bor. Am. 1:149.1831. (Standing Milkvetch).
#92 *Astragalus Laxmani* Jacq., in Torr., Ann. Lyc. Nat. Hist. N.Y. 2:178.1827.

In his diary for June 20, James cited an *Astragalus* that was in fruit and had purple and white flowers.[425] The collection may be Torrey's #92. If that is the case, the plant was collected along the Platte River slightly west of Gothenburg, Dawson County, Nebraska.

Astragalus agrestis Dougl. ex G. Don, Gen. Hist. Dichl. Pl. 2:258.1832. (Field Milkvetch).
#95 *Astragalus Hypoglottis* L., in Torr., Ann. Lyc. Nat. Hist. N.Y. 2:179.1827. "On the Platte and about the sources of the Canadian."

[420]JAMES [3], June 18.
[421]JAMES [1], I, 458; JAMES [2] in THWAITES [1], XV, 230.
[422]JAMES [1], II, 62; JAMES [2] in THWAITES [1], XVI, 57; JAMES [3], July 22.
[423]JAMES [3], August 5.
[424]JAMES [1], II, 95; JAMES [2] in THWAITES [1], XVI, 96. Events that occurred on August 4, 5, and 6 are listed under the date of August 4 in both editions.
[425]JAMES [3], June 20.

Astragalus hypoglottis β? *polyspermus* T. & G., Fl. No. Am. 1:328–29.1838. "On the Platte, and near the sources of the Canadian, *Nuttall! Dr. James!* May."

According to Barneby the James specimen at (NY) is a cotype of *Astragalus hypoglottis* β? *polyspermus* that Barneby treated as a synonym of *A. agrestis.*[426]

James compared this species with *A. galegoides* (*A. racemosus, q.v.*) stating that the former was "a most elegant species much smaller with purple flowers."[427] The two species of *Astragalus* were collected at the same time, and the comparison is appropriate.

In the *Account* on the same day only "species of astragalus" are listed.[428]

On July 30 the party traveled across the Don Carlos Hills, from Sierra Grande to Ute Creek, western Union County, New Mexico.

Astragalus ceramicus Sheldon var. **imperfectus** Sheldon, Minn. Bot. St. 1:19.1894. (Painted Milkvetch).

#101 *Orobus*? *longifolius* Nutt., in Torr., Ann. Lyc. Nat. Hist. N.Y. 2:180.1827. "Forks of the Platte."

If this plant were among the "several species of Astragalus" that James collected "about the forks of the Platte," the collection would have been made on June 23, 24, or 25 in Lincoln County or Keith County, Nebraska.[429]

Astragalus crassicarpus Nutt., in Fraser's Catalog. 1813. (Ground Plum).

In his diary, James referred to this plant as *A. carnosus,* which he collected with "other species of the same genus."[430] His collection was made on June 9 "in the open country" they encountered between Shell Creek and the Loup Fork, Platte County, Nebraska.

Three years later James listed both *A. missouriensis* and *A. laxmanii* (= *A. adsurgens* Pall. var. *robustior* Hook.) as having been seen, with *A. carnosus,* by June 9.[431] At that time, however, he was not yet in range of the first two species.

[426]BARNEBY [1], 621.
[427]JAMES [3], July 30.
[428]JAMES [1], II, 86; JAMES [2] in THWAITES [1], XVI, 85.
[429]JAMES [1], I, 468n.; JAMES [2] in THWAITES [1], XV, 241n.
[430]JAMES [3], June 9.
[431]JAMES [1], I, 433n.; JAMES [2] in THWAITES [1], XV, 200n.

Astragalus gracilis Nutt., Gen. No. Am. Pl. 2:100.1818. (Slender Milkvetch).

#97 *Astragalus gracilis* Nutt., in Torr., Ann. Lyc. Nat. Hist. N.Y. 2:179.1827. "On the Platte, and about the sources of the Canadian."

Upon reaching the forks of the Platte in Nebraska, James was in range of this species for most of the rest of the trip. Just where he made his collection is not certain. In the *Account,* however, plants collected on June 23–26 are listed together in one footnote.[432] Among those are "several species of Astragalus," which could have been collected along the South Platte from Lincoln County, Nebraska, to the Colorado line.

Astragalus lotiflorus Hook., Fl. Bor. Am. 1:152.1831. (Lotus Milkvetch).

#102 *Orobus dispar* Nutt., in Torr., Ann. Lyc. Nat. Hist. N.Y. 2:180.1827. "With the preceding ['Forks of the Platte.']."

Orobus dispar, with no description, was mentioned by James on June 24.[433] Under the same name it is also mentioned in the *Account.*[434] Plants collected on June 23–26 are listed together there in one footnote.

Orobus dispar is thought to be a synonym of *Astragalus tenellus,* a species out of range of the expedition's location at that time. Torrey, however, placed *A. tenellus* in synonymy under the later *A. gracilis* Nutt.[435] Hence, Torrey's #102 *O. dispar* would not be *A. tenellus.* What it may be is another matter. Because of the appearance of the plant (including flower size and color) and its distribution, we think it likely that James's plant was *A. lotiflorus.*

The plant was collected on the South Platte River as the party traveled between Sutherland, Lincoln County, and Ogallala, Keith County, Nebraska.

Astragalus mollissimus Torr. (Woolly Locoweed).

#93 *Astragalus mollissimus* Torr., Ann. Lyc. Nat. Hist. N.Y. 2:178–79.1827. "On the Platte."

James gave a detailed description in his diary of a plant that he called *Astragalus hypoglottis?*[436] The description fits *Astragalus mollissimus* very well.

---

[432]JAMES [1], I, 468n.; JAMES [2] in THWAITES [1], XV, 241n.
[433]JAMES [3], June 24 (erroneously dated June 23).
[434]JAMES [1], I, 468n.; JAMES [2] in THWAITES [1], XV, 241n.
[435]TORREY [2], 179.
[436]JAMES [3], June 25 (erroneously dated June 24).

Phaca villosa (Michx.) Nutt., Gen. No. Am. Pl. 2:97.1818. Only as to the plant Nuttall mentioned, from the "high hills of the Missouri." Other authors[437] have also placed *Phaca villosa,* in the sense that James used it,[438] under *A. mollissimus.*

The type (NY) of this species was collected on June 25 near the South Platte River, some two miles upstream from Ogallala, Keith County, Nebraska.

Astragalus plattensis Nutt. ex T. & G., Fl. No. Am. 1:332.1838. (Platte River Milkvetch).

#96 *Astragalus caryocarpus* in Torr., Ann. Lyc. Nat. Hist. N.Y. 2:179.1827. "On the Platte, and about the sources of the Canadian."

Torrey and Gray later identified this plant as *A. plattensis* and gave the location for both the Nuttall and James specimens as "[p]lains of the Platte."[439] The type is Nuttallian.

James referred to this plant in his diary for June 8.[440] His collection was made during their travel from the previous night's campsite on Rawhide Creek, just northwest of Fremont, Dodge County, to their June 8 camp on Shell Creek, northwest of Schuyler, Colfax County, Nebraska.

Astragalus racemosus Pursh, Fl. Am. Sept. 740. 1814. (Creamy Locoweed).

#94 *Astragalus racemosus* Pursh, in Torr., Ann. Lyc. Nat. Hist. N.Y. 2:179.1827. "On the Platte." Here the fruits are described as "stipitate triangular."

James, in his diary, called this plant *Astragalus galegoides,* a synonym of *A. racemosus,* and described the flowers as "yellowish white and large."[441]

The above descriptions of both the flowers and the fruits fit *A. racemosus* well.

In the *Account* on the same day, only "species of astragalus" are listed.[442]

On July 30 the party traveled across the Don Carlos Hills, from Sierra Grande to Ute Creek, western Union County, New Mexico.

---

[437]WATSON [1], 197; BRITTON AND BROWN, II, 379; BARNEBY [1], 736.
[438]JAMES [4], 186.
[439]TORREY AND GRAY [1], I, 332.
[440]JAMES [3], June 8.
[441]JAMES [3], July 30.
[442]JAMES [1], II, 86; JAMES [2] in THWAITES [1], XVI, 85.

Caesalpinia jamesii (T. & G.) Fisher, Bot. Gaz. 18:123.1893. (James Rushpea).

Hoffmanseggia jamesii T. & G., Fl. No. Am. 1:393.1840. "Sources of the Canadian, *Dr. James!*"

#112 *Pomaria glandulosa* Cav., in Torr., Ann. Lyc. Nat. Hist. N.Y. 2:193–94.1827. "On the Canadian."

James described this plant in his diary for the evening of July 26.[443] The type (NY) and at least a fragment of it (GH)[444] were collected in Bachicha Canyon, apparently near their campsite some eight miles north-northeast of the junction of State Highway 389 and U.S. Highway 160 in Las Animas County, Colorado.

Cassia chamaecrista L., Sp. Pl. 379. 1753. (Showy Partridge Pea).

#114 *Cassia Chamaecrista* L., in Torr., Ann. Lyc. Nat. Hist. N.Y. 2:194.1827. "On the Canadian."

James described this legume in his diary for August 5, calling it "Cassia nictitans?"[445] Reference is made to "a cassia" in the *Account*.[446] James's description would not rule out *C. nictitans,* but its distribution would.

On the morning of August 5 the party was but a few miles northeast of Logan, Quay County, New Mexico. By evening they had followed the Canadian River a few miles into Oldham County, Texas.

The southwestern variant of *C. chamaecrista* is sometimes recognized as *Cassia fasciculata* var. *rostrata* (Woot. & Standl.) B. L. Turner. The type locality for this variety is Logan, Quay County, New Mexico.

Cassia marilandica L., Sp. Pl. 378. 1753. (Wild Senna).

#113 *Cassia occidentalis* L., in Torr., Ann. Lyc. Nat. Hist. N.Y. 2:194.1827. "Sources of the Canadian."

If, as Torrey suggested, the plant were collected on the Canadian River, then it is more likely to be *C. marilandica* than any other broad-leaved species. *Cassia marilandica* occurs along the Canadian River in the eastern two-thirds of Oklahoma and continues into Arkansas.

If James collected the plant in Arkansas, another broad-leaved species, *C. obtusifolia* (*C. tora*), is a possibility.

No reference to this plant was found in James's diary.

---

[443]JAMES [3], July 26.
[444]FISHER, 150; ISELY [1], 194.
[445]JAMES [3], August 5.
[446]JAMES [1], II, 95; JAMES [2] in THWAITES [1], XVI, 96. In both editions, events that occurred on August 4, 5, and 6 are listed under the date of August 4.

Cassia nictitans L., Sp. Pl. 380. 1753. (Sensitive Partridge Pea).
In the *Account,* on September 3, James noted *Cassia nictitans* among the plants of the region.[447]
On that day the party traveled only a few miles and camped on the Canadian, about five miles northwest of Allen near the junction of Seminole, Hughes, and Pontotoc counties, Oklahoma.

Cercis canadensis L., Sp. Pl. 374. 1753. (Redbud).
#115 *Cercis canadensis* L., in Torr., Ann. Lyc. Nat. Hist. N.Y. 2:194.1827. "On the Canadian."
James stated in his diary for August 24 that *Cercis* is beginning to appear.[448] The plant is mentioned on that same day in the *Account.*[449]
On August 24 the party continued down the Canadian River, primarily through southwestern Blaine County, Oklahoma, to a point near Bridgeport. As usual, James was on the alert. He was near the westernmost known location for redbud along the Canadian.

Clitoria mariana L., Sp. Pl. 753. 1753. (Butterfly Pea).
#78 *Clitoria virginica* L., in Torr., Ann. Lyc. Nat. Hist. N.Y. 2:176.1827. "On the Arkansa, near the junction of the Canadian."
James listed *Clitoria virginica* in his diary for September 11.[450] At that time the party was traveling down the Arkansas, from a few miles below the mouth of the Canadian to just west of Sallisaw, Sequoyah County, near the middle of Oklahoma's eastern border. One day later in the *Account* James listed this plant as "vexillaria virginica."[451]
Inasmuch as *Centrosema virginianum* (L.) Benth. (which was based on *Clitoria virginiana* L.) is known in Oklahoma only on the southern border along the Red River from Marshall County eastward, *Clitoria mariana,* which does occur in Sequoyah County, seems much more likely to have been collected by James.

Dalea aurea Nutt. ex Pursh, Fl. Am. Sept. 740. 1814. (Silktop Dalea).
#84 *Dalea aurea* Nutt., in Torr., Ann. Lyc. Nat. Hist. N.Y. 2:177. 1827.
Dalea formosa is said by Torrey to have been collected with this

---

[447]JAMES [1], II, 156; JAMES [2] in THWAITES [1], XVI, 169.
[448]JAMES [3], August 24.
[449]JAMES [1], II, 141; JAMES [2] in THWAITES [1], XVI, 151.
[450]JAMES [3], September 11.
[451]JAMES [1], II, 171; JAMES [2] in THWAITES [1], XVI, 185.

species "[o]n the Platte."[452] *Dalea formosa,* however, was not collected on the Platte, so it is not at all certain where James collected *Dalea aurea.* To judge by its known range, the collection could have been made in any of the five states through which James traveled from June through August.

Dalea candida Michx. ex Willd., Sp. Pl. 3:1337.1802. (White Prairie Clover).
#80 *Petalostemum candidum* Michx., in Torr., Ann. Lyc. Nat. Hist. N.Y. 2:177.1827. "About the Forks of the Platte."
James mentioned this plant as *P. candidum* in his diary for June 26.[453] On that day the party traveled from near Ogallala, Keith County, Nebraska, to near Julesburg, Sedgwick County, Colorado. It is also mentioned under the same name in the *Account.*[454] Here plants collected on June 23–26 are listed together in one footnote.

Dalea cylindriceps Barneby, Mem. N.Y. Bot. Gard. 27:227.1977. (Massive Spike Prairie Clover).
#79 *Petalostemum macrostachyum* Torr., Ann. Lyc. Nat. Hist. N.Y. 2:176–77.1827. "About the Forks of the Platte." [Not *Dalea macrostachya* Moric., 1833].
James did not list this plant in his diary. If Torrey's location is correct, the type (NY) of *P. macrostachyum* would have been collected in Lincoln County, Nebraska, which is in known range of the species.

Dalea enneandra Nutt., in Fraser's Catalog, 1813. (Nine-Anther Prairie Clover).
#85 *Dalea laxiflora* Pursh, in Torr., Ann. Lyc. Nat. Hist. N.Y. 2:177.1827.
Torrey stated that *Dalea formosa* was collected with this species "[o]n the Platte."[455] *Dalea formosa,* however, was not collected on the Platte, so it is not at all certain where James collected *Dalea enneandra.* To judge by its known range, the collection could have been made in any of the five states through which James traveled from June through August.

[452]TORREY [2], 178.
[453]JAMES [3], June 26 (erroneously dated June 25).
[454]JAMES [1], I, 468n.; JAMES [2] in THWAITES [1], XV, 241n.
[455]TORREY [2], 178.

Dalea formosa Torr. (Feather Plume).
#86 *Dalea formosa* Torr., Ann. Lyc. Nat. Hist. N.Y. 2:177–78.1827.
"On the Platte."
This species is not known from anywhere on the Platte. "A beautiful Dalea," however, is mentioned in the *Account* on July 26.[456] Barneby, too, noted the reference in the Philadelphia edition of the *Account*.[457]
On July 26 the party traveled up Chacuaco Canyon and a few miles up Bachicha Canyon, Las Animas County, Colorado. There, we think, is where the type (NY) of *Dalea formosa* was collected.

Dalea jamesii (Torr.) T. & G., Fl. No. Am. 1:308.1838. (James Dalea).
#75 *Psoralea Jamesii* Torr., Ann. Lyc. Nat. Hist. N.Y. 2:175.1827. "Sandy plains of the Canadian." The type, according to Barneby, is at NY.[458]
Jamesia obovata Raf., Atl. Jour. 1:145.1832. This new genus and new species were based on Torrey's *Psoralea jamesii*.
Based on the known distribution of *D. jamesii*, the most likely place for James to have collected it on the Canadian is in Oldham County, Texas, August 6–8. Incidentally, we found the plant in abundance near the mouth of Turkey Creek, Pueblo County, Colorado. That location is very near James's July 16 campsite on the Arkansas.

Dalea lanata Sprengel, Syst. 3:327.1826. (Woolly Dalea).
#83 *Dalea, n.sp.*, Torr., Ann. Lyc. Nat. Hist. N.Y. 2:177.1827. "On the Platte. A beautiful species with scarlet flowers."
Dalea lanuginosa Nutt. ex T. & G., Fl. No. Am. 1:307.1838. Based on a Nuttall specimen from near Fort Smith, Arkansas. Cited also is "[o]n the Platte, *Dr. James!*" The name is preempted by *Dalea lanata* Spreng., 1826, doubtless based on the Nuttall plant (*cf.* Barneby).[459]
No mention of this plant is made in the diary; in the *Account* on August 20, however, James noted "a humble dalea," which we take to be *D. lanata*.[460]

---

[456]JAMES [6], II, 73; JAMES [7], II, 261.
[457]BARNEBY [2], 500.
[458]BARNEBY [2], 579.
[459]BARNEBY [2], 282.
[460]JAMES [1], II, 135; JAMES [2] in THWAITES [1], XVI, 144.

At the time, James was in western Dewey County, Oklahoma. *Dalea lanata* is not known from anywhere on the Platte.

Dalea purpurea Vent., Descr. Pl. Cels, pl. 40. 1800. (Purple Prairie Clover).

#82 *Petalostemum violaceum* Michx., in Torr., Ann. Lyc. Nat. Hist. N.Y. 2:177.1827. "About the Forks of the Platte."

James mentioned *P. violaceum* in his diary for June 26.[461] On that day the party traveled from near Ogallala, Keith County, Nebraska, to near Julesburg, Sedgwick County, Colorado.

It is also mentioned in the *Account* under the same name.[462] Plants collected on June 23–26 are listed together there in one footnote.

Dalea villosa (Nutt.) Sprengel, Syst. 3:326.1826. (Silky Prairie Clover).

#81 *Petalostemum villosum* Nutt., in Torr., Ann. Lyc. Nat. Hist. N.Y. 2:177.1827. "About the Forks of the Platte."

James does not list this plant in his diary. If Torrey's location is correct, the plant was collected in Lincoln County, Nebraska, which is in the known range of the species.

Desmanthus cooleyi (Eaton) Trel., Ark. Geol. Survey Rpt. 1888, 4:178.1891. (Cooley Desmanthus).

#106 *Acacia n.sp. Nutt. mss.*, in Torr., Ann. Lyc. Nat. Hist. N.Y. 2:191.1827. "Sources of the Canadian."

Desmanthus jamesii T. & G., Fl. No. Am. 1:402.1840. Here *Acacia cooleyi* Eaton, Man. ed. 5, 89, 1829 is cited as a synonym. Both names are based on Torrey's #106.

James described this plant in his diary for August 1.[463] There he noted the "conspicuous red gland at the insertion of the two lower leaflets. . . . Leaves sensitive."

In the *Account* the plant is described as "a yellow flowering sensitive plant. . . . Its leaves are twice pinnated, and manifestly irritable."[464] The yellow color of the flower is somewhat puzzling, and we wonder if the description here was based on *Acacia hirta*, which James evidently collected later in the trip, or which Nuttall collected in Arkansas Territory (see *A. hirta*). *Acacia hirta* does not occur so far west as New Mexico.

---

[461]JAMES [3], June 26 (erroneously dated June 25).
[462]JAMES [1], I, 468n.; JAMES [2] in THWAITES [1], XV, 241n.
[463]JAMES [3], August 1.
[464]JAMES [6], II, 89; JAMES [7], II, 276.

James collected the type (NY) on August 1 near their campsite at the confluence of Garcia Creek and Ute Creek, about six miles east and a little north of Yates, Harding County, New Mexico.

Desmanthus illinoensis (Michx.) MacM. ex Robins. and Fern., Man. 503. 1908. (Illinois Bundleflower).
#107 *Darlingtonia intermedia* Torr., Ann. Lyc. Nat. Hist. N.Y. 2:191.1827. "On the Canadian?"
Placing Torrey's name in synonymy is in accordance with Isely.[465]
The type of *Darlingtonia intermedia* could have been collected by James in any of the five states through which he traveled, Nebraska through Oklahoma.

Desmodium illinoense Gray, Proc. Am. Acad. Sci. 8:289.1870. (Illinois Tickclover).
#98 *Hedysarum canadense* L., in Torr., Ann. Lyc. Nat. Hist. N.Y. 2:179.1827. "On the Canadian, near its junction with the Arkansa."
James referred to "Hedysarum canadense?" in his diary for August 14.[466] On that day the party traveled down the Canadian River through Roberts County in the northeastern Texas panhandle. That area is out of range for *Hedysarum canadense* (*Desmodium canadense*). Because of the similarities of the leaves and fruits of *D. canadense* and *D. illinoense*, we believe that James's specimen belongs with the latter species, which does occur in that part of the Texas panhandle.
We find no other record of either *D. canadense* or *D. illinoense* from so far east in Oklahoma as the station reported by Torrey.

Desmodium sessilifolium (Torr.) T. & G., Fl. No. Am. 1:363.1840. (Sessileleaf Tickclover).
In his diary entry for August 22, written as James traveled through Dewey County in northwestern Oklahoma, he briefly described a "Hedysarum——?" that was about three feet high with a two-jointed fruit.[467]
Hedysarum boreale also occurs in that area, but three feet is too tall for this taxon.

Gleditsia triacanthos L., Sp. Pl. 1056. 1753. (Honey Locust).

[465]ISELY [2], 500.
[466]JAMES [3], August 14.
[467]JAMES [3], August 22.

In his diary for August 28, James noted the occurrence of the honey locust.[468] Once again he observed a species at its westernmost range along the Canadian River.

At that time the party was three or four miles northeast of Newcastle, near the McClain/Cleveland county line, Oklahoma.

On the preceding day (August 27) and the day following (August 29), honey locust is noted in the *Account*.[469]

Glycyrrhiza lepidota Pursh, Fl. Am. Sept. 480. 1814. (Wild Licorice).

#87 *Glycyrrhiza lepidota* Nutt., in Torr., Ann. Lyc. Nat. Hist. N.Y. 2:178.1827. "On the Platte, 200 miles above its confluence with the Missouri."

James collected this plant near the campsite of June 18, which was a few miles west-southwest of Overton, Dawson County, Nebraska.[470]

Gymnocladus dioica (L.) Koch, Dendrol. 1:15.1869. (Kentucky Coffee Tree).

#111 *Gymnocladus canadensis* Lam., in Torr., Ann. Lyc. Nat. Hist. N.Y. 2:193.1827. "On the Canadian."

On August 18 James encountered the Kentucky coffee tree at its westernmost range at their camp on the Canadian River near the mouth of West Creek, where the Packsaddle Bridge crosses the river in Ellis County, Oklahoma. James mentioned the tree, as "guilan-dina," in the *Account*.[471] Later, on August 24, in his diary and in the *Account*, James again noted its occurrence.[472] On that day the party traveled downstream, primarily through southwestern Blaine County, Oklahoma, to a point near Bridgeport.

Indigofera miniata Ort. var. **leptosepala** (Nutt.) Turner, Field & Lab. 24:104.1956. (Wild Indigo).

#77 *Indigofera, n.sp.*, Torr., Ann. Lyc. Nat. Hist. N.Y. 2:176.1827. "[A]llied to I. miniata. Flowers scarlet. This species was discovered in 1819, by Mr. Nuttall, on the Red River."

Torrey gave no location for James's plant, but the Torrey reference

[468]JAMES [3], August 28.
[469]JAMES [1], II, 145, 149; JAMES [2] in THWAITES [1], XVI, 156, 160.
[470]JAMES [1], I, 460; JAMES [2] in THWAITES [1], XV, 231; JAMES [3], June 18.
[471]JAMES [1], II, 131; JAMES [2] in THWAITES [1], XVI, 139.
[472]JAMES [1], II, 141; JAMES [2] in THWAITES [1], XVI, 151; JAMES [3], August 24.

(with incorrect page number) and "Plains of Arkansas, *Nuttall! Dr. James! Dr. Leavenworth!*" appear in Torrey and Gray under *I. leptosepala* Nutt. ex T. & G.[473]

In James's diary for August 16 appears the following: "An elegant procumbent plant belonging to Diadelphia Decandria with flowers of the size of Vicia pusilla colored pale vermillion."[474] On that date they were traveling down the Canadian River in Hemphill County, Texas.

Lathyrus eucosmus Butters & St. John, Rhodora 19:160.1917. (Peavine).

#100 *Lathyrus myrtifolius* Muhl., in Torr., Ann. Lyc. Nat. Hist. N.Y. 2:180.1827. No locality given.

James's specimen at (NY), cited as *L. eucosmus* by Hitchcock,[475] was collected on July 30 as the party traveled southwest across the Don Carlos Hills, from Sierra Grande to Ute Creek, western Union County, New Mexico.

James noted that the violet-purple flowers of this plant were large and "delightfully scented."[476]

Butters and St. John cited *A. A. & E. Gertrude Heller* no. *3658* (GH), an 1897 New Mexican collection, as the type.[477] The earlier James collection is here cited as from "Colorado."

Lathyrus polymorphus Nutt., Gen. No. Am. Pl. 2:96.1818. (Hoary Vetchling).

#99 *Lathyrus polymorphus* Nutt., in Torr., Ann. Lyc. Nat. Hist. N.Y. 2:180.1827. "On the Missouri and Platte, June."

James's collection at (NY) was verified by Hitchcock as being the typical form of this species and cited as being collected "'on the Missouri and the River Platte.'"[478]

James collected this plant on June 8 during the expedition's travel from the previous night's campsite on Rawhide Creek, just northwest of Fremont, Dodge County, to their June 8 camp on Shell Creek, northwest of Schuyler, Colfax County, Nebraska.[479]

On June 9, James remarked in his diary that in the open country he

[473]TORREY AND GRAY [1], I, 298–99.
[474]JAMES [3], August 16.
[475]HITCHCOCK [1], 72.
[476]JAMES [3], July 30.
[477]BUTTERS AND ST. JOHN, 161.
[478]HITCHCOCK [1], 72.
[479]JAMES [3], June 8.

met with a "most superb Lathyrus,"[480] which in the *Account* that same day he called *L. polymorphus*.[481] Torrey and Gray cited James specimens under both *L. ornatus* Nutt. and *L. polymorphus* Nutt.[482] *L. ornatus* is now considered to be a synonym of the latter. It seems very likely that the June 9 collection was also that species.

On June 9 the party traveled from Shell Creek to the Loup River, Platte County, Nebraska.

Lotus purshianus (Benth.) Clements & Clements, Rocky Mt. Fls. 183. 1914. (Deer Vetch).

#69 *Trigonella? americana* Nutt., in Torr., Ann. Lyc. Nat. Hist. N.Y. 2:174.1827. "On the Platte."

Trigonella americana Nutt., in James, Am. Phil. Soc. 2:186.1825. "On the Platte."

James's collection could very likely have been made in June on the Platte in the eastern two-thirds of Nebraska. The species is unknown along the Platte in Colorado.

James did not enter the range of this species again until August, when he was in Oklahoma.

Lupinus argenteus Pursh, Fl. Am. Sept. 468. 1814. (Silvery Lupine).

#105 *Lupinus decumbens* Torr., Ann. Lyc. Nat. Hist. N.Y. 2:191.1827. "On the southern branches of the Arkansa."

Torrey and Gray accepted the species and gave the same locality as Torrey did.[483]

In his diary for July 3, James described a "suffruticose" lupine that we believe became the type (NY) of *L. decumbens*.[484] On that day the party traveled west from Kuner, Weld County, and finally south up the South Platte River to about three miles south of Platteville, Weld County, Colorado.

It is not until July 4 that this "suffruticose species" is mentioned in the *Account*.[485] It was observed near their camp, which was seventeen miles farther up the South Platte River near Brighton, Adams County, Colorado.

[480]JAMES [3], June 9.
[481]JAMES [1], I, 433; JAMES [2] in THWAITES [1], XV, 200.
[482]TORREY AND GRAY [1], I, 277.
[483]TORREY AND GRAY [1], I, 381.
[484]JAMES [3], July 3.
[485]JAMES [1], I, 497; JAMES [2] in THWAITES [1], XV, 276.

Lupinus pusillus Pursh, Fl. Am. Sept. 468. 1814. (Small Lupine).
#104 *Lupinus pusillus* Pursh, in Torr., Ann. Lyc. Nat. Hist. N.Y.
2:191.1827. No locality given.

James mentioned this plant in the diary on June 23.[486] It was
collected on the south side of the South Platte River, a few miles
above its junction with the North Platte, Lincoln County, Nebraska.

Neptunia lutea (Leavenw.) Benth., Journ. Bot. 4:356.1842. (Yellow Puff).

Turner stated: "a specimen possibly from Oklahoma which bears a
note signed by Leavenworth, 'of James collection found first by
myself in 1820 on the prairies of Alabama.'"[487] Based on this
comment, *Neptunia lutea* is included here as a James collection.

James most likely would have made his collection along the Canadian River in August or September, in the eastern half of Oklahoma.

Oxytropis lambertii Pursh, Fl. Am. Sept. 740. 1814. (Locoweed).
#91 *Oxytropis Lamberti* Pursh, in Torr., Ann. Lyc. Nat. Hist. N.Y.
2:178.1827. "On the Missouri and Platte."

In his diary, James noted this species "on the steep woodless hills
along the Missouri bottoms."[488] His collection was made on May 25
in Iowa below the mouth of the Platte River.

Torrey and Gray cited a James specimen from the "[w]oodless hills
of the Missouri, from the Platte to the mountains."[489]

Prosopis glandulosa Torr. (Honey Mesquite).
#110 *Prosopis glandulosa* Torr., Ann. Lyc. Nat. Hist. N.Y. 2:192–
93, pl.2. 1827. "On the Canadian?"

The first mention of this plant is on August 2, after the party left the
Garcia Creek camp and continued down Ute Creek, mostly through
Harding County, and about four miles in southwest Union County,
New Mexico. In his diary, James spoke of "a shrub with spiny trunk
and branches and pinnated leaves resembling honey locust."[490]
Remarks on the plant were made in the *Account* on this date.[491]

Again on August 5, James commented on the plant and added that

---

[486]JAMES [3], June 23 (erroneously dated June 22).
[487]TURNER, 87.
[488]JAMES [3], May 25.
[489]TORREY AND GRAY [1], I, 339.
[490]JAMES [3], August 1 (under which date also appears the events of August 2).
[491]JAMES [1], II, 92; JAMES [2] in THWAITES [1], XVI, 92.

the legume "contains a considerable quantity of saccharine matter" that was pleasant to the taste.[492] Almost all of that day the party was along the Canadian River in Quay County, New Mexico.

Torrey and Gray cited a James specimen, under the name *Algarobia glandulosa* (Torr.) T. & G., from "[o]n the Canadian River" and added, "The pods were used for food by Major Long's party."[493]

The type (NY) was most likely collected on August 2. (Phototype, see fig. 24.)

Psoralea argophylla Pursh, Fl. Am. Sept. 475. 1814. (Silver Leaf Scurf Pea).

#73 *Psoralea canescens* Michx., in Torr., Ann. Lyc. Nat. Hist. N.Y. 2:175.1827. "With the preceding ['On the Missouri and Arkansa.']."

P. canescens is far out of range. The species along James's route that most closely resembles *P. canescens,* with its obovate to oval leaflets, is the above species.

Reference is made to this plant (as *P. incana,* a *nomen nudum*) in both the *Catalogue*[494] and the *Account.*[495] No listing for the species was found in the diary.

The date of collection given in the *Account* is June 14. On that day the party traveled south from the Loup River to the Platte, through Merrick County, Nebraska.

Psoralea cuspidata Pursh, Fl. Am. Sept. 741. 1814. (Tall-Bread Scurf Pea).

#72 *Psoralea cuspidata* Pursh, in Torr., Ann. Lyc. Nat. Hist. N.Y. 2:175.1827. "With the preceding ['On the Missouri and Arkansa.']."

James referred to this plant as *P. cuspidata.*[496] His collection was made on June 14 as the party traveled south from the Loup River to the Platte, through Merrick County, Nebraska.

Psoralea esculenta Pursh, Fl. Am. Sept. 475. 1814. (Breadroot).

#71 *Psoralea esculenta* Pursh, in Torr., Ann. Lyc. Nat. Hist. N.Y. 2:175.1827. "(Pomme blanche) On the Missouri and Arkansa. Used as food by the Pawnees and Canadian traders."

---

[492]JAMES [3], August 5.
[493]TORREY AND GRAY [1], I, 399.
[494]JAMES [4], 186.
[495]JAMES [1], I, 453n.; JAMES [2] in THWAITES [1], XV, 223n.
[496]JAMES [1], I, 453n.; JAMES [2] in THWAITES [1], XV, 223n.; JAMES [3], June 14 (included as part of the June 13 entry).

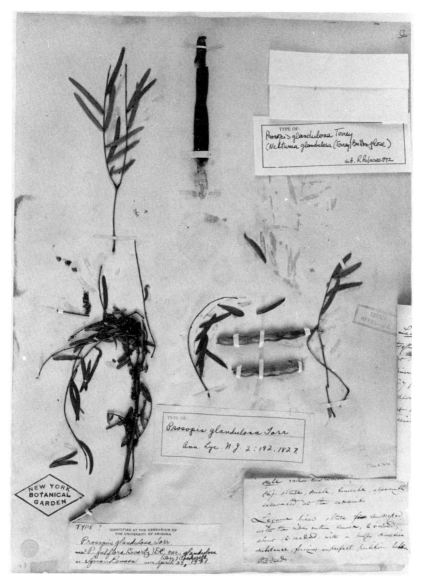

Fig. 24. Phototype of *Prosopis glandulosa* Torr. Courtesy New York Botanical Garden.

In his diary for June 13, James remarked, "The Pome blanche considerably used among the Indians is the root of a canescent, digitate leaved plant which is probably a Lupinus."[497]

In the *Account,* however, the name of the pomme blanche is corrected to *Psoralea esculenta.*[498] "It is eaten either boiled or roasted, and somewhat resembles the sweet potatoe."

On June 13 they were at the Pawnee Loup village, on the Loup River, Nance County, Nebraska.

James mentioned *Psoralea esculenta* again in the *Account* on June 14 as the party traveled south from the Loup River to the Platte through Merrick County, Nebraska.[499]

Psoralea lanceolata Pursh, Fl. Am. Sept. 475. 1814. (Lemon Scurf Pea).

#70 *Psoralea arenaria* Nutt., in Torr., Ann. Lyc. Nat. Hist. N.Y. 2:175.1827. "Sandy plains of the Arkansa and Platte."

James described a "trifoliate" plant that he referred to as a "Doubtful" *Phaca.*[500] His description could well be of *Psoralea lanceolata.* We find it curious, however, that the abundant dark glands, characteristic of the species, were not mentioned.

In addition James listed *Psoralea tenuiflora,* a species that also fits his description of the "Doubtful" *Phaca.*[501]

Based on distribution, James's "Doubtful" *Phaca,* collected on June 10 along the Loup River between Monroe, Platte County, and Merchiston, Nance County, Nebraska, could be either.

Psoralea tenuiflora Pursh, Fl. Am. Sept. 475. 1814. (Scurfy Pea).

James collected this plant on June 15 along the Platte River, either in Hall County or adjacent eastern Buffalo County, Nebraska.[502]

This may also be the "Doubtful" *Phaca* that James collected on June 10.

Robinia pseudoacacia L., Sp. Pl. 722. 1753. (Black Locust).

#90 *Robinia Pseudacacia* L., in Torr., Ann. Lyc. Nat. Hist. N.Y. 2:178.1827. "On the Canadian."

---

[497]JAMES [3], June 13.
[498]JAMES [1], I, 448; JAMES [2] in THWAITES [1], XV, 217.
[499]JAMES [1], I, 453n.; JAMES [2] in THWAITES [1], XV, 223n.
[500]JAMES [3], June 10.
[501]JAMES [4], 186.
[502]JAMES [3], June 15 (erroneously dated June 14).

It is possible that James collected the black locust along the Canadian or Arkansas rivers in extreme eastern Oklahoma; James, however, mentioned this tree in his diary only on March 30 as he was coming down the Ohio River en route to Engineer Cantonment.[503]

James noted this tree in the *Account* on August 27, while the party was camped at the junction of Buggy Creek and the Canadian River, about three and a half miles northeast of Minco, Grady County, Oklahoma.[504] The reference cannot be readily explained, as the location is too far west of the natural range for this tree in Oklahoma.

Schrankia nuttallii (DC. ex Britt. & Rose) Standley, Field Mus. Publ. Bot. 8:13.1930. (Sensitive Briar).

#109 *Schrankia uncinata* Willd., in Torr., Ann. Lyc. Nat. Hist. N.Y. 2:192.1827. "Plains of the Platte."

We are assuming that this plant is the "sensitive briar" mentioned in the diary.[505] James stated that it was not yet in flower.

The plant was collected on June 13 on the south side of the Loup River near the Nance/Merrick county line, about three miles north and a little east of Palmer, Nebraska.

Sophora nuttalliana Turner, Field & Lab. 24:15.1956. (White Loco).

#65 *Sophora? sericea* Nutt. [Not Andrews], in Torr., Ann. Lyc. Nat. Hist. N.Y. 2:174.1827. "On the Platte." Here Torrey described the "torrulous" fruit of James's immature specimens.

Torrey and Gray cited the Ann. Lyc. reference under *Sophora sericea* Nutt.[506]

No reference to this plant was found in the diary or the *Account,* but, based on the immature state of James's plants, his collection was most likely made in western Nebraska or along the South Platte River in Colorado.

Strophostyles helvola (L.) Britton, Britton & Brown, Ill. Fl. 2:338.1897. (Wild Bean).

#103 *Phaseolus perennis* Walt., in Torr., Ann. Lyc. Nat. Hist. N.Y. 2:180.1827. "On the Missouri."

---

[503]JAMES [3], March 30.
[504]JAMES [1], II, 145; JAMES [2] in THWAITES [1], XVI, 155.
[505]JAMES [3], June 13.
[506]TORREY AND GRAY [1], I, 390.

James mentioned this plant, as *Phaseolus perennis,* in his diary for September 3.[507] As that species is out of range for their location, it is likely that James had the very similar *S. helvola.*

The party traveled only a few miles and camped on the Canadian about five miles northwest of Allen near the junction of Seminole, Hughes, and Pontotoc counties, Oklahoma.

Thermopsis rhombifolia (Nutt. ex Pursh) Richards., in Frankl., First Jour. App. 737. 1823. (Yellow Pea).
#66 *Thermopsis rhombifolia* Nutt., in Torr., Ann. Lyc. Nat. Hist. N.Y. 2:174.1827. "On the Platte."
Based on the known range of this plant, the collection was probably made along the South Platte River in June in western Nebraska or northern Colorado.

Torrey and Gray cited a James specimen of *Thermopsis rhombifolia,* collected from the "[p]lains of the Platte."[508] We find no reference to this plant in James's diary.

Trifolium dasyphyllum T. & G., Fl. No. Am. 1:315.1838. (Whiproot Clover). "Summit of the Rocky Mountains, *Dr. James!*" Type: NY.
This plant would have been collected July 14 on Pikes Peak, El Paso County, Colorado.

Trifolium nanum Torr. (Dwarf Clover).
#8 *Trifolium nanum* Torr., Ann. Lyc. Nat. Hist. N.Y. 1:35, pl.3, fig.4. 1824. "With the preceding ['On James' Peak . . . near the region of perpetual snow.']." Type: NY.
This would have been collected July 14 on Pikes Peak, El Paso County, Colorado.

Vicia americana Muhl. ex Willd., Sp. Pl. 3:1096.1802. (American Vetch).
James spoke of species of *Vicia.*[509] *V. americana,* however, is the only native species within range.

The James collection was made on June 9 "in the open country" that they encountered between Shell Creek and the Loup River, Platte County, Nebraska.

---

[507]JAMES [3], September 3.
[508]TORREY AND GRAY [1], I, 388.
[509]JAMES [1], I, 433; JAMES [2] in THWAITES [1], XV, 200; JAMES [3], June 9.

Lemnaceae

Lemna minor L., Sp. Pl. 970. 1753. (Duckweed).
James noted this plant on July 1 in stagnant pools near the Platte.[510]
This collection was made a few miles east of Masters, Weld County,
Colorado.

Lentibulariaceae

Utricularia vulgaris L., Sp. Pl. 18. 1753. (Common Bladderwort).
#355 *Utricularia vulgaris* L., in Torr., Ann. Lyc. Nat. Hist. N.Y.
2:235.1827. "Ponds near the Platte."
On June 16, James referred to this plant in his diary as *U. vulgaris*
but gave no habitat.[511]
Reference is made in the *Account* to *U. longirostris* of Leconte, from
"some small ponds near the Platte."[512] The date there is also June 16,
at which time the party traveled along the Platte south of Gibbon to
south of Odessa, Buffalo County, Nebraska.

Liliaçeae

Allium perdulce S.V. Fraser, Trans. Kans. Acad. Sci. 42:124.1940.
(Wild Onion).
We chose this name only because James described the onion he
collected on June 7 as having purple flowers.[513] There are two other
species with pink to red flowers that occur in the area, namely *A.
drummondii* and *A. canadense* var. *lavendulare*.
On June 7 they were near the Elkhorn River, a few miles southeast
of Arlington, Washington or Dodge County, Nebraska.

Calochortus gunnisoni Wats., Bot. King's Exped. 348. 1871.
(Sego Lily).
#437 *Calochortus elegans* Pursh, in Torr., Ann. Lyc. Nat. Hist. N.Y.
2:250.1827. "Base of the Rocky Mountains."
James referred to this plant as *C. elegans,* a species not known so
far east as Colorado.[514] His collection was made on July 6 in Douglas

---

[510]JAMES [1], I, 493; JAMES [2] in THWAITES [1], XV, 272; JAMES [3], July 1.
[511]JAMES [3], June 16 (erroneously dated June 15).
[512]JAMES [1], I, 455; JAMES [2] in THWAITES [1], XV, 226.
[513]JAMES [3], June 7.
[514]JAMES [1], II, 3; JAMES [2] in THWAITES [1], XV, 289; JAMES [3], July 6.

County, Colorado, near the mouth of the canyon of the South Platte across the river from Waterton, Jefferson County.

Camassia scilloides (Raf.) Cory, Rhodora 38:405.1936. (Eastern Camass).

#440 *Scilla esculenta* in Torr., Ann. Lyc. Nat. Hist. N.Y. 2:251. 1827. "On the Arkansa, &c."

The only time that James was in range of this plant and at flowering time was while he was in Missouri. An additional clue, albeit a weak one, is an entry in his diary dated April 22.[515] It consists simply of "Hex. Mon." That was two days before James, Captain Bell, and Major Long arrived at St. Louis, as they traveled up the Mississippi from its junction with the Ohio.

Lloydia serotina (L.) Sweet, Hort. Brit. ed.2, 527. 1830. (Alp Lily).

#443 *Ornithogalum bracteatum* Torr., Ann. Lyc. Nat. Hist. N.Y. 2:251.1827. "On the Rocky Mountains."

Fenelonia bracteata (Torr.) Raf., Atl. Jour. 1:145.1832.

James's collection is the type of the species, and the species is the type of Rafinesque's genus *Fenelonia* (*cf.* Watson).[516]

James could have collected this alpine plant only on Pikes Peak, El Paso County, Colorado, July 14 or 15.

Polygonatum biflorum (Walt.) Ell., Bot. S.C. & Ga. 1:393.1817. (Solomon's Seal).

James made his collection, which he referred to in his diary as *P. multiflorum,* on June 2 "on the hills behind the cantonment." Engineer Cantonment was some five miles downstream on the Missouri River from Fort Calhoun, Washington County, Nebraska.

Ownbey referred all the material from Nebraska to *P. commutatum* (Schultes f.) A. Dietrich, largely because the plants are tetraploid.[517]

Smilax (Greenbriar).

James listed this genus in the *Account* on August 30, while the party was traveling along the Canadian River in Pottawatomie County, Oklahoma.[518] There James could have encountered either *S. bonanox* or *S. hispida.*

515JAMES [3], April 22.
516WATSON [3], 261.
517OWNBEY, 411.
518JAMES [1], II, 150; JAMES [2] in THWAITES [1], XVI, 161.

Yucca glauca Nutt., Fraser's Catalogue, 1813. (Soapweed).
#436 *Yucca filamentosa* Willd., in Torr., Ann. Lyc. Nat. Hist. N.Y. 2:250.1827. "Summit of dry ridges on the upper part of the Platte."
It is perplexing why Torrey used the epithet "filamentosa," unless perhaps he thought that Nuttall's *Y. glauca* was not specifically distinct. The very next species, and on the same page in Pursh's *Flora*,[519] is *Y. angustifolia,* based on a Nuttall collection from the Missouri. Nuttall also called it *Y. angustifolia,*[520] with no reference to either Fraser's *Catalogue* or to Pursh. Finally, James listed it as "Yucca angustifolia Nutt." in his *Catalogue*[521] and again as such, but without an author, in the *Account.*[522]
Reveal pointed out that Nuttall adequately described *Y. glauca* in Fraser's *Catalogue.*[523]
James's diary mentions "Yucca filamentosa?" on June 20, the day the party camped at the foot of the sandhills near Gothenburg, Dawson County, Nebraska, and again in August when they crossed the Texas panhandle.[524]

Zigadenus elegans Pursh, Fl. Am. Sept. 241. 1814. (White Camas).
#439 *Zigadenus chloranthus* Richards., in Torr., Ann. Lyc. Nat. Hist. N.Y. 2:251.1827. "On the Platte."
This species is found "in subalpine meadows and lower tundra."[525] The most likely location for James to have collected this species was on Pikes Peak, El Paso County, Colorado, July 13–15.

Zigadenus venenosus Wats. var. **gramineus** (Rydb.) Walsh ex Peck, Man. High. Pl. Oreg. 190. 1941. (Death Camas).
#438 *Zigadenus elegans* Pursh, in Torr., Ann. Lyc. Nat. Hist. N.Y. 2:251.1827. "Barren and waste places along the Arkansa."
James listed *Zigadenus elegans* in the *Account* and in his diary for July 12, while the party was camped on Fountain Creek, a branch of the Arkansas, near the town of Fountain, El Paso County, Colorado, at an elevation of about 5,500 feet.[526] Habitat and elevation, however,

[519]PURSH, 227.
[520]NUTTALL [5], I, 218.
[521]JAMES [4], 179.
[522]JAMES [1], I, 461; II, 120; JAMES [2] in THWAITES [1], XV, 232; XVI, 126.
[523]REVEAL, 52.
[524]JAMES [3], June 20 (erroneously dated June 19), August 15.
[525]WEBER [1], 435.
[526]JAMES [1], II, 21; JAMES [2] in THWAITES [1], XV, 312 (both entries for July 12); JAMES [3], July 12 (erroneously dated July 11 and including information for July 10, 11, and 12).

suggest that James collected *Z. venenosus* var. *gramineus*, a species found "in meadows on the plains and mesas."[527]

Linaceae

Linum sp. (Flax).
#39 *Linum rigidum* Pursh, in Torr., Ann. Lyc. Nat. Hist. N.Y. 2:171.1827. "On the Missouri."
Linum rigidum Pursh var. *rigidum* could have been collected on the Missouri, as indicated by Torrey, and hence near Engineer Cantonment, Washington County, Nebraska, during the first week of June. There is, however, no reference to *Linum* from "[o]n the Missouri" in James's diary or in the *Account*. Torrey and Gray cited *L.rigidum* "[f]rom the Missouri, *Nuttall! Dr. James!*"[528]

It is not until July 24 that James referred to *L. rigidum* in the diary or the *Account*.[529] This plant could have been *L. rigidum* var. *berlandieri* (Hooker) T. & G. or *L. puberulum* (Engelm.) Heller.

On that day James's party crossed the Arkansas River and headed southeast across Timpas Creek toward the Purgatoire River. To judge by the sequence of the diary entries, it appears that this collection could have been made three to six miles farther southeast of where they crossed Timpas Creek, perhaps during their midday halt in south-central Otero County, Colorado.

Linum lewisii Pursh, Fl. Am. Sept. 210. 1814. (Blue Flax).
#40 *Linum Lewisii* Pursh, in Torr., Ann. Lyc. Nat. Hist. N.Y. 2:171.1827. "Sources of the Platte, near the Rocky Mountains."
James mentioned this plant on July 5, the day that he made a side trip up Clear Creek, just north of Denver in Adams County, Colorado.[530]

Loasaceae

Cevallia sinuata Lag., Var. Cienc. 21:35.1805. (Stinging Cevallia).
Petalanthera hispida Nutt., Jour. Acad. Phil. 7:107–108.1834. Type: "In the Rocky Mountains, Dr. James."
Torrey and Gray stated, "This very interesting plant was collected

527 WEBER [1], 435.
528 TORREY AND GRAY [1], I, 204.
529 JAMES [1], II, 68; JAMES [2] in THWAITES [1], XVI, 65; JAMES [3], July 24.
530 JAMES [1], I, 501n.; JAMES [2] in THWAITES [1], XV, 281n.; JAMES [3], July 5.

by Dr. James in Long's Expedition."[531] The collection site is given as "[s]ources of the Canadian River, near the Rocky Mountains." In his diary for August 7, James gave a detailed description of this plant: "Cal. deeply 10 cleft. Cor. 0. Caps 1-celled 1-seeded. . . . Flowers in terminal capituli somewhat resembling Hydrophyllum . . . yellowish brown."[532] James also noted the barbellate hairs, a keen observation with just a hand lens.

On August 7 James traveled along the Canadian River in Oldham County, Texas.

Mentzelia decapetala (Pursh) Urb. & Gilg, Ber. Deut. Bot. Ges. 10:263.1892. (Ten-Petal Mentzelia).

#138 *Bartonia ornata* Pursh, in Torr., Ann. Lyc. Nat. Hist. N.Y. 2:199.1827. "On the sandy plains of the Canadian. In bud early in July."

James noted this plant in his diary for July 5, when he and three others made a side trip up "cannon-ball river" (Clear Creek), just north of Denver in Adams County, Colorado.[533] This plant is noted in the *Account* on July 4 near Brighton, Adams County, Colorado.[534] It is likely the plant that Torrey stated was in bud in July. James again noted this plant at their camp near the ford on the Arkansas River about three and a half miles north and a little west of Rocky Ford, Otero County, Colorado.[535]

In mid August along the Canadian River in the eastern Texas panhandle, James observed the "night-flowering bartonia."[536]

On August 27, when the party was camped on the Canadian River at the mouth of Buggy Creek near Minco, Grady County, Oklahoma, James commented in his diary that *Bartonia ornata* still occurred.[537] In the *Account* on that same day, however, James commented that "the bartonias had now disappeared."[538]

Present herbarium records would indicate an absence of *Mentzelia decapetala* in Grady County, although it occurs in close proximity.

[531]TORREY AND GRAY, [1], I, 536.
[532]JAMES [3], August 7.
[533]JAMES [3], July 5.
[534]JAMES [1], I, 497; JAMES [2] in THWAITES [1], XV, 276.
[535]JAMES [1], II, 63 (as July 21); JAMES [2] in THWAITES [1], XVI, 57 (as July 21); JAMES [3], July 22.
[536]JAMES [1], II, 120; JAMES [2] in THWAITES [1], XVI, 126.
[537]JAMES [3], August 27.
[538]JAMES [1], II, 146; JAMES [2] in THWAITES [1], XVI, 156.

Mentzelia nuda (Pursh) T. & G., Fl. No. Am. 1:535.1840. (Bractless Mentzelia).

#139 *Bartonia nuda* Sims, in Torr., Ann. Lyc. Nat. Hist. N.Y. 2:199.1827. "Sources of the Platte. In flower July 4th."

James referred to this plant in his diary on July 3 as *Bartonia nuda*.[539] On that day the party traveled west from Kuner, Weld County, and finally south up the South Platte River to about three miles south of Platteville, Weld County, Colorado.

On the next day, July 4, this plant is listed in the *Account* as being observed near camp.[540] The camp was seventeen miles farther up the South Platte River, near Brighton, Adams County, Colorado.

Mentzelia oligosperma Nutt., in Sims, Bot. Mag. 42: pl.1760. 1815. (Stickleaf).

#136 *Mentzelia aurea* Nutt., in Torr., Ann. Lyc. Nat. Hist. N.Y. 2:199.1827. "Near the Rocky Mountains."

#137 *Mentzelia oligosperma* Nutt., in Torr., Ann. Lyc. Nat. Hist. N.Y. 2:199.1827. "Sources of the Canadian."

On July 7, James in his diary described what must be this plant.[541] On the same day, in the *Account,* he listed "a beautiful little plant referrable to . . . Mentzelia" among the plants collected during the day.[542]

James made this collection on Sheep Mountain, about seven miles southwest of Waterton, on the north side of South Platte Canyon, Jefferson County, Colorado.

Again on July 30 James described this "decumbent Mentzelia," which he collected as they traveled from Sierra Grande, Union County, to Ute Creek, western Union County, New Mexico.[543]

Lobeliaceae

Lobelia cardinalis L., Sp. Pl. 930. 1753. (Cardinal Flower).

#247 *Lobelia fulgens* Pursh, in Torr., Ann. Lyc. Nat. Hist. N.Y. 2:216.1827. "On the Canadian."

James listed *Lobelia cardinalis* on August 27.[544] On that day, a

---

[539]JAMES [3], July 3.
[540]JAMES [1], I, 497; JAMES [2] in THWAITES [1], XV, 276.
[541]JAMES [3], July 7.
[542]JAMES [1], II, 8n.; JAMES [2] in THWAITES [1], XV, 294n.
[543]JAMES [1], II, 86; JAMES [2] in THWAITES [1], XVI, 85; JAMES [3] , July 30.
[544]JAMES [1], II, 145; JAMES [2] in THWAITES [1], XVI, 155; JAMES [3], August 27.

Sunday, the party remained in camp at the junction of Buggy Creek and the Canadian River, about three and a half miles northeast of Minco, Grady County, Oklahoma.

Lobelia siphilitica var. **ludoviciana** A. DC., Prodr. 7:377.1839. (Blue Cardinal Flower).

James mentioned "Lobelia syphillitica" in his diary for August 31.[545] The plant was found near the Canadian, about four miles southwest of Asher, Pottawatomie County, Oklahoma. That is near its westernmost range along the Canadian.

Loganiaceae

Spigelia marilandica (L.) L., Syst. ed.12. 734. 1767. (Indian-Pink).

#264 *Spigelia marilandica* L., in Torr., Ann. Lyc. Nat. Hist. N.Y. 2:219.1827. "Arkansa Territory."

Based on flowering time and distribution, James could have made his collection in the latter half of September along the Arkansas River in far-eastern Oklahoma, or in the state of Arkansas.

Loranthaceae

Phoradendron serotinum (Raf.) M.C. Johnst., Southwest. Nat. 2:45.1957. (Eastern Mistletoe).

#183 *Viscum verticillatum* Nutt., in Torr., Ann. Lyc. Nat. Hist. N.Y. 2:208.1827. "On the Canadian. Parasitic on elm-trees."

James, under the date of August 27, mentioned the mistletoe and stated that it was parasitic on elm.[546] On that day, a Sunday, the party remained in camp at the junction of Buggy Creek and the Canadian River, about three and a half miles northeast of Minco, Grady County, Oklahoma. We have no records of this mistletoe from farther up the Canadian than this early one of James.

In the *Account* on September 1 James again noted mistletoe along the Canadian River.[547] We estimate that the party traveled nineteen miles on this day and camped about two miles southeast of Konawa, Seminole County, Oklahoma.

[545]JAMES [3], August 31.
[546]JAMES [1], II, 145; JAMES [2] in THWAITES [1], XVI, 156; JAMES [3], August 27.
[547]JAMES [1], II, 152; JAMES [2] in THWAITES [1], XVI, 164.

Lythraceae

Ammannia coccinea Rottb., Pl. Hort. Havn. Desc. 7. 1773. (Tooth-cup).

#133 *Ammannia ramosior* L., in Torr., Ann. Lyc. Nat. Hist. N.Y. 2:199.1827. "On the Canadian?" Torrey also stated that the plant "[d]iffers somewhat from the A. ramosior of the Northern States, in the leaves being almost auriculate at the base."

Torrey and Gray cited a James specimen from "Arkansas" under *A. latifolia.*[548] Britton and Brown considered *A. latifolia sensu* Torrey and Gray to be *A. coccinea.*[549]

Based on flowering time and distribution, James probably collected the plant in August along the Canadian River in Oklahoma.

Lythrum alatum Pursh var. **lanceolatum** (Ell.) T. & G. ex Rothrock, in Wheeler, Rept. U.S. Geog. Surv. W. 100th Meridian, VI-Botany:120.1879. (Loosestrife).

#134 *Lythrum, n. sp. Nutt. mss.,* in Torr., Ann. Lyc. Nat. Hist. N.Y. 2:199.1827. "On the Missouri. *Dr. James and Dr. Baldwin.*"

There is no reason to doubt that the Baldwin specimen was collected along the Missouri. That was in late June to mid July 1819. James made the trip up that river in May of the next year, however, a little early for *Lythrum* to flower.

Torrey and Gray, under *L. alatum* Pursh var. γ, cited a James specimen from "Arkansas."[550]

On August 23, James briefly noted "Lythrum?" in his diary.[551] That is presumably the plant cited by Torrey and Gray. On that day the party followed the Canadian River through northeastern Custer County to the mouth of Bear Creek, Blaine County, Oklahoma. The date and location fit well with the flowering time and distribution of the plant.

Malvaceae

Callirhoe alceoides (Michx.) Gray, Mem. Am. Acad. n.s. 4:18. 1849. (Pl. Fendl.). (Pink Poppy Mallow).

#45 *Nuttallia involucrata* Nutt., in Torr., Ann. Lyc. Nat. Hist. N.Y.

[548]TORREY AND GRAY [1], I, 480.
[549]BRITTON AND BROWN, II, 578.
[550]TORREY AND GRAY [1], I, 481–82.
[551]JAMES [3], August 23.

2:172.1827, as to location, "Valley of the Loup Fork," and description, "Root large, soft, and edible," only.

Malva pedata β? *umbellata* T. & G., Fl. No. Am. 1:227.1838. "Valley of the Platte, *Dr. James!* . . . springing from a large soft edible root, in shape and size between a small turnip and a parsnip." Based on James's manuscript name *Sida macrorhiza.*

Callirhoe macrorhiza Gray, Mem. Am. Acad. n.s. 4:18.1849. (Pl. Fendl.). "The numerous stems . . . spring from a large edible root. . . . The petals are white or nearly so." *Malva pedata* β? *umbellata* and James's manuscript name *Sida macrorhiza* are cited as synonyms.

On June 9, near the campsite on the Loup River just west of the mouth of Looking Glass Creek, approximately two miles east of Monroe, Platte County, Nebraska, James collected the type (NY) of *C. macrorhiza.* In his diary, James described the plant and gave it the manuscript name *Sida macrorhiza.*[552] It is on this plant that Torrey and Gray based *Malva pedata* β? *umbellata.*[553]

Description is also given in the *Account,* under the date of June 9, for this plant: "with a large tuberous root which is soft and edible, being by no means ungrateful to the taste."[554] James further noted there that the plant lacks an exterior calyx, which is true for *C. alceoides* but not for *C. involucrata.*

Three days later James mentioned the abundance of this plant about the Pawnee Loup Indian village, which was located in the valley of the Loup River some four miles north and a half mile east of Palmer, Merrick County, Nebraska.[555] There, in addition, is a reference to Peale's sketch, "Figure 53." To date that sketch has not been found.

On the following day, June 13, he described the plant as it occurred about the village of the Pawnee Loup: "The root of Sida macrorhiza is large and edible in shape and size it is between the small turnip and a parsnip. The corrolla is large white and tinged with purple. The petals are cilliate fringed at the margin."

A specimen from the Pawnee villages is at (NY).

Callirhoe digitata Nutt., J. Acad. Nat. Sci. Philad. 2:181.1821. (Finger Poppy Mallow).

#43 *Nuttallia palmata* Dick, in Torr., Ann. Lyc. Nat. Hist. N.Y.

---

[552]JAMES [3], June 9.
[553]TORREY AND GRAY [1], I, 227.
[554]JAMES [1], I, 432–33; JAMES [2] in THWAITES [1], XV, 200.
[555]JAMES [3], June 12.

2:171.1827. The entry is not accompanied by either a description or a location. Torrey's reference is listed in synonymy in Gray[556] and Dorr[557] under *C. digitata* Nutt.

James was in range of *C. digitata* in early September, when he was in far-eastern Oklahoma as he neared Fort Smith, Arkansas.

Callirhoe involucrata (T. & G.) Gray, Mem. Am. Acad. n.s. 4:15.1849. (Pl. Fendl.). (Purple Poppy Mallow).
Malva involucrata T. & G., Fl. No. Am. 1:226.1838. "Valley of the Loup Fork of the Platte, *Dr. James!*"
#45 *Nuttallia involucrata* Nutt., in Torr., Ann. Lyc. Nat. Hist. N.Y. 2:172.1827, as to name only.

The type (NY) of *Callirhoe involucrata* was collected on the Platte River rather than on the Loup as indicated by Torrey and Gray.[558] This plant is mentioned erroneously in the *Account* on June 14 as "cristaria *coccinea*. Ph. (malva *coccinea*. N.)."[559] The party at that time was along the Platte about four miles southeast of Grand Island, Nebraska. The flower is described as having nearly the aspect of the common wild rose but deeper in color, characters of *C. involucrata* rather than *Sphaeralcea coccinea*.

In his diary three days later, James mentioned this plant as a dubious *Malva coccinea* and described his collection of a hispid plant with procumbent stems, with large scarlet flowers, and with three bracts subtending the calyx.[560] That description accurately fits *C. involucrata*. On June 17 the party traveled along the Platte River from south of Odessa, Buffalo County, to southwest of Overton, Dawson County, Nebraska, during which time the type of *C. involucrata* was collected.

Callirhoe leiocarpa R. Martin, J. Wash. Acad. Sci. 28(3):108.1938. (Tall Poppy Mallow).
#44 *Nuttallia digitata* Dick, in Torr., Ann. Lyc. Nat. Hist. N.Y. 2:172.1827. "Pawnee villages."

If Torrey's #43, *Nuttallia palmata*, is *C. digitata* (*q.v.*), then surely his #44, *Nuttallia digitata*, is something other than *C. digitata*.

If the Nebraska location given by Torrey is correct, the plant,

[556]GRAY [2], 301.
[557]DORR, 30.
[558]TORREY AND GRAY [1], I, 226.
[559]JAMES [1], I, 453; JAMES [2] in THWAITES [1], XV, 223.
[560]JAMES [3], June 17 (erroneously dated June 15).

lacking an involucre, could only be *C. alceoides* (*q.v.*) and is likely the specimen from the Pawnee villages at (NY).

If the Nebraska location is incorrect, then *C. leiocarpa* and *C. pedata* are the other two possible species that lack an involucre and that are in range of the route of the expedition. Of these two species only *C. leiocarpa* would have been in flower at the time its range was traversed by the expedition, on August 18–20 in Roger Mills or an adjacent county in western Oklahoma. The flowering time for *C. pedata* is April to early July, and its range was not reached by the expedition until early September in far-eastern Oklahoma.

Hibiscus laevis All., Auct. Syn. 31. 1773. (Halberdleaved Rose Mallow).

Hibiscus militaris Cav., Diss. 6:352, pl.198, fig.2. 1788.

#46 *Hibiscus militaris* Cav., in Torr., Ann. Lyc. Nat. Hist. N.Y. 2:172.1827. "Sandy plains of the Canadian."

We find no reference to this either in the diary or in the *Account*. Torrey's location could be correct, as this plant occurs along the Canadian in the eastern half of Oklahoma, where James traveled during the latter half of August.

Hibiscus lasiocarpus Cav., Diss. 3:159, pl.70, fig.1. 1787. (Woolly Rose Mallow).

#47 *Hibiscus grandiflorus* Michx., in Torr., Ann. Lyc. Nat. Hist. N.Y. 2:172.1827. "On the Arkansa."

James reported and described this plant on August 17 in his diary, as "H. grandiflorus," as he came down the Canadian River in eastern Hemphill County, Texas.[561] The Torrey reference is cited, under *H. lasiocarpus,* by Robinson in Gray.[562]

The *Account* for August 17 states, "The great flowering hibiscus is here a conspicuous and highly ornamental plant among the scattering trees in the low grounds."[563]

Collections of the species from as far west as the Texas panhandle are infrequent. Two, however, have come to our attention from Hemphill County. The first is Carleton in 1891, as cited by Holzinger.[564] This plant is again mentioned by Carleton, who states, "At Canadian City a splendid malvaceous plant (*Hibiscus lasiocarpus*

[561]JAMES [3], August 17.
[562]GRAY [2], 335.
[563]JAMES [1], II, 127; JAMES [2] in THWAITES [1], XVI, 135.
[564]HOLZINGER, 203.

Cav.) is common in the Canadian Valley."[565] The second record we have is *Rowell 10544* (OKL), from "Bottomlands of Canadian River, approx. 7 miles northeast of Canadian, Hemphill Co., Aug. 8, 1964."

Sphaeralcea angustifolia (Cav.) G. Don var. **cuspidata** Gray, Proc. Am. Acad. Sci. 22:293.1887. (Narrowleaf Globe Mallow). Based on the following:

#41 *Sida stellata* Torr., Ann. Lyc. Nat. Hist. N.Y. 2:171.1827. [Not of Cav., 1790]. "Sources of the Arkansa."

Sphaeralcea stellata (Torr.) T. & G., Fl. No. Am. 1:228.1838. "Margins of small brooks, near the sources of the Arkansas, *Dr. James!*" Type: NY.

James stated in his diary that the plant grew along "the margins of small running brooks."[566] The species is usually found on dry plains and in dry washes. In the country they were in at the time, the "running brooks" were dry washes most of the summer. That recent rains had fallen is known from the fact that, the next day, the Purgatoire River was in flood. In the *Account,* the land where the plant was collected is described as "sterile and sandy."[567]

James referred to the flowers as "pale vermillion,"[568] whereas Torrey called them "scarlet."[569]

The type was collected July 24, at or near Packers Gap, southeastern Otero County, Colorado.

Sphaeralcea coccinea (Nutt. in Fras. Cat.) Rydb., Bull. Torr. Bot. Club 40:58.1913. (Red False Mallow).

#42 *Malva coccinea* Nutt., in Torr., Ann. Lyc. Nat. Hist. N.Y. 2:171.1827. "Frequent on the low plains along the Platte."

James originally described this plant in his diary as a *Sida* with "large pale vermillion" flowers.[570] Here, too, is an indication that fig. 52 in Peale's sketches is of this plant. To date, that sketch has not been located.

Marginal notes in the diary, evidently entered later, indicate that James recognized that his plant was not a *Sida*. James made the collection on June 11 about the village of the Grand Pawnee on the

[565]CARLETON, 226.
[566]JAMES [3], July 24.
[567]JAMES [1], II, 68; JAMES [2] in THWAITES [1], XVI, 65.
[568]JAMES [3], July 24.
[569]TORREY [2], 171.
[570]JAMES [3], June 11.

Loup River, some seven miles southwest of Fullerton, Nance County, Nebraska.

Martyniaceae

Proboscidea louisianica (Mill.) Thell., Mem. Soc. Sci. Cherbourg IV. 38:480.1912. (Devil's Claw).
#269 *Martynia proboscidea* Ait., in Torr., Ann. Lyc. Nat. Hist. N.Y. 2:220.1827. "Sources of the Arkansa."
James listed "Martynia proboscidea" in his diary on July 20.[571] On that day the party traveled about twenty-six miles down the Arkansas from near Devine, Pueblo County, to near Olney Springs, Crowley County, Colorado.
The plant is listed in the *Account* on July 19, the day the party began its descent of the Arkansas from west of Pueblo near Turkey Creek, Pueblo County, to near Devine, Pueblo County, Colorado.[572]

Melastomataceae

Rhexia virginica L., Sp. Pl. 346. 1753. (Meadow Beauty).
#135 *Rhexia virginica* L., in Torr., Ann. Lyc. Nat. Hist. N.Y. 2:199.1827. "On the Arkansa, near its junction with the Canadian."
This species was listed by James in his diary on September 12.[573] On that same day in the *Account* the plant is noted as occurring about the evening's camp.[574] The party traveled in Sequoyah County, Oklahoma, from just west of Sallisaw to their camp near Muldrow.
Rhexia interior, a species not described until 1918, is, however, more frequent in the area where James collected his *Rhexia*.

Meliaceae

Melia azedarach L., Sp. Pl. 384. 1753. (Chinaberry).
#175 *Melia Azedarach* L., in Torr., Ann. Lyc. Nat. Hist. N.Y. 2:206.1827. "On the Canadian. Native."
This specimen would have been taken from a cultivated or an escaped plant and would not have been collected on the Canadian. It

[571]JAMES [3], July 20.
[572]JAMES [1], II, 51; JAMES [2] in THWAITES [1], XVI, 44.
[573]JAMES [3], September 12.
[574]JAMES [1], II, 171; JAMES [2] in THWAITES [1], XVI, 185.

could have been collected in the spring in Missouri, for example, or in September in Arkansas.

Menispermaceae

Calycocarpum lyoni (Pursh) Nutt., in A. Gray, Gen. Ill., 1:76. 1848. (Cupseed).

#11 *Menispermum lyoni* Pursh, in Torr., Ann. Lyc. Nat. Hist. N.Y. 2:165.1827. "On the Arkansa."

Menispermum lyoni was listed by James in his diary on September 11.[575] On that day the party traveled down the Arkansas from a few miles below the mouth of the Canadian to just west of Sallisaw, Sequoyah County, Oklahoma. In the *Account* one day later the plant is noted as occurring about the September 12 camp, which was near Muldrow, Sequoyah County, Oklahoma.[576]

Moraceae

Maclura pomifera (Raf.) Schneider, Ill. Handb. Laubh. 1:806. 1906. (Osage Orange).

#413 *Broussonetia tinctoria* Kunth. *Maclura aurantiaca* Nutt., in Torr., Ann. Lyc. Nat. Hist. N.Y. 2:246.1827. "In deep and fertile soils along the Arkansa and Canadian."

James recorded this plant in his diary on September 5,[577] and also explained that his earlier reference to it on August 15 was an error for *Cephalanthus.* In the *Account* under the same date, James spoke of the "bow-wood or Osage orange."[578] This was followed by a lengthy footnote concerning the characteristics, uses, and distribution of the plant.

On September 5 the party was crossing Hughes County, Oklahoma.

Morus microphylla Buckl., Proc. Acad. Phila. 1862:8.1862. (Texas Mulberry).

On August 2 James mentioned mulberry as occurring in the valley.[579] The only mulberry in the region is *M. microphylla.*

At that time the party had left the Garcia Creek camp and

---

[575]JAMES [3], September 11.
[576]JAMES [1], II, 171; JAMES [2] in THWAITES [1], XVI, 185.
[577]JAMES [3], September 5.
[578]JAMES [1], II, 158, 158–59n.; JAMES [2] in THWAITES [1], XVI, 170–71, 171n.
[579]JAMES [3], August 1, with the account of August 2 included there.

continued down Ute Creek, mostly through Harding County, New Mexico, except for about four miles in southwestern Union County.

Morus rubra L., Sp. Pl. 986. 1753. (Red Mulberry).
#412 *Morus rubra* L., in Torr., Ann. Lyc. Nat. Hist. N.Y. 2:246. 1827. "On the lower part of the Canadian."
James stated in his diary for August 19 that mulberry begins to make its appearance in the low grounds.[580] In the *Account* on August 18, this tree is noted near their camp on the Canadian River near the mouth of West Creek, where the Pack Saddle Bridge crosses the river in Ellis County, Oklahoma.[581]

In the *Account* on August 29 James listed "the linden" among the upland trees.[582] Inasmuch as linden does not occur in Oklahoma along the route of the expedition, James was surely seeing mulberry.

James again mentioned this tree in his diary on September 3.[583] In the *Account* for September 2 James stated that it is one of the common trees in the "dense forests of the river valley."[584] That is doubtless the location to which Torrey referred. On September 2 and 3 James was along the Canadian River in Seminole County or Pontotoc County, Oklahoma.

Nyctaginaceae

Abronia fragrans Nutt., Hooker's J. Bot. Kew Gard. Misc. 5:261. 1853. (Sweet Sand Verbena).
James indicated in his diary that he thought this was a new species and included a lengthy description, even mentioning the linear stigma, which he thought was bearded.[585] We think the "beard" was the abundant pollen that adheres to the side of the thread-like style. He also noticed the irregular placement of the stamens, leading him to think that the plant might be one of the "Polemonidae."

The specimen was collected June 27 while the party traveled up the South Platte River in northeastern Colorado from just west of Julesburg, Sedgwick County, to southeast of Crook, Logan County.

[580]JAMES [3], August 19.
[581]JAMES [1], II, 131; JAMES [2] in THWAITES [1], XVI, 139.
[582]JAMES [1], II, 149; JAMES [2] in THWAITES [1], XVI, 160.
[583]JAMES [3], September 3.
[584]JAMES [1], II, 155; JAMES [2] in THWAITES [1], XVI, 168.
[585]JAMES [3], June 27.

Mirabilis linearis (Pursh) Heimerl, Ann. Conserv. & Jard. Bot. Geneve 5:186.1901. (Narrowleaf Four-O'clock).
#368 *Oxybaphus angustifolius* in Torr., Ann. Lyc. Nat. Hist. N.Y. 2:237.1827. "On the Platte." There is no reference to this in the diary. Torrey's stated location could well be right.

Mirabilis multiflora (Torr.) Gray, in Torr., U.S. & Mex. Bound. Surv. 2:169.1859. (Colorado Four-O'clock).
#369 *Oxybaphus multiflorus* Torr., Ann. Lyc. Nat. Hist. N.Y. 2:237–38.1827. "About the Forks of the Platte."
The absence of the plant in Nebraska has caused Pilz, probably correctly, to think that it was collected in Colorado.[586] It is not mentioned in James's diary. The type (NY) was most likely collected in the latter half of July in Pueblo County, Colorado. Less likely, it may have been in Otero or Las Animas counties, or, in late July or early August, in New Mexico in Union, Harding, or Quay counties.

Mirabilis nyctaginea (Michx.) MacMill., Metasp. Minn. Val. 217. 1892. (Wild Four-O'clock).
#370 *Oxybaphus nyctaginea* [sic] in Torr., Ann. Lyc. Nat. Hist. N.Y. 2:238.1827.
Torrey gave no location, but James described a four o'clock in the diary.[587] The most helpful phrase is "stem with enlarged joints, subquadrangular." That well fits *M. nyctaginea.* James said it was in fig. 51, but we have been unable to locate it in any of Peale's sketches.
The plant was collected on June 7 near the Elkhorn River, a few miles southeast of Arlington, Washington or Dodge County, Nebraska.

Tripterocalyx micranthus (Torr.) Hook., J. Bot. Kew Gard. Misc. 5:261.1853. (Sand Puffs).
In his diary, James described a plant having a five-leaved "common calyx," the heads 10–20 flowered and the fruit with 3–5 "membranaceous spreading margins, resembling the valves of Rumex venosus."[588]
Torrey did not mention the James collection, so he evidently never saw it. The species, as an *Abronia,* was based by Torrey on a Fremont collection made twenty-two years after the James collection.[589]

---

[586]PILZ, 127.
[587]JAMES [3], June 7.
[588]JAMES [3], June 28.
[589]TORREY [4], 92.

James's plant was collected on June 28. On that day he traveled up the South Platte River from just east of Crook to a couple of miles west of Sterling, all in Logan County, Colorado.

Nymphaeaceae

Nelumbo lutea (Willd.) Pers., Syn. Pl. 1:92.1805. (Lotus).
#13 *Nelumbium luteum* Willd., in Torr., Ann. Lyc. Nat. Hist. N.Y. 2:165.1827. "On the Missouri and Arkansa, in stagnant waters."

No reference to this species was found in James's diary; on September 11 in the *Account,* however, James described "a deep morass, covered with the Nelumbo and other aquatic plants."[590]
On that day the party was traveling along the Arkansas River in Sequoyah County, Oklahoma.

Nyssaceae

Nyssa sylvatica Marsh., Arbustr. Am. 97. 1785. (Black Tupelo).
#140 *Nyssa biflora* Willd., in Torr., Ann. Lyc. Nat. Hist. N.Y. 2:200.1827. "On the Canadian."

The first reference by James to *Nyssa* occurred when he was far west of its range.[591] The tree was doubtless *Bumelia lanuginosa (q.v.)*.

James would have been within range of *Nyssa* as the party traveled along the Canadian and Arkansas rivers in extreme-eastern Oklahoma. *Nyssa* is mentioned in the *Account* three times during September.[592] The first two times, on September 1 and 2, James was still west of the known range and was again likely encountering *B. lanuginosa (q.v.)*. On September 11, however, he was in range when *Nyssa* is again mentioned. At that time the party was traveling along the Arkansas River in Sequoyah County, Oklahoma.

Oleaceae

Fraxinus pennsylvanica Marsh., Arbustr. Am. 51. 1785. (Green Ash).

James noted in his diary for September 3 "some ash" that was not very abundant among the trees of the forest.[593] It seems likely that he

[590]JAMES [1], II, 169; JAMES [2] in THWAITES [1], XVI, 182.
[591]JAMES [1], II, 142; JAMES [2] in THWAITES [1], XVI, 152.
[592]JAMES [1], II, 153, 155, and 169; JAMES [2] in THWAITES [1], XVI, 165, 168, and 183.
[593]JAMES [3], September 3.

was seeing green ash. On that day the party traveled only a few miles and camped on the Canadian about five miles northwest of Allen near the junction of Seminole, Hughes, and Pontotoc counties, Oklahoma.

Ash is listed one day earlier in the *Account* among the trees of the "dense forests of the river valley."[594]

Onagraceae

Calylophus lavandulifolius (T. & G.) Raven, Brittonia 16:286. 1964. (Lavenderleaf Evening Primrose).

In his diary, James listed an *Oenothera* that he thought was a new species; he gave it a name referring to the long flowers.[595] We think that this is the specimen that Torrey and Gray cited from "[p]lains of the Platte, *Dr. James! Nuttall!* ('near Scott's Bluffs')" when they described *Oenothera lavandulifolia*.[596] If that be the case, the type (NY) was collected June 27 along the South Platte River as the party traveled in northeastern Colorado from west of Julesburg, Sedgwick County, to southeast of Crook, Logan County.

Calylophus serrulatus (Nutt.) Raven, Brittonia 16:286.1964. (Yellow Evening Primrose).

#151 *Oenothera serrulata* Nutt., in Torr., Ann. Lyc. Nat. Hist. N.Y. 2:201.1827. "On the Canadian or Platte."

This species occurs in all five states through which James traveled.

Epilobium sp. (Willow-Herb).

The diary for June 20 lists "Epilobium palustre" without further comment.[597] At the time the party was near Gothenburg, Dawson County, Nebraska, but *E. palustre* is not recorded for this state.

E. coloratum Biehler, *E. adenocaulon* Hausskn., and *E. leptophyllum* Raf. are likely possibilities.

Gaura coccinea Pursh, Fl. Am. Sept. 733. 1814. (Scarlet Gaura).

#143 *Gaura coccinea* Pursh, in Torr., Ann. Lyc. Nat. Hist. N.Y. 2:200.1827. "On the Loup Fork, a branch of the Platte."

James's collection was made on June 9, according to the diary, on

---

[594]JAMES [1], II, 155; JAMES [2] in THWAITES [1], XVI, 168.
[595]JAMES [3], June 27.
[596]TORREY AND GRAY [1], I, 501.
[597]JAMES [3], June 20 (erroneously dated June 19).

an elevated ridge that the expedition began to encounter about three miles southeast of Platte Center, Platte County, Nebraska.[598] The ridge divides Shell Creek from the Loup River. This plant is listed in the *Account* on the same day.[599]

Gaura coccinea Nutt. ex Pursh var. **integerrima** Torr.
#145 *Gaura coccinea* β? *integerrima* Torr., Ann. Lyc. Nat. Hist. N.Y. 2:200–201.1827. "About the sources of the Canadian."
James described this plant in detail in his diary for August 1 and called it *Gaura angustifolia.*[600]
On that same date in the *Account* "two species of gaura" are noted to occur.[601] These two taxa are this variety and *G. villosa* (*q.v.*).
According to Raven and Gregory, the type is at NY.[602] It would have been collected on August 1 near the campsite at the confluence of Garcia Creek and Ute Creek, about six miles east and a little north of Yates, Harding County, New Mexico.
This variety is frequently treated as a synonym of the type variety.

Gaura coccinea Nutt. ex Pursh var. **parvifolia** (Torr.) Rickett, Kew Bull. 1934:57.1934. "On the Canadian."
#146 *Gaura parvifolia* Torr., Ann. Lyc. Nat. Hist. N.Y. 2:201.1827. "On the Canadian."
We find no mention of this plant in James's diary or in either edition of the *Account*. On August 8 in the *Account*, however, when describing *Gaura* (*Stenosiphon*) *linifolia*, he stated that it is the fifth species of the genus that they had "met with west of the Mississippi."[603] We account for the other four species as follows: *G. coccinea* on June 9, *G. parviflora* on July 27, and *G. coccinea* var. *integerrima* and *G. villosa* on August 1. It seems likely that *G. parvifolia* was collected, therefore, after the *Stenosiphon*. The type (NY) of *parvifolia* then would have been collected after August 8 somewhere along the Canadian River during August in the Texas panhandle or the western half of Oklahoma.
This taxon is sometimes considered to be a synonym of the type variety of *G. coccinea*.

[598]JAMES [3], June 9.
[599]JAMES [1], I, 433n.; JAMES [2] in THWAITES [1], XV, 200n.
[600]JAMES [3], August 1.
[601]JAMES [1], II, 89; JAMES [2] in THWAITES [1], XVI, 89.
[602]RAVEN AND GREGORY, 28.
[603]JAMES [1], II, 100; JAMES [2] in THWAITES [1], XVI, 102n.

Gaura mollis James, Long Exped. (Phila. ed.) 2:77.1823. (Velvet Leaf Gaura).

#141 *Gaura mollis* Nutt. *mss.*, in Torr., Ann. Lyc. Nat. Hist. N.Y. 2:200.1827. "South-west branches of the Arkansa."

Gaura parviflora Dougl. ex Hooker, Fl. Bor. Am. 1:208.1832.

In his diary for July 27, James referred to the "diminutive" size of the flowers[604] and suggested that, should it prove to be new, it should be called "G. parviflora."[605] In the *Account,* however, James described the species fully and proposed the name *Gaura mollis.*[606] That name has been overlooked for this taxon because many workers had previously believed that *Gaura mollis* HBK., Nov. Gen. & Sp. Pl. 6:93, pl.529. 1823, preempted *Gaura mollis* James. According to Stafleu and Cowan, the publication containing *G. mollis* HBK. appeared on August 6, 1823.[607] The *Account* containing James's *G. mollis* doubtless appeared much earlier in the year, as a dozen copies of the *Account* had been supplied to Secretary of War John C. Calhoun by January 3, 1823, thus making *G. mollis* James rather than *G. parviflora* Dougl. the earliest name for this taxon.

James remarked that the plant was collected "along the margin of the small stream which we are ascending."[608] He was then in Bachicha Canyon in southern Las Animas County, Colorado. That is where the type was collected.

In the *Account* on August 1, James again noted the occurrence of *G. mollis* about their campsite at the confluence of Garcia Creek and Ute Creek, about six miles east and a little north of Yates, Harding County, New Mexico.[609]

Gaura villosa Torr. (Hairy Gaura).

#144 *Gaura villosa* Torr., Ann. Lyc. Nat. Hist. 2:200.1827. "Sources of the Canadian."

In the diary for August 1, James described this plant in considerable detail and gave it a name.[610] On that same date in the *Account*

---

[604]JAMES [3], July 27.

[605]Interestingly, only a few years later Douglas found the same species in the Pacific Northwest and chose this same epithet. *G. parviflora* Dougl. is the name by which the species has been widely known.

[606]JAMES [1], II, 77n.; JAMES [2] in THWAITES [1], XVI, 75.

[607]STAFLEU AND COWAN, II, 371.

[608]JAMES [1], July 27.

[609]JAMES [1], II, 89; JAMES [2] in THWAITES [1], XVI, 89.

[610]JAMES [3], August 1.

"two new species of gaura" are noted.[611] This species and *G. coccinea* var. *integerrima* (*q.v.*) are the two taxa.

The type (NY) was collected near their campsite at the confluence of Garcia Creek and Ute Creek, about six miles east and a little north of Yates, Harding County, New Mexico.

Ludwigia decurrens Walt., Fl. Carol. 89. 1788. (Primrose Willow).

In his diary for September 9, James described this species fully and indicated that it was possibly new.[612] On that day the party traveled along the Canadian from just south of Porum, Muskogee County, to eight or ten miles above the junction of the Canadian and Arkansas rivers. Their camp would have been in extreme-southeastern Muskogee County, Oklahoma.

Oenothera albicaulis Pursh, Fl. Am. Sept. 733. 1814. (Prairie Evening Primrose).

When Pursh described this species, he thought that he was supplying a description for Nuttall's *Oe. albicaulis, a nomen nudum* which appeared in Fraser's *Catalogue,* 1813. Pursh's description, however, based on a Bradbury collection, proved to be of a different species. Four years later Nuttall attempted to maintain his name and provided a description.[613] He also provided, superfluously, the name *Oe. pinnatifida* for Pursh's *Oe. albicaulis.* Cited in Torrey and Gray, under *Oe. pinnatifida* Nutt., with *Oe. albicaulis* Pursh as a synonym, is "[p]lains of the Platte and Missouri, *Bradbury! Nuttall! Dr. James!*"[614] The Bradbury and Nuttall plants are from the Missouri, James's from the Platte.

If the information we have given concerning the type locality of *Oe. coronopifolia* is correct, we have no clue as to just where James collected *Oe. albicaulis* Pursh. If, however, our type locality of *Oe. coronopifolia* is incorrect, then that location may be the site for James's collection of *Oe. albicaulis* Pursh.

Oenothera caespitosa Nutt., Fraser's Catalogue, 1813. (White Stemless Evening Primrose).

This record is based only on James's June 27 diary entry, in which

---

[611]JAMES [1], II, 89; JAMES [2] in THWAITES [1], XVI, 89.
[612]JAMES [3], September 9.
[613]NUTTALL [5], I, 245–46.
[614]TORREY AND GRAY [1], I, 494.

he listed "Oe. caespitosa Nutt ??."[615] On that day he traveled in northeastern Colorado from near Julesburg, Sedgwick County, to southeast of Crook, Logan County.

Oenothera coronopifolia T. & G., Fl. No. Am. 1:495.1840. (Combleaf Evening Primrose).
#147 *Oenothera pinnatifida* Nutt., in Torr., Ann. Lyc. Nat. Hist. N.Y. 2:201.1827. "About the Forks of the Platte."
Torrey and Gray pointed out[616] that this new species is the *Oenothera pinnatifid sensu* Torr.,[617] non Nutt.
Under the date of June 23, James listed this plant in the diary as *Oenothera pinnatifida*.[618] The *Account* also mentions it.[619]
James may have collected the type (NY) of *Oenothera coronopifolia* on June 23 on the south side of the South Platte, just a few miles above its junction with the North Platte, Lincoln County, Nebraska. It is also possible that this is the location for James's collection of *Oenothera albicaulis* Pursh (see above).

Oenothera jamesii T. & G., Fl. No. Am. 1:493.1840. (Trumpet Evening Primrose). "On the Platte or Canadian River, *Dr. James!*" Type: NY. (Phototype, see fig. 25.)
Torrey commented that the flowers of this plant were larger than those of *O. biennis,* "and the tube of the calyx about four inches long."[620]
No mention of this plant is made in either edition of the *Account,* but in the diary for August 23 James described it in detail.[621] On that day the party followed the Canadian River through northeastern Custer County downstream to near the mouth of Bear Creek, Blaine County, Oklahoma.

Oenothera laciniata Hill, Veg. Syst. 12:64.1767. (Cutleaf Evening Primrose).
Oenothera sinuata, a synonym of *O. laciniata,* is listed by James.[622]
James collected "a small Oenothera" on June 7, near the Elkhorn

[615]JAMES [3], June 27.
[616]TORREY AND GRAY [1], I, 495.
[617]TORREY [2], 201.
[618]JAMES [3], June 23 (erroneously dated June 22).
[619]JAMES [1], I, 468; JAMES [2] in THWAITES [1], XV, 240–41.
[620]TORREY [2], 202.
[621]JAMES [3], August 23.
[622]JAMES [4], 179.

Fig. 25. Phototype of *Oenothera jamesii* T. & G. Courtesy New York Botanical Garden.

River, a few miles southeast of Arlington in Washington or Dodge County, Nebraska.[623]

Oenothera macrocarpa Nutt. var. **oklahomensis** (J.B.S. Norton) Reveal, Rhodora 70:43.1968. (Oklahoma Evening Primrose).

#150 *Oenothera macrocarpa* Pursh, in Torr., Ann. Lyc. Nat. Hist. N.Y. 2:201.1827. "On the Canadian. It differs from the ordinary variety in the leaves being perfectly smooth."

It is Torrey's remark about the smoothness of the leaves that leads us to think that James had the var. *oklahomensis*. Torrey and Gray referred to James's plant as *O. missouriensis*.[624]

In his diary for August 20, James listed "Oenothera macrocarpa Ph.," followed by a lengthy description and the comment that the plant grew on sandy ridges in scanty soil.[625] James commented on this plant in the *Account* on August 19, saying, "About the shelvings and crevices of the rocks the slender corrolla of the Oenothera *macrocarpa* . . . lay withering."[626] That fits the place the party camped on August 19 and left the next morning, August 20: They were on the Washita River drainage, probably in Roger Mills County, Oklahoma, a few miles southwest of Leedey, Dewey County.

Oenothera nuttallii Sweet, Hort. Brit. ed.2. 199. 1830. (White-Stemmed Evening Primrose).

#148 *Oenothera albicaulis* Nutt., non Pursh, in Torr., Ann. Lyc. Nat. Hist. N.Y. 2:201.1827. "Barren deserts, along the Platte."

Torrey and Gray, under *Oe. albicaulis* Nutt., included this Ann. Lyc. citation and stated, "Barrens along the Platte, *Nuttall, Dr. James!*"[627]

James mentioned *Oe. albicaulis* in his diary, without author or a word of description.[628] Because James referred in his diary to *Oenothera pinnatifida,* a Nuttallian name (see *Oenothera albicaulis* Pursh, above), and because Nuttall was indicated as the author of *Oenothera albicaulis* in the *Account*,[629] it seems exceedingly likely that he was using Nuttall's *Gen. No. Am. Pl.,* and hence was using *Oe. albicaulis* in the Nuttallian sense.

[623]JAMES [3], June 7.
[624]TORREY AND GRAY [1], I, 501–2.
[625]JAMES [3], August 20.
[626]JAMES [1], II, 134; JAMES [2] in THWAITES [1], XVI, 143–44.
[627]TORREY AND GRAY [1], I, 495.
[628]JAMES [3], June 28.
[629]JAMES [1], I, 484; JAMES [2] in THWAITES [1], XV, 259.

On June 28 James was traveling up the South Platte River from just east of Crook to a couple of miles west of Sterling, all in Logan County, Colorado.

Oenothera rhombipetala Nutt., in T. & G., Fl. No. Am. 1:493. 1840. (Fourpoint Evening Primrose).
In his diary for August 28, James described an *Oenothera*: "Stem nearly simple suffruticose. Tube of the calyx very small, divisions long marked with large and conspicuous red brown spots. 2–3 feet high. flowers small and numerous."[630] We take calyx "very small" as meaning "very slender." The calyx does frequently have the reddish-brown spots that he noted. As to "flowers small," that must have been in comparison to the other species of *Oenothera* he had seen during the past few weeks.
In addition to the species he listed, Torrey commented, "Five or six species . . . were collected by Dr. James on the Platte and Cana-dian."[631] One of those was likely *O. rhombipetala*.
On August 28 the party traveled downstream on the Canadian in Oklahoma from near Minco, Grady County, to three or four miles northeast of Newcastle near the McClain/Cleveland county line.

Oenothera villosa Thunb., Prodr. Fl. Cap. 75. 1792.[632] (Common Evening Primrose).
#149 *Oenothera biennis* L., in Torr., Ann. Lyc. Nat. Hist. N.Y. 2:201.1827. "Base of the Rocky Mountains."
James recorded this species on July 5.[633] That was the day that he made a side trip up Clear Creek, just north of Denver in Adams County, Colorado.

Stenosiphon linifolius (Nutt. ex James) Heynh., Nom. 2:704. 1840. (Stenosiphon).
Gaura linifolia Nutt. ex James, Long Exped. (Phila. ed.) 2:100. 1823.
#142 *Gaura linifolia* Nutt. mss. *James in Long's Exped.* ii. p. 100, in Torr., Ann. Lyc. Nat. Hist. N.Y. 2:200.1827. "On the upper part of the

---

[630]JAMES [3], August 28.
[631]TORREY [2], 201–2.
[632]*O. strigosa* (Rydb.) Mack. & Bush of many American authors. DIETRICH AND RAVEN, 382–83.
[633]JAMES [1], I, 50ln.; JAMES [2] in THWAITES [1], XV, 28ln. (as *Oe. diennis*); JAMES [3], July 5.

Canadian. A beautiful species, with white flowers. Mr. Nuttall found this plant on the Salt River."

Under the date of August 8, this plant was described by James in his diary[634] with nearly identical wording to that used in the Account.[635] On that day the expedition traveled down the Canadian River in Oldham County, Texas.

Since the original description was based on James's plant, it seems that the type (NY) should be the James collection from Texas. On this type sheet is also found the Nuttall collection from Salt River (Cimarron River in Oklahoma).

Ophioglossaceae

Botrychium virginianum (L.) Sw., in Schrad., J. Bot. 2:111.1802. (Rattlesnake Fern).

James reported this plant on May 29, along the Missouri River in the area of Engineer Cantonment.[636] That location was some five miles downstream from Fort Calhoun, Washington County, Nebraska.

Orchidaceae

Habenaria hyperborea (L.) R.Br., in Ait., Hort. Kew. ed.2, 5:193. 1813. (Northern Green Orchis).

#434 *Orchis dilatata* Pursh, in Torr., Ann. Lyc. Nat. Hist. N.Y. 2:250.1827. "Sources of the Platte and Arkansa."

James, too, referred to this plant as *Orchis dilatata*.[637] This species, however, grows at higher elevations than those at which James made his July 10 collection near Elephant Rock (7,400 feet), a mile or so east of Palmer Lake, El Paso County, Colorado.

It seems likely that James collected the similar *Habenaria hyperborea,* which occurs at the elevation of Palmer Lake.

Orobanchaceae

Orobanche multiflora Nutt., Jour. Acad. Nat. Sci. Phila. II. 1:179. 1848. (Broomrape).

---

[634]JAMES [3], August 8.
[635]JAMES [6], II, 100, 100n.; JAMES [7], II, 287, 355–56.
[636]JAMES [3], May 29.
[637]JAMES [1], II, 15n.; JAMES [2] in THWAITES [1], XV, 306n.; JAMES [3], July 10. All are erroneously dated July 11.

#331 *Orobanche ludoviciana* Nutt., in Torr., Ann. Lyc. Nat. Hist. N.Y. 2:231.1827. "Sources of the Canadian."

James described this plant in his diary for August 6.[638] For that same day in the *Account* a probable *Orobanche ludoviciana* is mentioned.[639]

The diary description of "large" purple flowers on a plant "sometimes nearly a foot high" is somewhat better for *O. multiflora,* a species not described until 1848.

On August 6, a Sunday, the party remained in camp on the Canadian River, approximately three miles east of the New Mexico/Texas line in Oldham County, Texas.

Papaveraceae

Argemone polyanthemos (Fedde) G.B. Ownb., Mem. Torr. Bot. Club 21:128.1958. (Prickly Poppy).

Argemone alba James, Long Exped. (Phila. ed.) 1:461.1823.[640] [Not of Raf., 1817].

#15 *Argemone mexicana* β *albiflora* DC., in Torr., Ann. Lyc. Nat. Hist. N.Y. 2:166.1827. "Along the Platte and Canadian rivers; abundant."

James referred in his diary for June 20 to a prickly poppy as *Argemone mexicana.*[641] Following his description he stated, "Probably an undescribed species."

The type of *A. alba* James was collected on June 20 on the sandhills near Gothenburg, Dawson County, Nebraska. This poppy may be found there along the roadsides today.

On July 21 James referred in the *Account* to "the white argemone"[642] and "the Mexican argemone"[643] while the party was camped on the Arkansas River, near Rocky Ford, Otero County, Colorado.

Again in mid August along the Canadian River in the eastern Texas panhandle, James was likely seeing this species when he noted argemone.[644]

[638]JAMES [3], August 6.

[639]JAMES [1], II, 96; JAMES [2] in THWAITES [1], XVI, 98. In both editions the information is included with that dated August 4.

[640]The description and comments are repeated in the London edition (see JAMES [7], II, 149).

[641]JAMES [3], June 20 (erroneously dated June 19).

[642]JAMES [1], II, 63.

[643]JAMES [2] in THWAITES [1], XVI, 57.

[644]JAMES [1], II, 120; JAMES [2] in THWAITES [1], XVI, 126.

Phrymaceae

Phryma leptostachya L., Sp. Pl. 601. 1753. (Lopseed).
The only reference we find to this is in the diary.[645] The plant would have been collected on August 25 along the Canadian River in Canadian County, Oklahoma.
No James specimen was found at NY.

Phytolaccaceae

Phytolacca americana L., Sp. Pl. 41. 1753. (Pokeweed).
#383 *Phytolacca decandra* L., in Torr., Ann. Lyc. Nat. Hist. N.Y. 2:240.1827. "On the Canadian and upper part of the Arkansa."
According to the *Account, Phytolacca* was noted as beginning to occur on August 14,[646] when we believe they were in Roberts County, Texas. That is far west for the species, but it has been collected along the Canadian in Hemphill County, Texas, which is immediately adjacent to the east of Roberts County.
Phytolacca is mentioned again in the *Account* for August 27, when they were in northern Grady County, Oklahoma,[647] but it is mentioned only once in the diary on August 29, when their location was Cleveland County, Oklahoma.[648]

Pinaceae

In the area where James traveled there are five species of conifers whose leaves are borne singly, and that is the number of such species James referred to in his diary and the *Account*. On July 10, James mentioned "two species of Abies" in the diary.[649] In the *Account* for that day are listed "the black and hemlock spruce (Abies *nigra* and A. *canadensis*)."[650] During their travel on July 10 from near Palmer Lake to their evening encampment at the Air Force Academy, El Paso County, Colorado, it is likely that the two species encountered were *Pseudotsuga menziesii* (Mirb.) Franco (Rocky Mountain Douglas-fir) and *Picea pungens* Engelm. (Blue spruce).

[645]JAMES [3], August 25.
[646]JAMES [1], II, 119; JAMES [2] in THWAITES [1], XVI, 125.
[647]JAMES [1], II, 146; JAMES [2] in THWAITES [1], XVI, 156.
[648]JAMES [3], August 29.
[649]JAMES [3], July 10 (erroneously dated July 11).
[650]JAMES [1], II, 15n. (erroneously dated July 11); JAMES [2] in THWAITES [1], XV, 306n. (dated "July 11th [10th and 11th]").

On July 14 James mentioned *Abies rubra, A. alba,* and *A. nigra* in the diary.[651] In addition to those three in the diary, James included *Abies balsamea* and *A. canadensis* in the *Account* on July 15.[652] They were all recorded as having been seen on Pikes Peak, El Paso County, Colorado. In addition to the Rocky Mountain Douglas-fir and Blue spruce, at this higher elevation James should have encountered *Abies concolor* (Gord. & Glend.) Lindl. ex Hildebr., (White fir), *Abies lasiocarpa* (Hook.) Nutt. (Subalpine fir), and *Picea engelmannii* Parry ex Engelm. (Engelmann spruce).

Torrey included only the following three: #429 *Pinus nigra* Pursh, #430 *Pinus canadensis* Pursh, and #431 *Pinus balsamea* L.[653] All three were stated to be from "[o]n the Rocky Mountains." Surely they refer to three of the five single-needled conifers that James should have encountered (as discussed above).

Pinus flexilis James, Long Exped. (Phila. ed.) 2:27, 34–35. 1823. (Limber Pine).

#428 *Pinus flexilis* James, in Torr., Ann. Lyc. Nat. Hist. N.Y. 2:249.1827. "On the Rocky Mountains, extending from their base to the region of perpetual frost."

In his diary James referred to this tree as "Pinus Banksiana?" and added, "Leaves 5 in a fascicle, branches remarkably flexible."[654] Many pages later, following most of the lengthy entry for August 14, James gave a full description of his new pine. There he remarked that this is the "P. Banksiana" of his earlier entry. The published description appears in the *Account* under the dates July 14 and 15.[655] The type was collected on July 14 on the slopes of Pikes Peak, El Paso County, Colorado.

Pinus ponderosa Dougl. ex Laws., Agr. Man. 354. 1836. (Ponderosa Pine).

#427 *Pinus resinosa* L., in Torr., Ann. Lyc. Nat. Hist. N.Y. 2:249. 1827. "On the Rocky Mountains."

On July 10 James mentioned *P. resinosa,* which has long needles.[656] The ponderosa pine would have been the only long-needled pine

[651]JAMES [3], July 14 (erroneously dated July 15).
[652]JAMES [1], II, 34; JAMES [2] in THWAITES [1], XVI, 25.
[653]TORREY [2], 250.
[654]JAMES [3], July 14 (erroneously dated July 15).
[655]JAMES [6], II, 27, 34–35; JAMES [7], II, 216, 224–25.
[656]JAMES [1], II, 15n., July 10 (erroneously dated July 11); JAMES [2] in THWAITES [1], XV, 306n., July 11 (as "July 11th [10th and 11th]"); JAMES [3], July 10 (erroneously dated July 11).

encountered as the party traveled southward from Dawson Butte, Douglas County, past Palmer Lake and on to their encampment at the Air Force Academy, El Paso County, Colorado.

Plantaginaceae

Plantago eriopoda Torr. (Redwool Plantain).
#367 *Plantago eriopoda* Torr., Ann. Lyc. Nat. Hist. N.Y. 2:237. 1827. "Depressed and moist situations along the Platte."
This same habitat is given in the *Account* for a plantago that James said was "manifestly allied to P. *eriophora* of Wallich, . . . to P. *attenuata* of the same work. . . . Its leaves, which are the size of those of P. *lanceolata*, are smooth, five nerved, with a few remote denticulations."[657]
Gray listed P. *attenuata* of the *Account* in synonymy under P. *eriopoda*, with the James specimen indicated as having come from Colorado.[658]
In his diary, James referred to this plant from along the Platte River as P. *glabra* and stated that it was "manifestly allied to P. eriophora."[659] The description given there is closely repeated in the *Account* for the plantago said to be allied to P. *eriophora* and P. *attenuata*.[660] The *Account* makes no mention of the name P. *glabra*.
James listed in his *Catalogue* Plantago glabra Nutt. from "moist soils and on the upper part of the Platte."[661] The name and location are those of his diary and refer to the plant that became the type of P. *eriopoda* Torr.
It is clear that all of these references are to the same collection, as evidenced from the dates and the similar descriptions and habitats.
#366 *Plantago glabra* Nutt., in Torr., Ann. Lyc. Nat. Hist. N.Y. 2:237.1827. "Moist soils on the upper part of the Platte." It will be noticed that this entry is almost identical to James's entry in his *Catalogue* for P. *glabra*. We think the *Catalogue* is the basis for Torrey's #366 entry. Torrey apparently included #366, P. *glabra* Nutt., in addition to #367, P. *eriopoda*, because he did not realize that the P. *glabra* of James's *Catalogue* is based on the same plant as Torrey's P. *eriopoda*. It is also possible that Torrey did not take P.

657JAMES [1], I, 455n.; JAMES [2] in THWAITES [1], XV, 226n.
658GRAY [4], 390.
659JAMES [3], June 15 (erroneously dated June 14).
660JAMES [1], I, 455n.; JAMES [2] in THWAITES [1], XV, 226n.
661JAMES [4], 175.

glabra solely from the *Catalogue.* He may have had another, or perhaps a mixed, collection of James's from along the Platte that in considerable part fit Nuttall's description of *P. glabra.* It may be that #366 refers to what later became *P. rugelii.*

Nuttall collected his plant, whose type is unknown, near Fort Mandan in 1811. He stated that the leaves were ovate and denticulate, the flowers scattered, and the bracts ovate and acuminate.[662] Little of this fits *P. eriopoda,* whose flowers are scattered but whose leaves are not ovate. The type specimen shows them to be four to eight times longer than broad and tapered at both ends, fitting very well James's "lanceolate" in his diary and Torrey's "lato-lanceolatis" in the original description. Further, the bracts of *P. eriopoda* are rounded at the top and not acuminate.

Nuttall's description of the leaves and inflorescence well fits *P. rugelii* Dcne., but the shape of the bracts does not. *P. rugelii,* which also occurs in North Dakota, was not described until 1852.

Gray,[663] Pilger,[664] and Bassett[665] all believed the application of *P. glabra* to be uncertain. We agree.

The type (NY) of *P. eriopoda* was collected by James on June 15 along the Platte River, either in Hall County or adjacent eastern Buffalo County, Nebraska.

Plantago patagonica Jacq., Icon. Pl. Rar. 2:9, pl.306. 1786–1793. (Woolly Plantain).

#364 *Plantago gnaphaloides* Nutt., in Torr., Ann. Lyc. Nat. Hist. N.Y. 2:236.1827. "On the Platte."

James mentioned this plant, as *P. Lagopus* Pursh, in his diary.[666] He referred to this plant on June 9, either as the party traveled up Shell Creek (from northwest of Schuyler, Colfax County, to southeast of Platte Center, Platte County) or at their evening's campsite on the Loup River just west of the mouth of Looking Glass Creek, approximately two miles east of Monroe, Platte County, Nebraska. On July 1, this plant is again mentioned as the party traveled west across the plain from near Fort Morgan, Morgan County, Colorado, to just east of Masters, Weld County, Colorado.

---

[662]NUTTALL [5], I, 100.
[663]GRAY [4], 392.
[664]PILGER, 98.
[665]BASSETT, 569.
[666]JAMES [3], June 9 and July 1.

The plant is referred to in the *Account* on June 9 and June 29.[667]

Platanaceae

Platanus occidentalis L., Sp. Pl. 999. 1753. (Sycamore).

In his diary for September 1, James commented that the sycamore "begins to appear along the river."[668] The tree is also noted that day in the *Account*.[669]

We estimate that the party traveled nineteen miles on September 1 and camped on the Canadian approximately two miles southeast of Konawa, Seminole County, Oklahoma. There the sycamore is near its westernmost range along the Canadian.

James continued to note the sycamore as the party traveled down the Canadian River.[670]

Polemoniaceae

Collomia linearis Nutt., Gen. No. Am. Pl. 1:126.1818.

#272 *Collomia linearis* Nutt., in Torr., Ann. Lyc. Nat. Hist. N.Y. 2:220.1827. "Sources of the Arkansa, near the Rocky Mountains."

James listed this in his *Catalogue* as *Collomia linearis* Nutt., "Near the Rocky Mountains."[671] This plant is known to occur in south-central Colorado in the Royal Gorge area on the Arkansas River, as Torrey's location would indicate. In his diary for June 27, however, James listed *Phlox linearis,* with a brief description: "Small, flower white, tube of the corrolla nearly strait."[672] On that day the party traveled in northeastern Colorado along the south side of the South Platte River, from west of Julesburg, Sedgwick County, to southeast of Crook, Logan County. There, too, the species is within its known range.

Gilia pinnatifida Nutt. ex Gray, Proc. Amer. Acad. Sci. 8:276. 1870.

On June 30, James described in detail in his diary a plant that must surely have become this species, as the characteristics he gave agree

[667]JAMES [1], I, 433, 488; JAMES [2] in THWAITES [1], XV, 200, 263.
[668]JAMES [3], September 1.
[669]JAMES [1], II, 152; JAMES [2] in THWAITES [1], XVI, 164.
[670]JAMES [1], II, 155, 161; JAMES [2] in THWAITES [1], XVI, 161, 174.
[671]JAMES [4], 176.
[672]JAMES [3], June 27.

well: The corolla lobes are rounded; the plant is viscid; the fruits are about equal to the length of the persistent calyx; the basal leaves are pinnatifid; and the cauline leaves are frequently linear.[673] James, however, stated, "Stamina unequal the three longer filaments bearing smaller anthers." That condition occurs in the material examined only infrequently.

James's collection likely was made near their evening camp, near the mouth of Bijou Creek, just west of Fort Morgan, Morgan County, Colorado.

The stated type locality for Nuttall's plant, "Lewis River [Snake River], Rocky Mts.,"[674] is a little northwest of the known range of the species. Perhaps Nuttall's collection came from the Green River in southern Wyoming.

Ipomopsis aggregata (Pursh) V. Grant, El Aliso 3:360.1956. (Skyrocket Ipomopsis).

#277 *Cantua aggregata* Pursh, in Torr., Ann. Lyc. Nat. Hist. N.Y. 2:220.1827. "With the preceding ['On the Canadian.']."

A detailed description of this plant was given by James in his diary for July 3.[675] On that day the party traveled west from Kuner, Weld County, and finally south up the South Platte River to about three miles south of Platteville, Weld County, Colorado.

Ipomopsis longiflora (Torr.) V. Grant, El Aliso 3:361.1956. (White Ipomopsis).

#278 *Cantua longiflora* Torr., Ann. Lyc. Nat. Hist. N.Y. 2:221. 1827. (Followed by Latin and English descriptions). "On the Canadian."

James described this plant in his diary for August 16.[676] All of that day the party was along the Canadian River in Hemphill County, Texas. There, then, is where the type (NY) was collected.

On August 6, James stated in the *Account* that they saw "an ipomopsis."[677] It is possible this date is incorrect, as the plant is recorded in the diary only for August 16.

Ipomopsis rubra (L.) Wherry, Bartonia No. 18. 56. 1936. (Standing Cypress).

[673]JAMES [3], June 30.
[674]CRONQUIST [1], IV, 120.
[675]JAMES [3], July 3.
[676]JAMES [3], August 16.
[677]JAMES [1], II, 96; JAMES [2] in THWAITES [1], XVI, 98.

#276 *Cantua coronopifolia* Willd., in Torr., Ann. Lyc. Nat. Hist. N.Y. 2:220.1827. "On the Canadian."

Based on the known distribution of this plant, it seems likely that it was collected in the eastern half of Oklahoma along the Canadian or Arkansas rivers in late August or early September.

Leptodactylon pungens (Torr.) Nutt., Jour. Acad. Phila. n.s. 1:157.1848.

#279 *Cantua pungens* Torr., Ann. Lyc. Nat. Hist. N.Y. 2:221.1827. (Followed by Latin and English descriptions). "Valley of the Loup Fork?"

The Loup River, especially that portion of it where James traveled, is far out of range of this species. It is probable that this new species was collected in late June or early July along the South Platte River, anywhere from Fort Morgan, Morgan County, Colorado to Denver.

#286 *Diapensia barbulata* Ell., in Torr., Ann. Lyc. Nat. Hist. N.Y. 2:223.1827. "Gravelly plains along the Platte. *Dr. James.*" Here Torrey remarked, "There were no specimens of this plant in the collection. I suspect there is some mistake in assigning it a station so far west."

James stated that the plant was "[o]n the gravelly plains of the Platte."[678] It seems likely that the location is correct and that James misidentified the plant. It now appears that this plant, which James called *Diapensia barbulata,* was what became *Leptodactylon pungens.*

On the type sheet (NY) is a note written by E. T. Wherry that states, "The Journal of the expedition shows that this is *not* from 'the Loup Fork' but from the Forks of the Platte, namely at lat. 41° 08', long. 100° 43'." This North Platte, Lincoln County, Nebraska, location, which is also a bit too far east for the species, is in reference to plants "approximating to Hoitzia."[679] Those, we believe, should be identified as *Phlox planitiarum* A. Nels., *q.v.*

Phlox pilosa L. var. **fulgida** Wherry, Bartonia No.12. 47. 1930. (Prairie Phlox).

#274 *Phlox aristata* Michx., in Torr., Ann. Lyc. Nat. Hist. N.Y. 2:220.1827. "Valley of the Loup Fork."

If Torrey's location is correct, this would have been collected during the second week of June at the west edge of its range, somewhere along the Loup River in Nance County, Nebraska.

[678]JAMES [4], 176.
[679]JAMES [1], I, 468n.; JAMES [2] in THWAITES [1], XV, 241n.

Phlox planitiarum A. Nels., Univ. Wyo. Publ. Bot. 1:49.1924. (Plains Phlox).

#275 *Phlox Hoodii* Richard., in Torr., Ann. Lyc. Nat. Hist. N.Y. 2:220.1827. "Valley of the Loup Fork."

The specific epithet *andicola* with varying authors is frequently used as the name for this taxon. Following his description of *P. Douglasii* var. *longifolia,* Gray commented that Nuttall had used the unpublished name *P. andicola* for this form.[680] Because *P. andicola* is cited, Gray's article has been taken as the place of publication for this Nuttallian name. We do not believe that the name, which was only incidentally mentioned by Gray, was ever validly published there or elsewhere.

Wherry, under the name *P. andicola* Nutt. ex Gray, accepted Torrey's location, stating further that the plant was collected "2 miles northeast of the present village of Duncan."[681] That is in Platte County, Nebraska, about four miles south of the Loup River, a location a little too far south and a little downstream from where the party intersected the Loup River. Anywhere along the Loup River where James traveled is too far east for *P. planitiarum.* It seems very likely that this is the plant that James referred to as "Hoitzia" in the *Account* and that it was collected at the forks of the Platte, Lincoln County, Nebraska, on June 23, or from there along the South Platte River to the Colorado line, June 24 to June 26.[682]

Polemonium delicatum Rydb., Bull. Torr. Bot. Club 28:29.1901. (Jacob's Ladder).

The type was collected by Rydberg and Vreeland from West Spanish Peak, Huerfano County, Colorado. The second of two specimens cited is "Colorado or New Mexico: Canadian?, Dr. James."

Literature indicates that this species occurs at elevations from 8,200 feet up to timberline.[683] James's plant would have been collected July 13–15 when he climbed Pikes Peak, El Paso County, Colorado, inasmuch as that was the only time he was at the proper elevation.

Polemonium foliosissimum (Gray) Gray, Syn. Fl. No. Am. 2¹:151. 1878. (Leafy Jacob's Ladder).

[680]GRAY [5], 254.
[681]WHERRY, 9.
[682]JAMES [1], I, 468n.; JAMES [2] in THWAITES [1], XV, 241n.
[683]DAVIDSON, 245; HARRINGTON, 441; WEBER [1], 259.

#271 *Polemonium mexicanum* in Torr., Ann. Lyc. Nat. Hist. N.Y. 2:220.1827. "On the Canadian?"

The frequency of occurrence and the distribution of *P. foliosissimum* along the route of the expedition in Colorado make it a more likely choice than the similar *P. occidentale*. James could have collected *P. foliosissimum* at several places in Colorado, from Weld County in late June to Pueblo County in mid July.

Polygalaceae

Polygala alba Nutt., Gen. No. Am. Pl. 2:87.1818. (White Milkwort).
#32 *Polygala alba* Nutt., in Torr., Ann. Lyc. Nat. Hist. N.Y. 2:168.1827. "On the Missouri."

In the diary, James mentioned this plant under the date of June 21.[684] On that day the party traveled a little more than twenty miles up the Platte from near Gothenburg, Dawson County, Nebraska, to about six miles west of Maxwell, Lincoln County, Nebraska.

P. torreyi G. Don, Gen. Hist. 1:360.1831. Based on "Polygala, nov. spec. Torrey in ann. lyc. new york, 2, p.164." (The page 164 is an error for 168, where Torrey's **#31** *Polygala n.sp.?* occurs). Here G. Don translated Torrey's Latin description of **#31** *Polygala n.sp.*, although the word "dissitis" is erroneously translated as "crowded" rather than "well-spaced." The location is given as "Native of North America on the Rocky Mountains."

Polygala jamesii Raf., Atl. Jour. 1:146.1832. Also based on **#31** *Polygala n.sp. ?* Torr., Ann. Lyc. Nat. Hist. N.Y. 2:168.1827. A Latin description is given, but no location is mentioned.

The only other places that we have found *P. jamesii* are in the *Index Kewensis* and *Index Rafinesquianus*.[685]

The sheet (NY) containing what is presumably the type of *P. torreyi* and the later *P. jamesii* has been annotated by S. F. Blake as *P. alba* Nutt.

The label for James's specimen reads "Polygala n.sp.? Ann. Lyc. 2: p.168." Neither the name *P. torreyi* nor *P. jamesii* appears on the sheet.

On the sheet, along with James's specimen, are two others, and we think that Blake's annotation refers to all three.

James could have made his second collection of *P. alba* in any of the five states through which he traveled.

---

[684]JAMES [3], June 21 (erroneously dated June 20).
[685]MERRILL, 151.

Polygonaceae

Eriogonum annuum Nutt., Trans. Am. Phil. Soc. n.s. 5:164.1835. (Annual Wild Buckwheat).

#389 *Eriogonum annuum, n.sp. Nutt. mss.*, in Torr., Ann. Lyc. Nat. Hist. N.Y. 2:241.1827. "Near the Rocky Mountains. Found also on the Arkansa by Mr. Nuttall. Root annual!"

Based on the time that this species is most usually in full flower and the area where it is most abundant, James likely collected it in August along the Canadian River in the Texas panhandle or in the western half of Oklahoma.

Eriogonum jamesii Benth., in DC., Prodr. 14:7.1856. (James's Wild Buckwheat).

#388 *Eriogonum sericeum* Pursh, in Torr., Ann. Lyc. Nat. Hist. N.Y. 2:241.1827. "Sources of the Platte."

Bentham indicated that Torrey's *E. sericeum* in the Ann. Lyc. is *E. jamesii*. A similar comment was later made by Torrey and Gray.[686]

We have been unable to locate a description in the diary of what became *E. jamesii*. The *E. sericeum* referred to in the diary is var. *flavescens,* which follows.[687]

The type of *E. jamesii* may be one of "several species of Eriogonum" James collected on July 26 near their encampment in Bachicha Canyon, about twelve miles northeast of the junction of State Highway 389 and U.S. Highway 160, Section 6, T32S, R56W, in southern Las Animas County, Colorado.[688]

Eriogonum jamesii var. **flavescens** Wats., Proc. Am. Acad. Sci. 12:255.1877.

In his diary for July 5, James listed "Eriogonum sericeum Ph." among the plants seen on his excursion up Clear Creek near Denver, Adams County, Colorado.[689] *E. sericeum* is also listed in the *Account* for this same location.[690]

James would have used Pursh's *Flora* in identifying the plant. Pursh described the flowers of *E. sericeum* as being "bright yellow"

---

[686]TORREY AND GRAY [2], 155.
[687]JAMES [3], July 5.
[688]JAMES [1], II, 73; JAMES [2] in THWAITES [1], XVI, 71.
[689]JAMES [3], July 5.
[690]JAMES [1], I, 501n.; JAMES [2] in THWAITES [1], XV, 281n.

and "covered with long silky down."[691] Thus, the plant that James saw must have been yellow flowered, as in variety *flavescens*.

Eriogonum tenellum Torr.

#390 *Eriogonum tenellum* Torr., Ann. Lyc. Nat. Hist. N.Y. 2:241. 1827. "With the preceding ['Near the Rocky Mountains.']." Type: NY.

James described this plant, which he thought was a new species of *Eriogonum,* in his diary.[692] In the *Account* on that day, James likely included it among the "several species of Eriogonum" collected about their encampment.[693]

The party was then camped in Bachicha Canyon, about twelve miles northeast of the junction of State Highway 389 and U.S. Highway 160, Section 6, T32S, R56W, in southern Las Animas County, Colorado.

Eriogonum umbellatum Torr. (Sulphur-Flower).

#391 *Eriogonum umbellatum* Torr., Ann. Lyc. Nat. Hist. N.Y. 2:241–42.1827. "With the preceding ['Near the Rocky Mountains.']."

The type (NY) was most likely collected on July 7 in Jefferson County, Colorado, when James crossed the South Platte and climbed to the southeast side of Sheep Mountain above the chasm of the Platte.

Oxyria digyna (L.) Hill, Hort. Kew. 158. 1768. (Alpine Sorrel).

#2 *Oxyria reniformis* R. Br., in Torr., Ann. Lyc. Nat. Hist. N.Y. 1:31.1824. "With the preceding ['On James' Peak . . . near the region of perpetual snow.']."

#386 *Oxyria reniformis* R. Br., in Torr., Ann. Lyc. Nat. Hist. N.Y. 2:240.1827. "Rocky Mountains."

James would have collected this on July 14 or 15 on Pikes Peak, El Paso County, Colorado. Torrey noted that James's collection was the second of this species from North America, the first having been from Labrador.[694]

Polygonum aviculare L., Sp. Pl. 362. 1753. (Knotweed).

#385 *Polygonum aviculare* β *glaucum* Torr., Ann. Lyc. Nat. Hist. N.Y. 2:240.1827. "*P. glaucum,* Nutt. gen.i.p.254. . . . Common on the Platte and Arkansa, near the Rocky Mountains."

[691]PURSH, 277.
[692]JAMES [3], July 26.
[693]JAMES [1], II, 73; JAMES [2] in THWAITES [1], XVI, 71.
[694]TORREY [1], 31.

Torrey's #385 would not have been Nuttall's *glaucum,* which is far out of range; it could well, however, have been one of the other species in the area that closely resembles *P. aviculare.*

James mentioned *P. aviculare* in his diary for June 12, the day that the party traveled up the Loup River past the Pawnee villages, Nance County, Nebraska.[695] It is mentioned again in the diary for June 14 as the party traveled south from the Loup River to the Platte through Merrick County, Nebraska.[696]

Polygonum lapathifolium L., Sp. Pl. 360. 1753. (Pale Smartweed) and

Polygonum virginianum L., Sp. Pl. 360. 1753. (Jumpseed).

James listed these plants in his diary for August 25.[697] On that day the party traveled along the Canadian from near Bridgeport, Caddo County, to northeast of Cedar Lake, Canadian County, Oklahoma.

On the same day a third species was mentioned as *P. persicaria.* It is possible that this Old World introduction was made by the Spanish into New Mexico and, like *Chenopodium album,* later came down the Canadian. It is also possible that James had some other species of the *Persicaria* group, perhaps *Polygonum persicarioides* (HBK.) Small.

Polygonum viviparum L., Sp. Pl. 360. 1753. (Alpine Bistort).

#7 *Polygonum viviparum* β *capitatum* Torr., Ann. Lyc. Nat. Hist. N.Y. 1:34.1824. "With the preceding ['On James' Peak . . . near the region of perpetual snow.']."

#384 *Polygonum viviparum* L., in Torr., Ann. Lyc. Nat. Hist. N.Y. 2:240.1827. "Rocky Mountains." Here Torrey concluded that his variety should not be maintained.

James would have collected the type on Pikes Peak, July 14 or 15, El Paso County, Colorado.

Rumex venosus Pursh, Fl. Am. Sept. 733. 1814. (Wild Begonia).

#387 *Rumex venosus* Pursh, in Torr., Ann. Lyc. Nat. Hist. N.Y. 2:241.1827. "Sandy plains on the upper part of the Platte."

In his diary for June 19, James wrote, "Rumex venosus? valves more

---

[695]JAMES [3], June 12.
[696]JAMES [3], June 14 (included as part of the June 13 entry).
[697]JAMES [3], August 25.

than an inch wide and beautifully colored."[698] For that same day in the *Account, Rumex venosus* is listed.[699]

The collection, marked "Long's Expedition Upper part of the Platte Dr. James." (NY), was made on the sandhills near Gothenburg, Dawson County, Nebraska.

Portulacaceae

Portulaca oleracea L., Sp. Pl. 445. 1753. (Purslane).

#152 *Portulaca oleracea* L., in Torr., Ann. Lyc. Nat. Hist. N.Y. 2:202.1827. "Sources of the Platte and Canadian. Indigenous."

James commented in his diary on the afternoon of July 1 about the abundance of this plant "in depressed and saline soils."[700] At that time the party was traveling from just west of Masters to near Kuner, Weld County, Colorado.

In the *Account* appears the remark that this species "is one of the most frequent plants about the base of the Rocky Mountains, particularly in places much frequented as licks by the bisons and other animals."[701] On that day, a Sunday, July 2, the party stayed in camp on the South Platte, near Kuner, Weld County, Colorado.

James mentioned the species again on August 1, at which time the party was camped at the confluence of Garcia and Ute creeks, about six miles east and a little north of Yates, Harding County, New Mexico.[702]

Years later Gray made this comment, "Common in cult. grounds around dwellings, and, as is thought, indigenous on the plains of Arkansas, Texas, and westward."[703] Inasmuch as the species is thought by some to be introduced into this country, it is possible that James collected a different species.

Portulaca pilosa L., Sp. Pl. 445. 1753. (Shaggy Portulaca).

#153 *Portulaca pilosa* L., in Torr., Ann. Lyc. Nat. Hist. N.Y. 2:202.1827. "With the preceding ['Sources of the Platte and Canadian.']; common." "The specimens of this plant were all in fruit, so that the color of the corolla cannot be ascertained."

---

[698]JAMES [3], June 19.
[699]JAMES [1], I, 461n.; JAMES [2] in THWAITES [1], XV, 233n.
[700]JAMES [3], July 1.
[701]JAMES [1], I, 494; JAMES [2] in THWAITES [1], XV, 273.
[702]JAMES [3], August 1.
[703]GRAY [2], 263.

Portulaca mundula I.M. Johnston, Jour. Arn. Arb. 29:195.1948. Treating *P. mundula* as a synonym is in accordance with Matthews et al.[704]

James made no mention of this plant in his diary, but in the *Account* for July 30, he spoke of a species of *Portulaca* "observed on the Arkansa."[705] The leaf axils were described as pilose and the leaves "narrower than in *P. oleracea*." This purslane is likely *P. pilosa,* but if the flowers were yellow, then James's plant may have been *P. parvula* Gray, itself a questionable species.

James probably made his collection July 22–24 near Rocky Ford, Otero County, Colorado.

Talinum calycinum Engelm., in Wisliz., Tour Northern Mex. 88. 1848. (Fameflower).

#154 *Talinum, n.sp. Nutt. mss.*, in Torr., Ann. Lyc. Nat. Hist. N.Y. 2:202.1827. "On the Canadian. A polyandrous species, with large purple flowers."

Torrey and Gray doubtless referred to this plant under *Talinum teretifolium* Pursh, where they cited a James specimen from "Arkansas."[706] The species is far out of range, as presently understood, of James's route. James very probably collected his plant in mid August in western Oklahoma. August is late for *T. calycinum* to flower, but August collections are not unknown.

Talinum parviflorum Nutt., in T. & G., Fl. No. Am. 1:197.1838. (Prairie Fameflower).

On June 28, in his diary, James described this plant as "Pent. Mon." followed by a lengthy description.[707] Here the calyx is described as "2-leaved persistent"; the seeds as numerous attached to a columella; the leaves as radical, linear lanceolate and fleshy; and the "[s]cape and flowers somewhat resembling those of drosera rotundifolia."

Many authors list the sepals as being deciduous, but we have seen several specimens from the western part of the Great Plains whose sepals are still present in fruiting condition.

A "very small white-flowered species of talinum" was listed in the *Account* among the plants collected on June 27.[708] That is

---

[704]MATTHEWS, KETRON, AND ZANE, 71.
[705]JAMES [1], II, 86; JAMES [2] in THWAITES [1], XVI, 86.
[706]TORREY AND GRAY [1], I, 197.
[707]JAMES [3], June 28.
[708]JAMES [1], I, 484; JAMES [2] in THWAITES [1], XV, 259.

doubtless the same plant that James described in his diary a day later.

On June 28 James traveled up the South Platte River from just east of Crook, to a couple of miles west of Sterling, all in Logan County, Colorado.

Potamogetonaceae

In the genus *Potamogeton* we cannot be sure of all the species that are referred to by James[709] or Torrey.[710]

The following are only possible identifications for some of the species:

Potamogeton diversifolius Raf., Med. Repos. Hex. II. 5:354.1808. (Waterthread Pondweed).

#450 *Potamogeton diversifolium* Bart., *sensu* Torr., Ann. Lyc. Nat. Hist. N.Y. 2:252.1827. "Sources of the Canadian?"

Potamogeton diversifolius Bart. (1815) is a later homonym.

On July 30 the party traveled across the Don Carlos Hills, from Sierra Grande to Ute Creek, western Union County, New Mexico; James listed a *Potamogeton* for that day.[711] Where he found a suitable habitat for a *Potamogeton* is hard to say. Possibly there was a pool in Ute Creek, which was otherwise dry that day.

Potamogeton gramineus L., Sp. Pl. 177. 1753. (Variable Pondweed).

James referred to this plant as "Potamogeton gramineum" in the diary,[712] and no other reference is made to it except in the *Catalogue*.[713] On that day, June 16, James collected near the Platte River in Buffalo County, Nebraska.

Potamogeton illinoensis Morong, Bot. Gaz. 5:50.1880. (Shining Pondweed).

James collected a *Potamogeton* that he called *P. lucens* on June 13, after the party crossed the Loup River to the south side near the Nance/Merrick county line, Nebraska.[714]

[709]JAMES [1], I, 455; JAMES [2] in THWAITES [1], XV, 226; JAMES [3], June 13, 16, July 30; JAMES [4], 176.
[710]TORREY [2], 252.
[711]JAMES [3], July 30.
[712]JAMES [3], June 16 (erroneously dated June 15).
[713]JAMES [4], 176.
[714]JAMES [3], June 13.

Potamogeton natans L., Sp. Pl. 126. 1753. (Floatingleaf Pond-weed).

#448 *Potamogeton natans* L., in Torr., Ann. Lyc. Nat. Hist. N.Y. 2:252.1827. "Ponds near the Platte."

In the *Account* on June 16, this plant is said to occur in "some small ponds near the Platte."[715]

The collection was made near the Platte River in Buffalo County, Nebraska.

Potamogeton nodosus Poir., in Lam., Enc. Meth. Bot., Suppl. 4:535.1816. (Longleaf Pondweed).

#449 *Potamogeton fluitans* L., in Torr., Ann. Lyc. Nat. Hist. N.Y. 2:252.1827. "With the preceding ['Ponds near the Platte.']."

James listed *P. fluitans* in his diary for June 16.[716] On that same day in the *Account* this plant is said to occur in "some small ponds near the Platte."[717]

The collection was made near the Platte River in Buffalo County, Nebraska.

Primulaceae

Androsace carinata Torr. (Rock-Jasmine).

#1 *Androsace carinata* Torr., Ann. Lyc. Nat. Hist. N.Y. 1:30, pl.3, fig.1.1824. "On James' Peak . . . near the region of perpetual snow."

#357 *Androsace carinata* Torr., Ann. Lyc. Nat. Hist. N.Y. 2:235. 1827. "With the preceding ['Rocky Mountains.']."

James collected the type (fragment at GH, *fide* Robbins)[718] of this species on July 14 on Pikes Peak, El Paso County, Colorado.

Androsace occidentalis Pursh, Fl. Am. Sept. 137. 1814. (Western Rock-Jasmine).

#358 *Androsace occidentalis* Nutt., in Torr., Ann. Lyc. Nat. Hist. N.Y. 2:235.1827. "On the Platte."

James without doubt collected this early-flowering species in Nebraska in June.

---

[715]JAMES [1], I, 455; JAMES [2] in THWAITES [1], XV, 226.
[716]JAMES [3], June 16 (erroneously dated June 15).
[717]JAMES [1], I, 455; JAMES [2] in THWAITES [1], XV, 226.
[718]ROBBINS, 148.

Androsace septentrionalis L., Sp. Pl. 142. 1753. (Northern Rock-Jasmine).

#359 *Androsace septentrionalis* Willd., in Torr., Ann. Lyc. Nat. Hist. N.Y. 2:235.1827. "With the preceding? ['On the Platte.']."

Based on flowering time and known distribution, James probably collected this species in July in Colorado.

Dodecatheon pulchellum (Raf.) Merrill, Jour. Arn. Arb. 29:212. 1948. (Shooting Star).

#360 *Dodecatheon Meadia* L., in Torr., Ann. Lyc. Nat. Hist. N.Y. 2:236.1827. "Within the Rocky Mountains."

James referred to this plant in his diary on July 7.[719] There and in the *Account* for the same day[720] it is called *Dodecatheon integrifolium*. In 1840, Rafinesque named this western-American plant *Exinia pulchella*.[721]

On July 7 James ascended the South Platte from the chasm to a point about seven miles southwest of Waterton, Jefferson County, Colorado. This plant still occurs there.

Primula angustifolia Torr. (Alpine Primrose).

#6 *Primula angustifolia* Torr., Ann. Lyc. Nat. Hist. N.Y. 1:34, pl.3, fig.3. 1824. "With the preceding ['On James' Peak . . . near the region of perpetual snow.']."

#356 *Primula angustifolia* Torr., Ann. Lyc. Nat. Hist. N.Y. 2:235. 1827. "Rocky Mountains."

This type (NY) was collected July 14 on Pikes Peak, El Paso County, Colorado.

Samolus ebracteatus HBK. var. **cuneatus** (Small) Henrickson, Southwest. Nat. 28:311.1983. (Water Pimpernel).

#363 *Samolus ebracteatus* Kunth, in Torr., Ann. Lyc. Nat. Hist. N.Y. 2:236.1827. "Saline soils near the base of the Rocky Mountains."

The only other reference to the James collection that we have found is in Gray, where the Torrey reference is cited.[722]

Based on the known distribution of this taxon, James would have collected it in August along the Canadian River in the Texas panhandle or in the western half of Oklahoma.

---

[719]JAMES [3], July 7 (erroneously dated July 8).
[720]JAMES [1], II, 8n.; JAMES [2] in THWAITES [1], XV, 294n.
[721]RAFINESQUE [2], 185.
[722]GRAY [4], 64.

Samolus parviflorus Raf., Am. Monthly Mag. 2:176.1818. (Water Pimpernel).

#362 *Samolus Valerandi* L., in Torr., Ann. Lyc. Nat. Hist. N.Y. 2:236.1827. "On the Canadian."

In his diary for September 8 James listed *Samolus valerandi,* now considered to be an Old World species.[723] On that day the party traveled down the Canadian River along the McIntosh/Pittsburg county line and camped that night on the north side of the river at the south end of Muskogee County, Oklahoma.

Steironema ciliatum (L.) Raf., Ann. Gen. Phys. 7:193.1820. (Fringed Loosestrife).

#361 *Lysimachia ciliata* L., in Torr., Ann. Lyc. Nat. Hist. N.Y. 2:236.1827. "With the preceding ['Within the Rocky Mountains.']."

James referred to this plant as *Lysimachia ciliata.*[724] His collection was made on July 6 in Douglas County, Colorado, near the mouth of the canyon of the South Platte across the river from Waterton.

Ranunculaceae

Anemone sp.

In his diary, James stated that his collection resembled *A. aconitifolia.*[725] That is a synonym of *A. canadensis,* a species whose habitat is damp ground.

James's collection was made on dry prairie where *A. virginiana* or *A. cylindrica* are more likely to occur. No James specimen of either of these two species, however, was found at NY.

This June 6 collection was made near Big Papillion Creek, near Kennard, Washington County, Nebraska.

Anemone canadensis L., Syst. ed.12. 3:App.231.1768. (Meadow Anemone).

#2 *Anemone pennsylvanica* L., in Torr., Ann. Lyc. Nat. Hist. N.Y. 2:163.1827.

James referred to this plant in his diary as *Anemone dichotoma,* a synonym of *A. canadensis.*[726] His collection was made on June 8 during their travel from the previous night's campsite on Rawhide

[723]JAMES [3], September 8.
[724]JAMES [1], II, 3n.; JAMES [2] in THWAITES [1], XV, 288n.; JAMES [3], July 6.
[725]JAMES [3], June 6.
[726]JAMES [3], June 8.

Creek, just northwest of Fremont, Dodge County, to their camp on Shell Creek, northwest of Schuyler, Colfax County, Nebraska.

Anemone caroliniana Walt., Fl. Car. 157. 1788. (Carolina Anemone).
#1 *Anemone tenella* Pursh, in Torr., Ann. Lyc. Nat. Hist. N.Y. 2:163.1827. "[O]n the Platte." This may be in reference to one of the collections discussed below.
A collection, which James made on May 30 and referred in his diary to *A. tenella,* a synonym of *A. caroliniana,* was found "on dry and elevated woodless hills about the cantonment" some five miles downstream on the Missouri River from Fort Calhoun, Washington County, Nebraska.[727] It is not until June 9 that James listed A. *tenella* in the *Account.*[728] In addition to that plant there are several others listed in the same footnote. According to the diary, some of these plants were collected before June 9, others after that date.
James made a second collection of *A. caroliniana* on June 12 and referred to it in his diary as *A. pinnatifida,* a European species.[729] Very possibly he meant *A. multifida,* a species that is also out of range in eastern Nebraska. The June 12 collection site was near the Loup River between the villages of the Pawnee Republics and the Pawnee Loups, Nance County, Nebraska. That is between the towns of Fullerton and Palmer.

Anemone patens L., Sp. Pl. 538. 1753. (Pasque Flower).
#3 *Anemone ludoviciana* Nutt., in Torr., Ann. Lyc. Nat. Hist. N.Y. 2:163.1827. "Council Bluffs."
Anemone ludoviciana Nutt., in James, Am. Phil. Soc. 2, n.s.:183. 1825. "About Council Bluffs."
No James specimen or other reference to a James collection of the pasque flower has been found.

Aquilegia coerulea James, Long Exped. (Phila. ed.) 2:15.1823. (Colorado Columbine).
#9 *Aquilegia coerulea* James, in Torr., Ann. Lyc. Nat. Hist. N.Y. 2:164.1827. "About the higher parts of the Rocky Mountains. Flowers in June." Type: NY. (Phototype, see fig. 26.)
In his diary for July 10 James indicated that the plant was found in

[727]JAMES [3], May 30.
[728]JAMES [1], I, 433n.; JAMES [2] in THWAITES [1], XV, 200n.
[729]JAMES [3], June 12.

Fig. 26. Phototype of *Aquilegia coerulea* James. Courtesy New York Botanical Garden.

the vicinity of Palmer Lake.[730] That could have been before the party arrived at Palmer Lake, and hence in southern Douglas County. Based on the habitat given in the diary, it seems more likely, however, that the collection was made during the midday rest on July 10 while on Monument Creek, near the base of Elephant Rock ("Castle Rock" of Seymour's illustration),[731] a mile or so east of Palmer Lake, El Paso County, Colorado. James described his new species in the *Account* under events for July 10.[732]

Later, James also mentioned seeing the plant at timberline on Pikes Peak, where he noted that the flowers were "much more intensely coloured."[733] Munz discussed the variability.[734]

The species would later become the state flower of Colorado.

Caltha leptosepala DC., Syst. Veg. 1:310.1818. (Marsh Marigold).
#8 *Caltha sagittata* Cav., in Torr., Ann. Lyc. Nat. Hist. N.Y. 2:164.1827. "In streams, within the Rocky Mountains." Latin and English descriptions are included.

In the diary James indicated the plant to be a possible new species, gave it a name referring to the leaf shape, and provided the following description: "Leaves oblong cordate reniform or deeply cordate at the base, obtuse, minutely serrulate. Scape simple somewhat angular or grooved. After flowering becoming longer than the leaves. Petals numerous, white. Styles about 10."[735]

Gray, under *C. leptosepala*, cited Torrey's name and the Ann. Lyc. reference in synonymy.[736]

Psycrophila auriculata Raf., Atl. Jour. 1:144.1832. This name is based on Torrey's description in the Ann. Lyc.

Caltha auriculata (Raf.) Merrill, Jour. Arn. Arb. 29:211.1948. Merrill here included in synonymy *C. leptosepala* var. *rotundifolia* Huth (1891). Hitchcock, however, considered var. *rotundifolia* to be a variety of *C. biflora* DC. (1818).[737] He placed *C. auriculata* in synonymy under *C. leptosepala*.

[730]JAMES [3], July 10 (erroneously dated July 11).

[731]First published in the atlas of the Philadelphia edition of the *Account* and later reprinted by FULLER AND HAFEN, 157.

[732]JAMES [6], II, 15n.; JAMES [7], II, 345 (erroneously dated July 11 in both editions).

[733]JAMES [1], II, 28; JAMES [2] in THWAITES [1], XVI, 17.

[734]MUNZ, 130.

[735]JAMES [3], July 14.

[736]GRAY [1], 40.

[737]HITCHCOCK [2], 335.

James's plant, the type of *Psycrophila auriculata,* was collected July 14 as James ascended Pikes Peak, El Paso County, Colorado.

Clematis ligusticifolia Nutt. ex T. & G., Fl. No. Am. 1:9.1838. (Western Clematis).

James listed "Clematis virginica?" in his diary for July 5.[738] This same species is cited in the *Account* for the same day.[739] If we assume James's identification was nearly right in that he had a *Clematis* that greatly resembled *C. virginiana,* then there is no doubt but that he had the Nuttallian species that was described eighteen years later.

On July 5 James made a side trip up Clear Creek, just north of Denver in Adams County, Colorado.

Clematis pitcheri Torr. & Gray, Fl. No. Am. 1:10.1838. (Pitcher's Clematis).

In his diary for August 27, James mentioned a plant under the tentative name of "Clematis cylindrica?" and specified that the styles were not plumose.[740]

On that day, a Sunday, the party remained in camp at the junction of Buggy Creek and the Canadian River, about three and a half miles northeast of Minco, Grady County, Oklahoma.

Delphinium virescens Nutt., Gen. No. Am. Pl. 2:14.1818. (Plains Larkspur).

#4 *Delphinium virescens* Nutt., in Torr., Ann. Lyc. Nat. Hist. N.Y. 2:163.1827. "On the Missouri."

James referred to this plant in his diary as *Delphinium exaltatum,* a species that is out of range.[741] His collection was made near their campsite of June 6 on Big Papillion Creek, near Kennard, Washington County, Nebraska.

Ranunculus amphibius James, Long Exped. (Phila. ed.) 1:498. 1823.

#7 *Ranunculus Purshii* Richardson *sensu* Torr., Ann. Lyc. Nat. Hist. N.Y. 2:163.1827. "Sources of the Platte."

Gray stated, under *Ranunculus natans* C. A. Meyer, "To this, rather

---

[738]JAMES [3], July 5.
[739]JAMES [1], I, 501n.; JAMES [2] in THWAITES [1], XV, 281n.
[740]JAMES [3], August 27.
[741]JAMES [3], June 6.

than to R. *multifidus,* should be referred . . . R. *Purshii* of Torr. in
Ann. Lyc. N.Y. ii. 162." (Error for '163').[742]

Later, again under R. *natans,* Gray described the petals as "about 2
lines long," listed in synonymy the Torrey reference in the Ann. Lyc.,
and added, "Rocky Mountains of Colorado, subalpine or lower," and
included James as a collector.[743]

The diary for July 4 contains the following description of a
Ranunculus: "Leaves reniform 4–5 cleft divisions cuneate border
crenate. Stems slender floating Leaves long petioled all alike joints of
the stem rooting. Petals obovate rather narrow Fls. yellow larger than
those of R. fluviatilis with which it grows."[744]

In the *Account* the following appears as a footnote under the date of
July 4: "Other plants were collected about this encampment, among
which we distinguished an interesting species of Ranunculus, having
a flower somewhat larger than that of R. *fluviatilis* with which it
grows, often extending, however, to some distance about the margins
of the pools in which it is principally found. R. *amphibius*; slender,
floating or decumbent, leaves reniform, four or five lobed, divisions
cuneate-oblong, margin crenate, petioles long and alternate. The
submersed leaves are, in every respect, similar to the floating ones."[745]

Clearly, the descriptions in the diary and in the *Account* apply to
the same plant. They apply poorly to the subgenus Batrachium (e.g.,
R. *circinatus* var. *subrigidus, q.v.*). The descriptions, however, fit well
the plant that has been called R. *natans,* an 1830 name that R.
amphibius antedates.

James collected the type on July 4 along the South Platte River,
three or four miles south of Brighton, Adams County, Colorado.

Ranunculus circinatus Sibth. var. **subrigidus** (W. Drew) L. Benson, Amer. Midl. Naturalist 40:240.1948. (White Water-Crowfoot).

In his *Supplement,* Benson placed R. *amphibius* James in synonymy
under the above taxon, giving as the type locality "'Platte River west
of the mouth of Portera's Creek.'"[746] A specimen at NY is indicated as
being the holotype of R. *amphibius* James. Also on the sheet, closely
adjacent to the specimen, has been affixed a label, almost certainly in
James's handwriting, reading "Ranunculus amphibius N.S.?"; nearby

[742]GRAY [7], 366.
[743]GRAY [1], 25.
[744]JAMES [3], July 4.
[745]JAMES [6], I, 498n.; JAMES [7], II, 342.
[746]BENSON [1], 368.

on the sheet is written "Long's Exped. Dr. James." There is no reason to doubt Benson's identification. That it is James's *R. amphibius,* however, is another matter. We believe that the label has been affixed to the wrong specimen.

James most likely collected his specimen of *R. circinatus* var. *subrigidus* in June along the Platte in Nebraska.

Ranunculus cymbalaria Pursh, Fl. Am. Sept. 392. 1814. (Shore Buttercup).

R. Cymbalaria Pursh, in Torr. & Gray, Fl. No. Am. 1:17.1838. "Salt plains of the Platte, *Dr. James!*"

In the diary for Sunday, June 18, James listed "Ranunculus pygmaeus?" and described it as follows: "Leaves all radical, long petioled, round cordate and deeply crenate. Scape exceeding the leaves. Receptacle columnar."[747] On the following day he mentioned it again, "growing in the sand of the River bank."

There seems to be no reason to doubt that the plant described in the diary and the James specimen cited by Torrey and Gray are one and the same.

This buttercup would have been collected along the Platte River about six miles west-southwest of Overton, Dawson County, Nebraska.

Thalictrum dasycarpum Fisch. & Lall., Ind. Sem. Hort. Petrop. 8:72.1842. (Purple Meadow Rue).

James made two collections of this plant, each time referring them in his diary to *T. cornuti.* The first collection was made on May 30 in the vicinity of Engineer Cantonment, some five miles downstream on the Missouri River from Fort Calhoun, Washington County, Nebraska. On June 9, James made his second collection of this plant on an elevated ridge that they began to encounter about three miles southeast of Platte Center, Platte County, Nebraska.

Rhamnaceae

Rhamnus caroliniana Walt., Fl. Carol. 101. 1788. (Indian Cherry).

#62 *Rhamnus carolinianus* Walt., in Torr., Ann. Lyc. Nat. Hist. N.Y. 2:174.1827.

We have found no reference to this tree in James's diary; he could,

---

[747]JAMES [3], June 18.

however, have encountered it along the Canadian or Arkansas rivers in eastern Oklahoma from McIntosh County eastward to Fort Smith.

Rosaceae

Agrimonia sp. (Agrimony).
The name "Agrimonia parviflora" appears in James's diary for September 1.[748] The name has been applied to not only Aiton's *A. parviflora* but also to *A. pubescens* and *A. rostellata,* both of Wallr., 1842. All three of these species occur in the area the party was in at the time.
On September 1 they traveled along the Canadian River at the south end of Pottawatomie County, Oklahoma.

Cercocarpus montanus Raf., Atl. Jour. 1:146.1832. (Mountain Mahogany).
#132 *Cercocarpus fothergilloides* HBK., in Torr., Ann. Lyc. Nat. Hist. N.Y. 2:198.1827. "On the Rocky Mountains."
Cercocarpus parvifolius Nutt. ex T. & G., Fl. No. Am. 1:427.1840. "Rocky Mountains in bushy ravines near the sources of the Platte, *Dr. James! Nuttall!*"
Rafinesque based his name on Torrey's *C. fothergilloides.* Torrey included a full description.
Cercocarpus grows in the area where the South Platte River comes out of the mountains near Waterton and Kassler, Jefferson County, Colorado, and across the river along the hogbacks near where the party camped on July 6 and 7. James's specimen, which became the type (NY), was very likely collected in this area.

Dryas octopetala L. subsp. **hookeriana** (Juz.) Hultén, Fl. Alas. 6:1046.1945. (Mountain Avens).
#121 *Dryas octopetala* L., in Torr., Ann. Lyc. Nat. Hist. N.Y. 2:195.1827. "On the Rocky Mountains, in latitude 39°."
James collected this tundra species on July 14 near the summit of Pikes Peak, El Paso County, Colorado.

Geum aleppicum Jacq. var. **strictum** (Ait.) Fernald, Rhodora 37:294.1935. (Yellow Avens).
The diary for Sunday, June 18, mentions *Geum strictum* as one of

[748]JAMES [3], September 1.

the plants in flower.[749] James was then on the Platte River, about six miles west-southwest of Overton, Dawson County, Nebraska.

Geum macrophyllum Willd. var. **perincisum** (Rydb.) Raup, Rhodora 33:176.1931. (Large-Leaved Avens).

It seems very likely that this is the plant James referred to in his diary for July 5 as "Geum virginianum?"[750]

That day James made a side trip up "Canon Ball Creek" (Clear Creek), just north of Denver in Adams County, Colorado.

Geum rossii (R.Br.) Ser. var. **turbinatum** (Rydb.) C.L. Hitchc., Univ. Wash. Publ. Biol. 17(3):112.1961. (Alpine Avens).

#4 *Potentilla nivalis* Torr., Ann. Lyc. Nat. Hist. N.Y. 1:32, pl.3, fig.2. 1824. "With the preceding ['On James' Peak, one of the highest of the Rocky Mountains, 10,000 feet above the level of the ocean, near the region of perpetual snow.']."

#123 *Geum triflorum* Pursh, Fl. ii. p. 736. Potentilla nivalis, *nobis,* in *Ann. Lyc. nat. hist. New-York,* i. p.32, t.3. f.1. in Torr., Ann. Lyc. Nat. Hist. N.Y. 2:195.1827. "On the Rocky Mountains."

Torrey and Gray cited the first reference (Ann. Lyc. 1) under *Geum rossii* and cited a James specimen from James Peak, then cited the second reference (Ann. Lyc. 2) under variety β, and cited "Rocky Mountains, *Dr. James!*"[751]

In view of abundant collections now, variety β seems to be within the range of variability of var. *turbinatum.*

In 1897, Rydberg indicated that the name of Torrey's new species, *Potentilla nivalis,* was preempted by Lapeyrouse (1782); he provided the new name, *Geum turbinatum.*[752]

James's type was collected on July 14 or 15 on the slopes of Pikes Peak, El Paso County, Colorado.

Holodiscus dumosus (Nutt. in Hook.) Heller, Cat. No. Am. Pl. 4. 1898. (Ocean Spray).

#120 *Spiraea discolor* Pursh?, in Torr., Ann. Lyc. Nat. Hist. N.Y. 2:195.1827. "On the Rocky Mountains."

Spiraea ariaefolia β *discolor* (Pursh) T. & G., Fl. No. Am. 1:416.

[749]JAMES [3], June 18.
[750]JAMES [3], July 5.
[751]TORREY AND GRAY [1], I, 424.
[752]RYDBERG [3], 91.

1840. Cited here in synonymy are Pursh's name, the Ann. Lyc. reference, and *Spiraea dumosa* Nutt., *mss.* Three specimens are also cited: the James specimen (this anent the Torrey reference), Nuttall (referring without doubt to Nuttall's type of his *mss.* name based on his plant collected on the North Platte River in Wyoming), and the Lewis plant from the Kooskoosky River, Idaho (the type of Pursh's *S. discolor*).

James would have collected his plant in July somewhere between Denver and Cañon City, Colorado.

Physocarpus monogynus (Torr.) Coult., Contr. U.S. Nat. Herb. 2:104.1891. (Mountain Ninebark).

#119 *Spiraea monogyna* Torr., Ann. Lyc. Nat. Hist. N.Y. 2:194. 1827. "On the Rocky Mountains."

The type (NY) that James referred to as *S. opulifolia* was collected on July 7 in the ravines of the foothills of Sheep Mountain on the north side of South Platte Canyon, Jefferson County, Colorado.[753]

S. opulifolia var. *pauciflora* T. & G., Fl. No. Am. 1:414.1840. "Rocky Mountains in about lat. 40°, *Dr. James!*" (as to the Ann. Lyc. reference), "Blue Mountains, Oregon Territory, *Nuttall!*" (as to *S. pauciflora* Nutt. *mss.*), "and at Kettle Falls of the Oregon, *Douglas*" (as to an unnamed variety of *Spiraea opulifolia* in Hook., Fl. Bor. Am. 1:171.1832).

The Nuttall specimen from southeast Oregon and the Douglas specimen from northeast Washington are out of range of *P. monogynus.*

Potentilla anserina L., Sp. Pl. 495. 1753. (Silverweed).

James mentioned this species on July 4, after they camped at 10:30 A.M. on the South Platte River on the north end of Henderson Island about four miles south of Brighton, Adams County, Colorado.[754]

Potentilla arguta Pursh, Fl. Am. Sept. 736. 1814. (Tall Cinquefoil).

#126 *Potentilla pennsylvanica* β *arguta* Seringe, in Torr., Ann. Lyc. Nat. Hist. N.Y. 2:197.1827. "On the Missouri."

It is likely that this was collected along the Missouri in May or in eastern Nebraska in the first half of June. Torrey and Gray, however, under *Potentilla arguta,* cited the Ann. Lyc. reference and

---

[753]JAMES [1], II, 8n.; JAMES [2] in THWAITES [1], XV, 295n.; JAMES [3], July 7 (erroneously dated July 8).

[754]JAMES [1], I, 498n.; JAMES [2] in THWAITES [1], XV, 277n.; JAMES [3], July 4.

added "west to the Rocky Mountains in lat. 42⁰, *Dr. James*; June–July."[755]

Potentilla concinna Richards., in Franklin's Jour. 739. 1823.
#128 *Potentilla humifusa* Nutt., in Torr., Ann. Lyc. Nat. Hist. N.Y. 2:197.1827. "On the Missouri."
Nuttall's *P. humifusa* was collected on the Missouri near Fort Mandan, North Dakota. James's route intersected the known range of *P. concinna* only in Colorado and New Mexico.

Potentilla fruticosa L., Sp. Pl. 495. 1753. (Shrubby Cinquefoil).
#129 *Potentilla fruticosa* L., in Torr., Ann. Lyc. Nat. Hist. N.Y. 2:197.1827. "On the Rocky Mountains."
Torrey and Gray listed a James specimen from "along the Rocky Mountains to lat. 42⁰."[756]
James mentioned this plant on July 14, when they were ascending Pikes Peak, El Paso County, Colorado.[757]

Potentilla hippiana Lehm., Stirp. Pug. 2:7.1830. (Woolly Cinquefoil).
#130 *Potentilla leucophylla* Torr., Ann. Lyc. Nat. Hist. N.Y. 2:197.–98.1827. [Not of Pall., 1773]. "Sources of the Platte."
James listed a *Potentilla* in his diary[758] with a description so similar to that of Torrey that there is little doubt both refer to the same plant. Torrey and Gray cited a James specimen of this from "in the Rocky Mountains to the sources of the Platte."[759]
The type (NY) of *Potentilla leucophylla* was collected almost certainly on July 30 as the party traveled across the Don Carlos Hills, from Sierra Grande to Ute Creek, western Union County, New Mexico.

Potentilla paradoxa Nutt., in T. & G., Fl. No. Am. 1:437.1840. (Bushy Cinquefoil).
#127 *Potentilla supina* L., in Torr., Ann. Lyc. Nat. Hist. N.Y. 2:197.1827. "On the Mississippi and Missouri."

---

[755]TORREY AND GRAY [1], I, 445–46.
[756]TORREY AND GRAY [1], I, 445.
[757]JAMES [1], II, 26; JAMES [2] in THWAITES [1], XVI, 15; JAMES [3], July 14 (erroneously dated July 15).
[758]JAMES [3], July 30.
[759]TORREY AND GRAY [1], I, 438.

The identification is based on the species fitting a combination of three known items—pinnate leaves, the locality, and the habitat.

In his diary James stated, "Potentilla— —? with pinnate leaves. Hab. with Ranunculus pygmaeus in the sand of the river bank."[760]

The plant was collected on June 19 along the Platte River between Overton and Gothenburg, Dawson County, Nebraska.

Prunus angustifolia Marsh., Arbustr. Am. 111. 1785. (Chickasaw Plum).

#116 *Prunus Chicasa* Michx., in Torr., Ann. Lyc. Nat. Hist. N.Y. 2:194.1827. "On the Arkansa; common. Truly indigenous."

In his diary for June 18, James mentioned "Prunus chicasa?" as being abundant about the Loup villages. They passed through the villages more than a week before, but no mention was made of *Prunus* at that time.[761]

The Chickasaw Plum does not occur in the northern half of Nebraska. What James was referring to is not certain. Some writers have suggested that the plum was cultivated by the Indians. It is also possible that James was seeing the sand cherry, *Prunus besseyi, q.v.*

James noted "Osage plum" in the *Account* on August 13 when they were along the Canadian River in eastern Hutchinson County, Texas.[762] That, too, was likely *P. angustifolia*. A few miles farther downstream, James referred to this plum as "plum bushes."[763]

In his diary for September 3, James referred to the "species of Prunus" found there and "nearly to the sources of the river."[764] At that time the party was along the Canadian in Seminole and Pontotoc counties, Oklahoma, where four species of *Prunus* (*P. americana, P. angustifolia, P. gracilis,* and *P. mexicana*) meet these conditions.

Prunus besseyi Bailey, Bull. Cornell Agric. Exp. Sta. 70:261.1894. (Sand Cherry).

The sand cherry, which James called *Prunus depressa* in his diary for June 18, is likely this species.[765] At the time the party was camped west-southwest of Overton, Dawson County, Nebraska.

This may also be the species that James observed along the Loup

[760]JAMES [3], June 19.
[761]JAMES [3], June 18.
[762]JAMES [1], II, 117; JAMES [2] in THWAITES [1], XVI, 123.
[763]JAMES [1], II, 120; JAMES [2] in THWAITES [1], XVI, 126.
[764]JAMES [3], September 3.
[765]JAMES [3], June 18.

River in Nebraska, which he called "Prunus chicasa" (*Prunus angustifolia, q.v.*).

Prunus serotina Ehrh., Beitr. Naturk. 3:20.1788. (Black Cherry).

James reported black cherry in the *Account* on August 29, as the party traveled from near Newcastle to north of Lexington, Cleveland County, Oklahoma.[766]

We have no other record of this species occurring quite so far west along the Canadian River, but it is recorded from Seminole and Pontotoc counties, Oklahoma, at a location that the expedition would reach on September 1.

If the tree has not been eradicated or overlooked along the river in Cleveland County, then perhaps the *Account* erred in referring to the tree at that time.

Rosa blanda Ait., Hort. Kew. 2:202.1789. (Smooth Wild Rose).

This rose was mentioned in James's diary for June 13.[767] James briefly described it on that same day in the *Account*.[768] The name is accepted chiefly because the flowering time and the range are in harmony with the itinerary of the expedition.

The plant was noted after the party had left the Pawnee Loup village and crossed the Loup River to its south side near the Nance/ Merrick county line, three miles north and a little east of Palmer, Nebraska.

Rubus deliciosus Torr. (Boulder Raspberry).

#125 *Rubus deliciosus* Torr., Ann. Lyc. Nat. Hist. N.Y. 2:196.1827. "On the Rocky Mountains."

Curiously, Torrey's description of this new species contains characters that fit both *Rubus parviflorus* and *R. odoratus*. For example, he described the flowers as occurring "in a terminal corymbose panicle . . . purple." The flowers of *Rubus deliciosus* are solitary and white.

It is possible that Torrey had on hand mixed material when he wrote his description of *R. deliciosus*. The type sheet (NY), however, appears not to be mixed.

Torrey quoted James concerning the large and delicious fruits. The fruits of *Rubus deliciosus* are anything but delicious.

---

[766]JAMES [1], II, 149; JAMES [2] in THWAITES [1], XVI, 160.
[767]JAMES [3], June 13.
[768]JAMES [1], I, 448; JAMES [2] in THWAITES [1], XV, 218.

James made a collection of *Rubus* on July 7 during an excursion into the mountains from the mouth of South Platte Canyon.[769] He referred to it in his diary as "Rubus spectabilis approaching R. odoratus. fruit highly and pleasingly flavored." His collection was made in the ravines of the foothills of Sheep Mountain about seven miles southwest of Waterton on the north side of South Platte Canyon, Jefferson County, Colorado.

In the *Account* on this same day James noted finding "a few large and delicious raspberries, of a species approaching the flowering raspberry (rubus odoratus), but with smaller leaves, and a more branching stem."[770]

It is possible that Torrey obtained the information on the fruit size and flavor from the *Account* and assumed the *Rubus* noted on July 7 to be the same as his *R. deliciosus*. The large, delicious raspberry found by James on Sheep Mountain was more likely *R. idaeus* subsp. *melanolasius* (Dieck) Focke. In addition, James could have encountered *R. deliciosus,* as it, too, occurs abundantly on Sheep Mountain.

There is, of course, Gray's explanation: "The fruit, by the way, is mawkish, and far from 'delicious.' The natural explanation of its having been termed so by Dr. James is that, in his hurried rush for the mountains, in the too restricted time allowed him by Major Long, he was so nearly starved that any edible fruit must have been to him delicious."[771]

In his diary for July 30, when the party traveled from Sierra Grande, Union County, to Ute Creek, western Union County, New Mexico, James stated, "The same species [of *Rubus*] as inhabits the Rocky mountains now in flower here has the cor. large and white."[772] On that same day in the *Account* it is described as "an unarmed rubus."[773] It may have been the similar *R. neomexicanus* Gray, as its flowering time, unlike that of the *R. deliciosus,* extends throughout the summer in New Mexico.

Rubus occidentalis L., Sp. Pl. 493. 1753. (Black Raspberry).

#124 *Rubus Idaeus* var. *americanus* Torr., Ann. Lyc. Nat. Hist. N.Y. 2:196.1827. "In rocky woods, near Council Bluff on the Missouri." James's type specimen was collected on May 29, in deep ravines

---

[769]JAMES [3], July 7 (erroneously dated July 8).
[770]JAMES [1], II, 7; JAMES [2] in THWAITES [1], XV, 293.
[771]GRAY [8], 389.
[772]JAMES [3], July 30.
[773]JAMES [1], II, 86; JAMES [2] in THWAITES [1], XVI, 85.

along the Missouri River in the area of Engineer Cantonment, some five miles downstream from Fort Calhoun, Washington County, Nebraska.

Torrey and Gray cited Torrey's new variety and James's specimen from Council Bluff as a synonym of *R. occidentalis.*[774]

Sibbaldia procumbens L., Sp. Pl. 284. 1753.

Torrey and Gray included among the collectors of this species "(near perpetual snow), *Dr. James!*"[775]

Inasmuch as this species is known only from subalpine to alpine regions, James's specimen would have been collected on Pikes Peak, July 13–15, El Paso County, Colorado.

Torrey included with #122 *Geum virginianum* a variety, "β *trilobum.*"[776] His description reads "foliis radicalibus trilobis ternatisve. With the preceding." Whether the "preceding" refers to *Geum virginianum* or to Torrey's #121 *Dryas octopetala* is not clear. If it is to the latter, an alpine species, then Torrey's variety, with the James specimen as the type, may well be *Sibbaldia procumbens.*

Rubiaceae

Cephalanthus occidentalis L., Sp. Pl. 95. 1753. (Buttonbush).

#193 *Cephalanthus occidentalis* L., in Torr., Ann. Lyc. Nat. Hist. N.Y. 2:209.1827. "On the Canadian."

James stated in his diary on August 15 that "Maclura aurantiaca?" begins to occur.[777] Three weeks later (September 5), however, James wrote that the plant he mistook earlier for *Maclura* was "no other than a young plant of the Cephalanthus occidentalis."[778]

In the *Account* one day earlier, on August 14, James noted "cephalanthus."[779]

On August 15 the party was traveling down the Canadian River in Roberts and Hemphill counties, Texas. Stands of *Cephalanthus occidentalis* remain there today, at the westernmost range of the species along the Canadian.

---

[774]TORREY AND GRAY [1], I, 453.
[775]TORREY AND GRAY [1], I, 433.
[776]TORREY [2], 195.
[777]JAMES [3], August 15.
[778]JAMES [3], September 5.
[779]JAMES [1], II, 119; JAMES [2] in THWAITES [1], XVI, 125.

Diodia teres Walt., Fl. Carol. 87. 1788. (Rough Buttonweed).
#196 *Spermacoce diodina* Michx., in Torr., Ann. Lyc. Nat. Hist. N.Y. 2:209.1827. "On the Canadian."

James listed "Diodia tetragona?" in his diary for August 29.[780] The species is listed two days earlier in the *Account*[781] and has been considered to be synonymous,[782] or perhaps synonymous,[783] with *Diodia virginiana* L. var. *latifolia* T. & G., which is out of range. The name *Spermacoce diodina* is listed in synonymy under *Diodia teres* in both Torrey and Gray[784] and Fernald and Griscom.[785]

On August 29 the party traveled about twenty miles and camped on the Canadian about three miles north of Lexington, Cleveland County, Oklahoma.

Galium circaezans Michx., Fl. Bor. Am. 1:80.1803. (Woods Bedstraw).
#195 *Galium circaezans* Michx., in Torr., Ann. Lyc. Nat. Hist. N.Y. 2:209.1827. "On the Missouri."

Based on flowering time and distribution, it is possible that James collected this species along the Missouri River in Missouri prior to his arrival at Engineer Cantonment. The species, however, does occur in eastern Nebraska, where James traveled in early June.

Rutaceae

Zanthoxylum americanum Mill., Gard. Dict. ed.8, no.2. 1768. (Prickly Ash).

James referred to "prickly ash" in his diary on September 11, when the party traveled down the Arkansas from a few miles below the mouth of the Canadian to just west of Sallisaw, Sequoyah County, Oklahoma.[786]

James later listed *Z. fraxineum,* which is a synonym of *Z. americanum.*[787]

---

[780]JAMES [3], August 29.
[781]JAMES [1], II, 146; JAMES [2] in THWAITES [1], XVI, 156.
[782]TORREY AND GRAY [1], II, 29.
[783]FERNALD AND GRISCOM, 308.
[784]TORREY AND GRAY [1], II, 29.
[785]FERNALD AND GRISCOM, 307.
[786]JAMES [3], September 11.
[787]JAMES [4], 190.

Salicaceae

Populus angustifolia James, Long Exped. (Phila. ed.) 1:497.1823. (Narrowleaf Cottonwood).

#425 *Populus angustifolia* in Torr., Ann. Lyc. Nat. Hist. N.Y. 2:249.1827. Following a Latin description, Torrey adds, "P.angustifolia,James in Long's Ex.i.p.497" and "Sources of the Platte." Type: NY.

James listed this tree in his diary as a new species, although under a different epithet.[788] In the *Account* for July 4 a brief description is given, with "P.angustifolia,J." as a footnote.[789]

July 4 was largely spent encamped on the South Platte River near Brighton, Adams County, Colorado.

Populus deltoides Bartr. ex Marsh., Arbustr. Am. 106. 1785.

#426 *Populus angulata* Willd., in Torr., Ann. Lyc. Nat. Hist. N.Y. 2:249.1827. "On all the western rivers to the Mountains."

Torrey's #426 evidently includes the two varieties of *P. deltoides* that are found along the western rivers along which James traveled:

var. **deltoides** (Eastern Cottonwood).

James referred to this cottonwood as *Populus angulata* in his diary for September 3.[790] The cottonwood is mentioned one day earlier in the *Account*.[791]

The party traveled only a few miles and camped on the Canadian, about five miles northwest of Allen near the junction of Seminole, Hughes, and Pontotoc counties, Oklahoma.

James discussed *Populus angulata* again in the *Account* on September 8, when the party traveled along the Canadian River from near Eufaula, McIntosh County, to a few miles south of Porum, Muskogee County, Oklahoma.[792]

var. **occidentalis** Rydb., Mem. N.Y. Bot. Gard. 1:15.1900. (Plains Cottonwood).

In his diary for July 22, James remarked that the "point on which we are encamped is sparingly covered with a growth of cottonwood intermixed

---

[788]JAMES [3], July 4.
[789]JAMES [6], I, 497; JAMES [7], II, 181–82.
[790]JAMES [3], September 3.
[791]JAMES [1], II, 155; JAMES [2] in THWAITES [1], XVI, 168.
[792]JAMES [1], II, 164–65n.; JAMES [2] in THWAITES [1], XVI, 177–78n.

with the Populus tremuloides and some willows."[793] This same remark is made in the *Account* one day earlier at the same location.[794]

At the time, they were camped on the Arkansas River near Rocky Ford, Otero County, Colorado.

Populus tremuloides Michx., Fl. Bor. Am. 2:243.1803. (Quaking Aspen).

#424 *Populus tremuloides* Michx., in Torr., Ann. Lyc. Nat. Hist. N.Y. 2:249.1827. "On the upper part of the Arkansa, and about the base of the Rocky Mountains."

James noted the quaking aspen on July 10 near the base of Elephant Rock, a mile or so east of Palmer Lake, El Paso County, Colorado.[795]

James noted cottonwood intermixed with this aspen and willows again at their camp on the Arkansas River near Rocky Ford, Otero County, Colorado.[796] The reference to aspen is curious since present-day records do not indicate the occurrence of quaking aspen that far east in Colorado.

Salix amygdaloides Anderss., Ofvers. Kgl. Sv. Vet. Akad. Forh. 15:114.1858. (Peachleaf Willow).

On June 18 James wrote in his diary, "The small island opposite our encampment has a low growth of willows from 8–10 feet high and a few of a different species considerably higher."[797] Based on the height of the willow and its range, we take the higher to be the above. James mentioned willow in the *Account* on this same day.[798]

At the time their camp was a few miles west-southwest of Overton, Dawson County, Nebraska.

Salix caroliniana Michx., Fl. Bor. Am. 2:226.1803. (Coast Plain Willow).

If our assumption is correct that in June when James referred to *Salix angustata* he had *S. lutea* (*q.v.*), then his reference on September 8 to *S. angustata* must also be to a similar-appearing species that occurs in the area.[799]

[793]JAMES [3], July 22.

[794]JAMES [1], II, 62; JAMES [2] in THWAITES [1], XVI, 57.

[795]JAMES [1], II, 15n.; JAMES [2] in THWAITES [1], XV, 306n.; JAMES [3], July 10. All references are erroneously dated July 11.

[796]JAMES [1], II, 62; JAMES [2] in THWAITES [1], XVI, 57; JAMES [3], July 22.

[797]JAMES [3], June 18.

[798]JAMES [1], I, 458; JAMES [2] in THWAITES [1], XV, 230.

[799]JAMES [1], II, 164; JAMES [2] in THWAITES [1], XVI, 177.

Both *S. exigua* subsp. *interior* and *S. caroliniana* are in range, but the latter more nearly resembles *S. angustata*.

On September 8 the party traveled along the Canadian River from near Eufaula, McIntosh County, to a few miles south of Porum, Muskogee County, Oklahoma.

Salix eriocephala Michx., Fl. Bor. Am. 2:225.1803. (Diamond Willow).

Based on range, this seems to be one of the willows growing on the island that are mentioned under *S. amygdaloides* (*q.v.*).

Salix exigua Nutt. subsp. **interior** (Rowlee) Cronquist, Vasc. Pl. Pac. NW. Part 2. 51.1964. (Sandbar Willow).

#423 *Salix longifolia* Muhl.?, in Torr., Ann. Lyc. Nat. Hist. N.Y. 2:248–49.1827. "On the western rivers, to the Rocky Mountains; common."

The same remarks apply as in the preceding.

Salix humilis Marsh., Arb. Am. 140. 1785. (Prairie Willow).

James referred to this plant in his diary as *Salix conifera*.[800] His collection was made on May 29 on elevated, woodless plains in the area of Engineer Cantonment, some five miles downstream on the Missouri River from Fort Calhoun, Washington County, Nebraska. The only prairie species in range is *S. humilis*.

Salix lutea Nutt., No. Am. Sylva 1:63.1842. (Yellow Willow).

James referred to this plant in his diary as *Salix angustata*.[801] His collection was made on May 29 along the banks of the Missouri River in the area of Engineer Cantonment, some five miles downstream from Fort Calhoun, Washington County, Nebraska. That location is out of range for *S. angustata*, but well within range of the similar *S. lutea*.

Sapindaceae

Cardiospermum halicacabum L., Sp. Pl. 366. 1753. (Balloon-Vine).

#51 *Cardiospermum Halicacabum* L., in Torr., Ann. Lyc. Nat. Hist.

---

[800]JAMES [3], May 29.
[801]JAMES [3], May 29.

N.Y. 2:172.1827. "On the Missouri, and very abundant on the Canadian 200 miles above its confluence with the Arkansa. Dr. James states that it is undoubtedly a native."

James listed this species in his *Catalogue* with the same information Torrey provided, except for the reference to the Missouri.[802] The *Account* mentions it under the date of August 27, stating: "sometimes cultivated in the gardens, and said to be a native of the East Indies."[803] James's diary includes it, with a description, one day later.[804]

Many subsequent authors consider this vine to be an introduction from the American tropics. We do not know how it got introduced into central Oklahoma so early. It still occurs in sandy meadows along the floodplain of the Canadian.

We place their camp of Sunday, August 27, where they laid over for a day, at the junction of Buggy Creek and the Canadian, near Minco, Grady County, Oklahoma. From there, on August 28, the party traveled to within three or four miles to the northeast of Newcastle, near the McClain/Cleveland county line.

Sapindus drummondii Hook. & Arn., Bot. Beechey Voy. 281. 1838. (Soapberry).

#50 *Sapindus Saponaria* L., in Torr., Ann. Lyc. Nat. Hist. N.Y. 2:172.1827. "The station of this plant is not recorded. It was probably found about the sources of the Platte."

In his diary, James described what he thought was a possible new species:[805]

Oct. Mon. Cal. of 5 leaves, nearly flat, but the divisions are somewhat concave. Cor. of 5 linear lanceolate petals which are somewhat tomentose on the upper side and margins. Anthers capitate, lower half of the filaments tomentose. Style simple Stigma very small Germ 3-seeded, 2 of them often abortive. Stamina exserted. Flowers small, white, in a thyrse or cyme.

After describing the pinnate leaves, James continued, "About 10–12 feet high the leaves and trunk having somewhat the aspect of some species of Juglans."

This plant was collected on August 3 in Harding County, New

[802]JAMES [4], 180.
[803]JAMES [1], II, 145; JAMES [2] in THWAITES [1], XVI, 155.
[804]JAMES [3], August 28.
[805]JAMES [3], August 3.

Mexico, as the party traveled thirty miles down Ute Creek, starting from a few miles south of Bueyeros.

Sapotaceae

Bumelia lanuginosa (Michx.) Pers., Syn. Pl. 1:237.1805. (Chittamwood).

James first noted the occurrence of "nyssa" on August 26, as the men traveled away from the Canadian River.[806] On that day the party traveled through southwestern Canadian County to the mouth of Buggy Creek in northwestern Grady County, central Oklahoma.

James noted "nyssa" again on September 1 and 2, on which days the party was still in central Oklahoma, in Seminole and Pontotoc counties.[807]

Nyssa occurs in extreme-eastern Oklahoma and thence through the eastern United States. It is likely that James was seeing *Bumelia lanuginosa,* a tree of the south-central United States that would have been unfamiliar to an easterner. It, like *Nyssa,* has alternate, simple, entire leaves, a combination of characters found in very few tree species in temperate North America.

Saxifragaceae

Heuchera bracteata (Torr.) Ser., in DC., Prodr. 4:52.1830. (Bracted Alum-Root).

#168 *Tiarella? bracteata* Torr., Ann. Lyc. Nat. Hist. N.Y. 2:204–205.1827. "On the Rocky Mountains."

Based on the distribution of this species, James could have collected the type from July 6–15 on his travels from the chasm of the Platte, Douglas County, to his return from Pikes Peak, El Paso County, Colorado.

We found this species on Sheep Mountain along the South Platte in Jefferson County, Colorado, an area that James explored on July 7.

Heuchera parvifolia Nutt. ex T. & G., Fl. No. Am. 1:581.1840. (Common Alum-Root).

Following the original description Torrey and Gray cited, along with a Nuttall collection, "Rocky Mountains, *Dr. James!*"

[806]JAMES [1], II, 142; JAMES [2] in THWAITES [1], XVI, 152.
[807]JAMES [1], II, 153, 155; JAMES [2] in THWAITES [1], XVI, 165, 168.

Based on the range of this species, James must have made his collection in July along the Front Range from near Denver to Cañon City, Fremont County, Colorado.

Ribes sp.

Torrey and Gray mentioned a fragment of *Ribes* collected by James "in the Rocky Mountains (about lat. 41⁰) which may be the R. irriguum of Douglas."808

James's route is out of the known range of *R. irriguum.* We are unable to determine just what James had.

Ribes aureum Pursh, Fl. Am. Sept. 164. 1814. (Golden Currant).

#160 *Ribes aureum* Pursh, in Torr., Ann. Lyc. Nat. Hist. N.Y. 2:203.1827. "About the base of the Rocky Mountains."

James referred to this shrub by name on July 5, when he made a side trip up "cannon-ball river" (Clear Creek), just north of Denver in Adams County, Colorado.809

Ribes odoratum Wendl. f., in Bartl. and Wendl., Beitr. Bot. 2:15. 1825. (Buffalo Currant).

James mentioned *Ribes aureum* in his diary for August 5.810 It is not clear whether he collected the plant or was commenting on the plentiful currants. Most of that day the party traveled down the Canadian River in Quay County, New Mexico, in an area out of range of *R. aureum.*

James mentioned *Ribes floridum* in his diary on August 27.811 That, too, must have been *Ribes odoratum,* as it is the only species that occurs near their location that day; they were near the junction of Buggy Creek and the Canadian River, about three and a half miles northeast of Minco, Grady County, Oklahoma.

Saxifraga bronchialis L. subsp. austromontana (Wieg.) Piper, Contr. U.S. Nat. Herb. 11:313.1906. (Spotted Saxifrage).

#163 *Saxifraga bronchialis* Willd., in Torr., Ann. Lyc. Nat. Hist. N.Y. 2:204.1827. "On the Rocky Mountains."

The only other reference we find to this collection is in Torrey and

---

808TORREY AND GRAY [1], I, 547–48.
809JAMES [1], I, 501; JAMES [2] in THWAITES [1], XV, 280; JAMES [3], July 5.
810JAMES [3], August 5.
811JAMES [3], August 27.

Gray, where, under *S. bronchialis,* the James specimen and the Torrey reference are cited.[812]

Based on the distribution of this species, James could have encountered it from July 6–15 on his travels from the chasm of the South Platte, Douglas County, to his return from Pikes Peak, El Paso County, Colorado.

We collected this species in Limekiln Valley, El Paso County; James was in this area on July 11–12.

Saxifraga flagellaris Willd., in Sternb., Rev. Saxifr. 25. 1810. (Whiplash Saxifrage).

#162 *Saxifraga flagellaris* Sternb., in Torr., Ann. Lyc. Nat. Hist. N.Y. 2:203.1827. "On the Rocky Mountains."

Again, the only other reference we find to this James collection is in Torrey and Gray, where a James specimen and the Torrey reference are given.[813]

Because of the elevation at which this plant grows, it almost certainly was collected July 13–15 on Pikes Peak, El Paso County, Colorado.

Saxifraga rhomboidea Greene, Pittonia 3:343.1898.

#161 *Saxifraga nivalis* L., in Torr., Ann. Lyc. Nat. Hist. N.Y. 2:203.1827. "On the Rocky Mountains."

James referred to this plant in his diary and the *Account* as *S. nivalis,* a species limited to the Old World.[814] On that day James ascended the South Platte above the chasm to a point about seven miles southwest of Waterton, Jefferson County, Colorado.

On July 14, the day James climbed Pikes Peak, El Paso County, Colorado, he again listed *Saxifraga nivalis* in his diary.[815]

Telesonix jamesii (Torr.) Raf., Fl. Tellur. 2:69.1837. (James's Saxifrage).

#164 *Saxifraga Jamesii* Torr., Ann. Lyc. Nat. Hist. N.Y. 2:204.1827. "On the Rocky Mountains."

Of this species, Weber remarked, "Abundant on talus slopes along the Cog Railway near Windy Point on Pikes Peak, at one site in Rocky

---

[812]TORREY AND GRAY [1], I, 564.

[813]TORREY AND GRAY [1], I, 564.

[814]JAMES [3], July 7 (erroneously dated July 8); JAMES [1], II, 8n.; JAMES [2] in THWAITES [1], XV, 295n.

[815]JAMES [3], July 14 (erroneously dated July 15).

Mountain National Park, and on granite tors in the Platte River drainage."[816]

James's excursion from the chasm of the Platte on July 7 did not bring him far enough into the mountains to reach the "granite tors in the Platte River drainage." In his ascent of Pikes Peak on July 14, however, he passed Windy Point. It is there, almost certainly, that James collected the type (NY) of this beautiful, purple-flowered plant.

From the cog railway we have seen *Telesonix* in vegetative condition in the rock crevices just below Windy Point.

Scrophulariaceae

Agalinis sp.

#314 *Gerardia purpurea* L., in Torr., Ann. Lyc. Nat. Hist. N.Y. 2:228.1827.

Gerardia purpurea occurs in eastern Nebraska and flowers in August and September, but James went through the area in June. There are, however, three species that occur along James's route that flower at the time of year he was there.

During late August or early September, the following three purple-flowered species could have been found in Oklahoma: *A. aspera, A. fasciculata,* and *A. heterophylla.*

Agalinis auriculata (Michx.) Blake, Rhodora 20:71.1918.

#313 *Gerardia auriculata* Michx., in Torr., Ann. Lyc. Nat. Hist. N.Y. 2:228.1827.

On August 31, James described as a *Gerardia* a hirsute plant with "[l]eaves ovate-lanceolate sessile. Flowers large purple."[817] We believe that is the above species, which has been infrequently collected in Oklahoma.

On August 31 the party remained in camp on the Canadian River, about four miles southwest of Asher, Pottawatomie County, Oklahoma.

Agalinis tenuifolia (Vahl) Raf., New Fl. Bot. No. Am. 2:64.1837.

In his diary for August 14, James described as a *Gerardia* a plant with "[s]tem erect sparingly branched, subquadrangular. Leaves

---

[816]WEBER [1], 318.
[817]JAMES [3], August 31.

linear opposite Flowers purple, in a terminal leafy panicle."[818] We take that to be the above species, as it is the only one in range with these characters.

On August 14 the party traveled down the Canadian River through Roberts County, in the northeastern Texas panhandle.

Aureolaria grandiflora (Benth.) Pennell, Rhodora 20:135.1918. (False Foxglove).

James listed "Gerrardia flava" in his diary for September 1.[819]

Based on the color and size of the flower and the distribution, we believe his collection must have been of *A. grandiflora*.

We estimate that the party traveled nineteen miles on September 1 and camped on the Canadian, approximately two miles southeast of Konawa, Seminole County, Oklahoma.

Besseya plantaginea (James) Rydb., Bull. Torr. Bot. Club 30:280. 1903. (Foothills Besseya).

Veronica plantaginea James, Trans. Am. Phil. Soc. n.s. 2:173.1825. Type: NY.

James found this plant after the party left Palmer Lake on July 10.[820] The next date that he entered in his diary, however, was July 13, when, he wrote, he started for Pikes "High Peak."[821] His plant, then, could have been collected on July 10, 11, or 12. During those three days they were in El Paso County, traveling southwestward along the foothills from Palmer Lake to the Air Force Academy to Rock Creek, not far from Fort Carson. On the 12th, they rode eastward to near the town of Fountain, Colorado.

Castilleja integra Gray, in Torr., Bot. Mex. Bound. 119.1859. (Paintbrush).

#324 *Euchroma purpurea* Nutt. mss., in Torr., Ann. Lyc. Nat. Hist. N.Y. 2:230.1827. "On the Arkansa."

James did not reach the region where *Castilleja* (*Euchroma*) *purpurea* grows until long after its flowering time.

Castilleja integra is suggested because of its flower color, flowering time, and distribution. James could have collected it in southeastern Colorado or adjacent New Mexico in late July.

---

[818]JAMES [3], August 14.
[819]JAMES [3], September 1.
[820]JAMES [3], July 10 (erroneously dated July 11).
[821]JAMES [3], July 13 (erroneously dated July 14).

Castilleja occidentalis Torr. (Western Yellow Paintbrush).
#325 *Castilleja occidentalis* Torr., Ann. Lyc. Nat. Hist. N.Y. 2:230. 1827. "On the Rocky Mountains." Type: NY.
This high-altitude species would have been collected by James July 13–15 on his trip to the top of Pikes Peak, El Paso County, Colorado.

Castilleja sessiliflora Pursh, Fl. Am. Sept. 738. 1814. (Downy Paintbrush).
#322 *Euchroma grandiflora* Nutt., in Torr., Ann. Lyc. Nat. Hist. N.Y. 2:230.1827. "Mouth of the Platte."
E. grandiflora is listed as a synonym of *C. sessiliflora* in Gray[822] and Pennell.[823]
James likely collected this plant in June or July in Nebraska or along the South Platte in Colorado.

Chionophila jamesii Benth., in DC., Prodr. 10:331.1846. (Snow-Lover). "[I]n montibus Scopulosis Americae borealis juxta nives perpetuas (James!)."
On July 14, James described in his diary "a small plant somewhat resembling Penstemon with erect flowers" that he collected near the summit of Pikes Peak, El Paso County, Colorado.[824] The plant became the type (isotype: NY *fide* Pennell)[825] of *Chionophila jamesii*.
On the type sheet (NY) of *Penstemon jamesii* is a note in which Torrey indicated that he had given Hooker a portion of the plants, which Torrey had originally called *P. albidum*. It was this portion on which *Chionophila jamesii* was based.
The species is the basis of the new genus *Chionophila*.

Lindernia dubia (L.) Pennell, Acad. Nat. Sci. Phila. Monogr. No.1, 141. 1935. (Yellowseed False Pimpernel).
#329 *Lindernia dilatata* Muhl., in Torr., Ann. Lyc. Nat. Hist. N.Y. 2:231.1827. "On the Canadian."
Lindernia attenuata was listed by James in his diary for September 9.[826] On that day the party traveled along the Canadian from just south of Porum, Muskogee County, to within eight or ten miles upstream from the junction of the Canadian and Arkansas rivers.

---

[822]GRAY [4], 298.
[823]PENNELL [2], 523.
[824]JAMES [3], July 14 (erroneously dated July 15).
[825]PENNELL [1], 324.
[826]JAMES [3], September 9.

Their camp would have been in extreme-southeastern Muskogee County, Oklahoma.

Following N. H. Holmgren,[827] *L. dubia* is here considered to include *L. anagallidea. L. dilatata* in turn is considered a synonym of *L. anagallidea.*

Mimulus floribundus Dougl., in Lindl., Bot. Reg. 13: pl.1125. 1828. (Many-Flowered Mimulus).

#10 *Capraria pusilla* Torr., Ann. Lyc. Nat. Hist. N.Y. 1:36.1824. "With the preceding, ['On James' Peak, one of the highest of the Rocky Mountains, 10,000 feet above the level of the ocean, near the region of perpetual snow.'] and on the sides of the Rocky Mountains, in crevices of rocks." Not *Mimulus pusillus* Benth. (1846).

James's type collection was made between July 6 and 18 from near Denver to Royal Gorge at Cañon City, Colorado.

Mimulus glabratus HBK. var. **jamesii** (T. & G.) Gray, Syn. Fl. No. Am. ed.2, 2(1): Suppl.447. 1886. (Smooth Mimulus).

Mimulus glabratus HBK. var. *fremontii* (Benth.) Grant, Ann. Mo. Bot. Gard. 11:190.1924.

Mimulus jamesii T. & G. ex Benth., in DC., Prodr. 10:371.1846. "Ad fontes planitierum Missouriensium (James! Engelmann!)." Information written in James's handwriting on the type sheet (NY) indicates that on May 27, 1820, James collected the type in "clear running water near the Missouri River, between the [Council] Bluffs and the mouth of the Beyer River." At that time James was along the Missouri River in Pottawatamie County, Iowa, a short distance downstream from Engineer Cantonment. Also on the type sheet is written "Lindernia?" "Lindernia? fl. flat. [?] in clear running water" is also listed among the plants collected on May 27 in the diary.

It seems likely that the plant James called "Lindernia?" became the type of *Mimulus jamesii.*

Again on June 30, as the party traveled along the South Platte between Brush and Fort Morgan, Morgan County, Colorado, James mentioned in his diary a plant growing in a spring of clear water.[828] He described it as being "the same plant [*Lindernia*] resembling Gratiola as was noticed in those [springs] about Council Bluffs."

On July 7, James described in his diary "a small subdecumbent

827HOLMGREN, IV, 350.
828JAMES [3], June 30.

plant with opposite pedunculated leaves. Flowers yellow somewhat resembling those of Gratiola."[829] That plant could well be this species or *Mimulus guttatus* DC. On July 7 James ascended the South Platte above the chasm, about seven miles southwest of Waterton, Jefferson County, Colorado.

Pedicularis sp.

#311 *Pedicularis flammea* L., in Torr., Ann. Lyc. Nat. Hist. N.Y. 2:228.1827. "On the Rocky Mountains, *Dr. James.* There were no specimens of this plant in the collection."

James listed *P. flammea* "On the Rocky Mountains" in his *Catalogue.*[830]

P. flammea is a species that grows to be only about three inches tall but which is out of range. There are at least three short species in range that James could have seen: *Pedicularis parryi, P. canadensis* subsp. *fluviatilis,* and *P. scopulorum.*

Pedicularis groenlandica Retz., Prodr. Fl. Scand. ed. 2, 145. 1795. (Elephant-Head).

#310 *Pedicularis groenlandica* Willd., in Torr., Ann. Lyc. Nat. Hist. N.Y. 2:228.1827. "On the Rocky Mountains."

This species was most likely collected July 14, during James's ascent of Pikes Peak, El Paso County, Colorado.

Penstemon albidus Nutt., Gen. No. Am. Pl. 2:53.1818. (White Beardtongue).

For the entry in Torrey see *Penstemon jamesii.*[831]

James listed this plant, with a question mark, in his diary for June 12.[832] The date and location for this species are very good, and there is no reason to doubt the identification.

The party traveled that day through the Pawnee Republic village up the Loup River to the Pawnee Loup village, all in Nance County, Nebraska.

Penstemon ambiguus Torr. (Pink Plains Penstemon).

#315 *Pentstemon ambiguum* Torr., Ann. Lyc. Nat. Hist. N.Y. 2:228–29.1827. "Near the Rocky Mountains." Type: NY.

---

[829]JAMES [3], July 7 (erroneously dated July 8).
[830]JAMES [4], 184.
[831]TORREY [2], 229.
[832]JAMES [3], June 12.

In his diary for August 3, James described this plant fully.[833] The type was collected in Harding County, New Mexico, as the party traveled thirty miles down Ute Creek, starting from a few miles south of Bueyeros.

Penstemon angustifolius Nutt. ex Pursh, Fl. Am. Sept. 738. 1814. (Narrow-Leaved Penstemon).
P. coeruleus Nutt., Gen. No. Am. Pl. 2:52.1818.
Torrey's #321 *P. coeruleum* became Bentham's *P. torreyi* (*q.v.*).
It is not known what specimen from the Long Expedition Bentham saw when he listed the following under *P. coeruleus:* "in planitie Missouriensi pr. Fort Mandan, etc. (Nutt.! Long! Bradbury!)."[834] The range as given by Bentham, however, is good for *P. angustifolius,* and this plant would have been in flower at the time that James was in its range in Nebraska and northeastern Colorado in June.

Penstemon eriantherus Pursh, Fl. Am. Sept. 737. 1814. (Crested Beardtongue).
#320 *Pentstemon cristatum* Nutt., in Torr., Ann. Lyc. Nat. Hist. N.Y. 2:229.1827. "Forks of the Platte."
James mentioned this plant in the diary under the date of June 23,[835] and it was also listed in the *Account,*[836] all as *P. cristatum.*
James collected the plant on the south side of the South Platte River, a few miles above its junction with the North Platte, Lincoln County, Nebraska.

Penstemon glaber Pursh, Fl. Am. Sept. 738. 1814.
#319 *Pentstemon erianthera* Nutt., *P. glabra* Pursh, in Torr., Ann. Lyc. Nat. Hist. N.Y. 2:229.1827. "Sources of the Platte."
The closest the party got to the currently known range of this species (seventy-five to eighty miles) was on June 25, when they spent the day in camp on the South Platte River, a few miles west of Ogallala, Keith County, Nebraska. Perhaps it was there that James made his collection.

Penstemon glaber Pursh var. **alpinus** (Torr.) Gray, Proc. Am. Acad. Sci. 6:60.1862. (Alpine Penstemon).

---

[833]JAMES [3], August 3.
[834]BENTHAM, 325.
[835]JAMES [3], June 23 (erroneously dated June 22).
[836]JAMES [1], I, 468n.; JAMES [2] in THWAITES [1], XV, 241n.

#9 *Pentstemon alpina* Torr., Ann. Lyc. Nat. Hist. N.Y. 1:35.1824. "With the preceding ['On James' Peak, one of the highest of the Rocky Mountains, 10,000 feet above the level of the ocean, near the region of perpetual snow.']."

Pennell explained that the name is unfortunate, as the "plant rarely reaches timber line and grows mostly upon the lower mountain slopes and foothills."[837] Among the several specimens cited from Colorado in Pennell are one from Denver and one from Evans, Weld County.

James listed "Penstemon erianthera," i.e., *P. glaber* Pursh, on July 4 and 14.[838] We think it likely that one of these is the type (NY) of Torrey's *P. alpina.* On July 4 the party was encamped most of the day on the South Platte River near Brighton, Adams County, Colorado. On July 14 James ascended Pikes Peak, El Paso County, Colorado.

Penstemon gracilis Nutt., Gen. No. Am. Pl. 2:52.1818. (Slender Penstemon).

#316 *Pentstemon gracile* Nutt., in Torr., Ann. Lyc. Nat. Hist. N.Y. 2:229.1827. "Along the Platte."

James referred in his diary to this plant as *P. gracile.*[839] His collection was made on June 14 as the party traveled south from the Loup River to the Platte through Merrick County, Nebraska.[840]

Penstemon grandiflorus Nutt., Fraser's Catalogue, 1813. (Large Beardtongue).

#317 *Pentstemon grandiflorum* Nutt., in Torr., Ann. Lyc. Nat. Hist. N.Y. 2:229.1827. "Mouth of the Platte to the Rocky Mountains. Also on the Canadian. Flowers May–Aug."

In the *Account* on August 19, James listed this species as *P. bradburii.*[841] At that time the expedition was on the Washita River drainage, probably in Roger Mills County, Oklahoma, a few miles southwest of Leedey, Dewey County.

Penstemon jamesii Benth., in DC., Prodr. 10:325.1846. (James

[837]PENNELL [1], 348.

[838]JAMES [1], I, 498n., II, 28; JAMES [2] in THWAITES [1], XV, 277n., XVI, 17; JAMES [3], July 4.

[839]JAMES [3], June 14 (included as part of the June 13 entry).

[840]In the *Account* (JAMES [1], I, 455n.; JAMES [2] in THWAITES [1], XV, 226n.) this plant is listed among the plants collected on June 15 and 16.

[841]JAMES [1], II, 134; JAMES [2] in THWAITES [1], XVI, 144.

Penstemon). "[I]n montibus Scopulosis (James in itinere Longii!). P. albidus Torr.! ann. Lyc. N.York. p.229 non Nutt."

#318 *Pentstemon albidum sensu* Torr., Ann. Lyc. Nat. Hist. N.Y. 2:229.1827. "Near the Rocky Mountains." As indicated by Gray, *P. jamesii* is *P. albidum sensu* Torrey in part.[842]

In his diary for July 30, James listed a *Penstemon* with a brief description that could apply to *P. jamesii*.[843] In the *Account* on this day a "pentstemon" is listed.[844] That plant, which likely became the type (NY), was collected as the party traveled across the Don Carlos Hills, from Sierra Grande to Ute Creek, western Union County, New Mexico.

Penstemon torreyi Benth., in DC., Prodr. 10:324.1846. (Torrey Penstemon). "[V]ersus montes Scopulosos (iter Long.!). P. coeruleus Torr.! pl. Rocky-M. p.229, non Nutt." Type: NY.

#321 *Pentstemon coeruleum?* Nutt., in Torr., Ann. Lyc. Nat. Hist. N.Y. 2:229.1827. No locality is given. "The flowers in my specimens are faded too much to ascertain what was the original colour. They appear to have been purple."

This plant is frequently treated as a variety of *P. barbatus*.

James described this plant in his diary on July 10.[845] The type locality is on Monument Creek, somewhere between Elephant Rock, near Palmer Lake, and their campsite on the grounds of the Air Force Academy, El Paso County, Colorado.

Penstemon whippleanus Gray, Proc. Am. Acad. Sci. 6:73.1862.

P. glaucus Graham var. *stenosepalus* Gray, *l.c.* 6:70.1862. A James specimen from Pikes Peak was the first one of this variety cited by Gray; Pennell, however, designated *Parry 261* (NY) from the headwaters of Clear Creek etc., Colorado, as the lectotype.[846]

The James collection (NY) is the earlier and was made on July 14 or 15 on Pikes Peak, El Paso County, Colorado.

Scrophularia lanceolata Pursh, Fl. Am. Sept. 419. 1814. (Figwort).

#328 *Scrophularia lanceolata* Pursh, in Torr., Ann. Lyc. Nat. Hist.

---

[842]GRAY [4], 265.
[843]JAMES [3], July 30.
[844]JAMES [1], II, 86; JAMES [2] in THWAITES [1], XVI, 86.
[845]JAMES [3], July 10 (erroneously dated July 11).
[846]PENNELL [1], 377.

N.Y. 2:230.1827. "Sources of the Platte. *Dr. James.*" "This plant is not in the collection."

The plant was mentioned by James in his diary and in the *Account* on July 4.[847] On that day the party camped before noon on the South Platte River, a few miles south of Brighton, Adams County, Colorado.

Veronica catenata Pennell, Rhodora 23:37.1921. (Speedwell).

#327 *Veronica Anagallis* L., in Torr., Ann. Lyc. Nat. Hist. N.Y. 2:230.1827. "On the Platte."

The diary reads, "Veronica annagallis? Stem erect obtusely quadrangular. leaves opposite sessile, sharply serrate Flowers axillary sessile crowded root creeping. jointed. Resembles V. Beccabunga."[848]

This plant was listed merely as "Veronica approaching V. *beccabunga*" in the *Account.*[849]

James's "sessile leaves" would eliminate *V. americana.* His "serrate leaves" better suggest *V. anagallis-aquatica.* "Flowers axillary and sessile" is puzzling. Perhaps the specimen was quite young, if indeed it were a *Veronica. V. catenata* is chosen as more likely because of the unlikelihood of *V. anagallis-aquatica* being introduced so far west so early.

The plant that James described was collected on June 20 along the Platte River near Gothenburg, Dawson County, Nebraska.

The type of *V. catenata* was collected by Rydberg in Fall River County in the southwest corner of South Dakota, adjacent to Nebraska.

Veronicastrum virginicum (L.) Farw., Drugg. Circ. 61:231.1917. (Culver's Root).

#326 *Leptandra virginica* Nutt., in Torr., Ann. Lyc. Nat. Hist. N.Y. 2:230.1827. "On the Arkansa."

Based on flowering time and distribution, James would have made his collection between September 10 and 13 along the Arkansas River in Sequoyah County, Oklahoma.

Solanaceae

Physalis lobata Torr. (Purple-Flowered Ground-Cherry).

[847]JAMES [1], I, 498n.; JAMES [2] in THWAITES [1], XV, 277n.; JAMES [3], July 4.

[848]JAMES [3], June 20 (erroneously dated June 19).

[849]JAMES [1], I, 461n.; JAMES [2] in THWAITES [1], XV, 233n. (as approaching "V. *deccabunga*").

#302 *Physalis lobata* Torr., Ann. Lyc. Nat. Hist. N.Y. 2:226.1827.
"On the Canadian?" Type: NY.

James collected a plant that he thought was a *Physalis* on July 25,
while the party was on Chacuaco Creek not more than six miles
above its junction with the Purgatoire River, Las Animas County,
Colorado.[850]

That is the only *Physalis* mentioned in the diary during the time
that James was in the range of *P. lobata.*

According to Torrey's original description, the flower is "small,
greenish." The flowers are large and purplish. Presumably the dis-
crepancy was caused by the imperfect condition of the original
specimen.

Physalis heterophylla Nees, Linnaea 6:463.1831.
see *Physalis pubescens.*

Physalis pubescens L., Sp. Pl. 183. 1753. (Downy Ground-
Cherry).

#303 *Physalis pubescens* Willd., in Torr., Ann. Lyc. Nat. Hist. N.Y.
2:227.1827. "On the Missouri."

The reference from Linnaeus and from Willdenow refer to the
same species.

James mentioned a *Solanum* in his diary for May 6, while he was at
Loutre Lick, Missouri.[851] A paragraph later he suggested that it was a
Physalis.

On May 30, while at Engineer Cantonment on the Missouri River,
some five miles downstream from Fort Calhoun, Washington County, Nebraska, James wrote, "The Solanum first observed on the rocky
hills at Loutre Lick is very abundant in the dry grassy plains in this
vicinity."[852]

On June 19 James wrote, "The plant found at Loutre Lick and called
Solanum——? is a Physalis and is abundant on the Platte."[853] On that
day the party traveled along the Platte River between Overton and
Gothenburg, Dawson County, Nebraska.

Central Missouri is in good range for *P. pubescens,* and it seems
likely that the plant from Loutre Lick was the one to which Torrey
referred. What the two collections from Nebraska may be is less

---

[850]JAMES [3], July 25.
[851]JAMES [3], May 6.
[852]JAMES [3], May 30.
[853]JAMES [3], June 19.

certain. *Physalis pubescens* occurs in Nebraska but infrequently. To judge by abundance, these collections are likely *P. heterophylla* Nees and/or *P. virginiana* Miller.

Physalis virginiana Mill., Gard. Dict. ed. 8, no.4, 1768.
see *Physalis pubescens.*

Solanum carolinense L., Sp. Pl. 187. 1753. (Horse-Nettle).
#306 *Solanum carolinense* Dun., in Torr., Ann. Lyc. Nat. Hist. N.Y. 2:227.1827. "On the Missouri and along the Platte to the mountains."

James could have collected this species in June near Engineer Cantonment or along the Loup River in Nebraska. His collection could also have been made in the latter half of August along the Canadian River in Oklahoma.

Gleason commented that this species was "originally native in the se. states."[854] We are uncertain how rapidly the range of this species extended to include the area crossed by the Long Expedition.

Solanum dimidiatum Raf., Aut. Bot. 107. 1840. (Western Horse-Nettle).
#307 *Solanum platyphyllum* Dun., in Torr., Ann. Lyc. Nat. Hist. N.Y. 2:227.1827. No location given.
Solanum torreyi Gray, Proc. Am. Acad. 6:44.1866.

The first reference cited by Gray in the Proc. Am. Acad. is #281, *S. mammosum,* in Pl. Lindh. The second is *S. platyphyllum* of Torrey in the Ann. Lyc. reference above. The New York Botanical Garden type specimen microfiche shows a James specimen collected on the Long Expedition as a type of *Solanum torreyi.* The microfiche index lists two specimens. The second we interpret to be from a specimen grown at the Cambridge Botanic Garden from seeds of a Charles Wright collection made in the mid 1800s.

James described the plant as "Solanum caroliniense ?" in his diary for August 21, stating that it was about three feet tall, the sinuate-pinnatifid leaves 5–6 inches long, the flower large, purple, and the berry large.[855]

On August 21 the party was traveling down the Canadian River in Dewey County, Oklahoma.

---

[854] GLEASON [2], III, 201.
[855] JAMES [3], August 21.

Solanum elaeagnifolium Cav., Icon. & Descript. Pl. 3:22, pl. 243. 1795. (Silverleaf Nightshade).

#309 Solanum flavidum Torr., Ann. Lyc. Nat. Hist. N.Y. 2:227–28.1827. "The exact locality of this plant is not recorded."

In his diary for July 25, James gave a lengthy description of what he thought was a new species of a plant resembling *Solanum*.[856] His description and that of Torrey's #309 are very similar and must surely refer to the same species. Gray placed Torrey's species in synonymy under *S. elaeagnifolium*.[857]

James remarked that he collected the plant in the morning. The party made their midday stop near the mouth of Iron or Minnie canyon on the Purgatoire. The type of *S. flavidum*, then, came from near this stream and within two or three miles north or south of the Otero/Las Animas county line, Colorado.

Solanum jamesii Torr. (Wild Potato).

#308 Solanum Jamesii Torr., Ann. Lyc. Nat. Hist. N.Y. 2:227.1827. "The station was not recorded, but is probably on the Arkansa."

In Torrey's original description he stated that the plant was an annual. Later he remarked that James's collection was "erroneously described as annual."[858]

In his diary for July 30, James described a *Solanum* that fits fairly well this species and appears to be the type (NY) collection.[859]

On July 30 the party traveled southwest across the Don Carlos Hills, from Sierra Grande to Ute Creek, western Union County, New Mexico.

Solanum nigrum L., Sp. Pl. 186. 1753. (Black Nightshade).

James observed this plant for the first time on August 5.[860] On that day the party crossed from Quay County, New Mexico, into Oldham County, Texas, in the Texas panhandle. The plant appears to have been collected near their evening's campsite.

Solanum rostratum Dun., Hist. Nat. Solanum 234, pl.24. 1813. (Buffalo Bur).

#304 Nycterium luteum Donn. *Androcera lobata* Nutt. *Solanum*

---

[856]JAMES [3], July 25.
[857]GRAY [4], 230.
[858]TORREY [3], 151.
[859]JAMES [3], July 30.
[860]JAMES [3], August 5.

heterandrum Pursh, in Torr., Ann. Lyc. Nat. Hist. N.Y. 2:227.1827. "Common throughout all the country along the course of the Platte and upper parts of the Arkansa."

James referred to this plant in his *Catalogue* as *Androcera lobata;*[861] in the diary[862] and *Account*[863] it is referred to as *Solanum heterandrum*. The plant was collected on June 19 "about marmot holes" between Overton and Gothenburg, Dawson County, Nebraska.

Solanum triflorum Nutt., Gen. No. Am. Pl. 1:128.1818. (Cut-Leaved Nightshade).

#305 *Solanum triflorum* Nutt., in Torr., Ann. Lyc. Nat. Hist. N.Y. 2:227.1827. "On the Platte, commencing near the Pawnee villages and continuing to the mountains; almost invariably found near the habitation of the marmots or prairie dogs."

The habitat is given in the references below as evidence that all refer to the same plant.

Solanum hirsutum James, Trans. Am. Phil. Soc. n.s. 2:176.1825. [Not *S. hirsutum* Dunal, 1813]. "Habitat on the Platte, commencing near the Paunee Villages, and continuing to the mountains. I have never seen it, except immediately about the burrowing places of the marmots or prairie dogs, where it is almost constantly found."

James described this plant in his diary, remarking that it was "probably a distinct species" that differed from *S. triflorum* in being hirsute.[864] Here, too, James gave the habitat as "in the loose soil about the burrows of the marmot or prairie dog." A description and habitat similar to the one in the diary are also found in the *Account.*[865]

James's type collection was likely made on June 14 as the party traveled south from the Loup River to the Platte through Merrick County, Nebraska.

Sparganiaceae

Sparganium eurycarpum Engelm., in Gray, Man. Bot. ed.2. 430. 1856. (Bur-Reed).

James referred to this plant as *Sparganium ramosum* on June 13, the

---

861JAMES [4], 177.
862JAMES [3], June 19.
863JAMES [1], I, 453n.; JAMES [2] in THWAITES [1], XV, 223n. (both under June 14).
864JAMES [3], June 14 (erroneously included as part of June 13).
865JAMES [1], I, 453n.; JAMES [2] in THWAITES [1], XV, 223n.

day the party crossed the Loup River and camped about three miles north and a little east of Palmer, Merrick County, Nebraska.[866]

Typhaceae

Typha latifolia L., Sp. Pl. 971. 1753. (Broad-Leaved Cat-Tail).

This name appears in James's diary for July 4.[867] On that day the party camped before noon on the South Platte River, a few miles south of Brighton, Adams County, Colorado.

Ulmaceae

Celtis laevigata Willd., Berl. Baumz. ed.2. 81. 1811. (Sugar Berry).

In his diary for September 3 James mentioned this hackberry as *Celtis occidentalis,* a species that is unlikely for James's location.[868] In the *Account,* hackberry is mentioned a day earlier.[869]

The party traveled only a few miles and camped on the Canadian, about five miles northwest of Allen near the junction of Seminole, Hughes, and Pontotoc counties, Oklahoma.

Celtis reticulata Torr. (Net-Leaved Hackberry).

#414 *Celtis reticulata* Torr., Ann. Lyc. Nat. Hist. N.Y. 2:247.1827. "Base of the Rocky Mountains."

Under the genus name *Prunus,* James described in his diary for July 25 what he believed was a new species.[870] Phrases such as "leaves alternate obliquely cordate" and "peduncles axillary solitary one flowered" leave no doubt about this being a *Celtis.* As *Celtis reticulata* is the only species of this genus that occurs where James was that day, there is no doubt as to what his description refers.

The type (NY) was collected on July 25 on Chacuaco Creek, not more than six miles above its junction with the Purgatoire River, Las Animas County, Colorado.

Ulmus alata Michx., Fl. Bor. Am. 1:173.1803. (Winged Elm).

The first mention of *U. alata* by James occurs in the *Account* under

---

[866]JAMES [3], June 13.
[867]JAMES [3], July 4.
[868]JAMES [3], September 3.
[869]JAMES [1], II, 155; JAMES [2] in THWAITES [1], XVI, 168.
[870]JAMES [3], July 25.

the date of August 15.[871] That was an error that is explained under *U. americana,* which follows.

On September 3, however, James stated in his diary that *U. alata* "begins to be abundant" and that *U. americana* is also present.[872] The *Account* mentions these two species of elm, but in the entry for September 2.[873]

The party was now, and for the first time, in good range of *U. alata.* On September 3 the party traveled only a few miles and camped on the Canadian about five miles northwest of Allen, near the junction of Seminole, Hughes, and Pontotoc counties, Oklahoma.

Ulmus americana L., Sp. Pl. 226. 1753. (American Elm).

When James mentioned *Ulmus americana,* as well as *U. alata,* in his diary for September 3, he was in eastern Pontotoc County, Oklahoma, and in good range for both species.[874]

In his diary for August 15, James stated that *U. americana* begins to occur.[875] The *Account* for August 15, however, reads: "Near our camp was a scattering grove of small-leaved elms. This tree (the U. alata, N.) is not known in the Eastern states; . . . it is usually of a smaller size than the ulmus americana, and is distinguished from it by the smallness of the leaves and the whiteness of the trunk."[876] In the *Account* one day earlier, August 14, James mentioned "small-leaved elm."[877]

James's confusion is understandable. In western Oklahoma and the adjacent Texas panhandle, the tree long passing as *U. americana,* perhaps quite correctly, differs in several respects. The tree is low and very wide, characters that could easily be environmental. The leaves are frequently very rough above, much as in *U. rubra.* They are also smaller than in typical *U. americana.* We measured the length of the blade of over 100 leaves of elm from western Oklahoma and adjacent Texas. The average length was between 5 and 6 cm. The two largest were 7.5 cm. The usual size of *U. americana* is 8 to 14 cm.

On August 15 the party was traveling down the Canadian River in Roberts and Hemphill counties, Texas.

The mention in the *Account* of elm near the campsite of August 5

[871]JAMES [1], II, 121–22; JAMES [2] in THWAITES [1], XVI, 128.
[872]JAMES [3], September 3.
[873]JAMES [1], II, 155; JAMES [2] in THWAITES [1], XVI, 168.
[874]JAMES [3], September 3.
[875]JAMES [3], August 15.
[876]JAMES [1], II, 121–22; JAMES [2] in THWAITES [1], XVI, 128.
[877]JAMES [1], II, 119; JAMES [2] in THWAITES [1], XVI, 125.

and 6 (along the Canadian River at the western edge of the Texas panhandle) is an apparent error,[878] as this tree is not recorded closer to that camp than the eastern edge of the Texas panhandle.

James mentioned thickets of elm and other trees in the *Account* early on August 26, when they were northeast of Cedar Lake, Canadian County, Oklahoma.[879]

Ulmus thomasii Sarg., Silva No. Am. 14:102.1902. (Rock Elm).

James referred to this plant in his diary as the European *U. nemoralis.*[880] His collection was likely of *U. thomasii,* a species that occurs along the Missouri River.

James made his collection on May 29 in the area of Engineer Cantonment, some five miles downstream on the Missouri River from Fort Calhoun, Washington County, Nebraska.

Umbelliferae

Eryngium diffusum Torr. (Eryngo).

#177 *Eryngium diffusum* Torr., Ann. Lyc. Nat. Hist. N.Y. 2:206–207.1827. "On the Canadian." Type: NY.

No mention of this plant is made in the diary; in the *Account* on August 20, however, James noted that the ground was covered "with a purple mat" of eryngo.[881] It is interesting that they found so much of it, as it is an infrequently collected plant in Oklahoma.

At the time James collected the type they were in western Dewey County, Oklahoma.

Heracleum sphondylium L. subsp. **montanum** (Schleich. ex Gaud.) Briquet, in Schinz & R. Keller, Fl. Schweiz, ed.2, 1:372.1905. (Cow Parsnip).

#179 *Heracleum Sphondylium* L., in Torr., Ann. Lyc. Nat. Hist. N.Y. 2:207.1827. "On the Missouri."

We have found no reference to this plant in James's diary; however, based on distribution and flowering time, it could have been collected in May near Engineer Cantonment on the Missouri River or in July along the front range in Colorado.

---

[878]JAMES [1], II, 96; JAMES [2] in THWAITES [1], XVI, 98.
[879]JAMES [1], II, 142; JAMES [2] in THWAITES [1], XVI, 152.
[880]JAMES [3], May 29.
[881]JAMES [1], II, 135; JAMES [2] in THWAITES [1], XVI, 144.

Oreoxis humilis Raf., in Seringe, Bull. Bot. 1:217.1830. (Alpine Parsley).

Rafinesque's name is based on a description by Torrey of an unnumbered and unnamed umbellifer immediately following his #179.[882]

James's type (NY) collection could have been made only on July 14 on the tundra of Pikes Peak, El Paso County, Colorado, where it is said to be endemic.

Sium suave Walt., Fl. Carol. 115. 1788. (Water Parsnip).

#178 *Sium latifolium* L., in Torr., Ann. Lyc. Nat. Hist. N.Y. 2:207.1827. "Base of the Rocky Mountains."

This collection was made on July 5 when James made a side trip up "cannon-ball river" (Clear Creek), just north of Denver in Adams County, Colorado.[883]

Urticaceae

Parietaria pensylvanica Muhl., in Willd., Sp. Pl. 4:955.1806. (Pellitory).

#411 *Parietaria pennsylvanica* Willd., in Torr., Ann. Lyc. Nat. Hist. N.Y. 2:246.1827. No location given.

In view of the long flowering period and the wide distribution of the species, it is not possible to know where James collected it.

Valerianaceae

Valeriana capitata Pallas subsp. **acutiloba** (Rydb.) F. G. Meyer, Ann. Mo. Bot. Gard. 38:407.1951. (Valerian).

In his diary for July 14 James included the following: "Tri. Mon. A plant resembling——[word not legible, perhaps Diodia] Hab. about the borders of rocks at the base of the last cone."[884] We are interpreting this plant to be a *Valeriana* of the alpine region. July 14 is the day that James climbed Pikes Peak, El Paso County, Colorado; his plant was collected just below the summit.

[882]TORREY [2], 207.
[883]JAMES [1], I, 50ln.; JAMES [2] in THWAITES [1], XV, 281n.; JAMES [3], July 5.
[884]JAMES [3], July 14 (erroneously dated July 15).

Verbenaceae

Phyla cuneifolia (Torr.) Greene, Pittonia 4:47.1899. (Fog Fruit).
#353 *Zapania cuneifolia* Torr., Ann. Lyc. Nat. Hist. N.Y. 2:234.
1827. "On the Platte."
The type sheet (NY) contains a Latin description as given by
Torrey, but there is no additional information. The species occurs
over much of the route of the expedition.

Phyla lanceolata (Michx.) Greene, Pittonia 4:47.1899. (Northern
Fog Fruit).
#352 *Zapania lanceolata* Pursh, in Torr., Ann. Lyc. Nat. Hist. N.Y.
2:234.1827. "On the Platte?"
Based on the known range of the species, there is no reason to doubt the
locality; hence, it could have been collected in June in Nebraska.

Verbena bipinnatifida Nutt., Jour. Acad. Nat. Sci. Philad. 2:123.
1821. (Dakota Vervain).
#349 *Verbena bipinnatifida* Nutt., in Torr., Ann. Lyc. Nat. Hist.
N.Y. 2:233.1827. "About the lead mines of Missouri."
James listed "Verbena Aubletia" in his diary, a name that is a
synonym of *Verbena canadensis*.[885] At the time, however, James was
not in range of this species. He presumably had the similar but not-
yet-described *V. bipinnatifida*.
Torrey's location, "[a]bout the lead mines of Missouri" is surely
incorrect, as this species in known in Missouri from only one west-
central county. James encountered the lead mines in eastern Missouri, along the Mississippi River south of St. Louis.
James's plant was collected June 19, between Overton and Gothenburg, Dawson County, Nebraska.

Verbena simplex Lehm., Ind. Sem. Hort. Hamb. 17. 1825. (Narrow-Leaved Vervain).
#351 *Verbena angustifolia* Michx., in Torr., Ann. Lyc. Nat. Hist.
N.Y. 2:234.1827. "Near St. Louis."
James reached the area "[n]ear St. Louis" too early for the flowering of this species; as he traveled up the Missouri River toward
Engineer Cantonment, however, he could have encountered it in mid
to late May.

[885]JAMES [3], June 19.

It is also possible for James to have made his collection in early September along the Canadian River in far-eastern Oklahoma. Late-August specimens are known from Muskogee County, Oklahoma, a county through which the expedition traveled September 8–10.

Verbena stricta Vent., Hort. Cels. 53. 1800. (Hoary Vervain).

#350 "a" *Verbena stricta* Vent. β? *mollis* Torr., Ann. Lyc. Nat. Hist. N.Y. 2:234.1827. "On the Arkansa?"

Torrey's new variety is said to have been collected "[o]n the Arkansa?" It is considered to be a synonym of *Verbena stricta*. The type may be at NY. Moldenke, under locality undetermined, cited "*James s.n.* [Long's 1st Exped.]."886

Verbena mollis (Torr.) Raf., Atl. Jour. 1:146.1832. The reference here is to Torrey's #360, obviously an error for #350.

If the Arkansas locality is correct, the collection could have been made along the Arkansas River in July in Colorado, or in early September in eastern Oklahoma. We think it is more likely that this is the *Verbena* that James referred to in his diary on June 29 as *V. urticifolia*.887 On that day James traveled from near Sterling, Logan County, to Messex, Washington County, Colorado. At the time, he was out of range of *V. urticifolia*.

Violaceae

Hybanthus linearis (Torr.) Shinners, Field & Lab. 19:126.1951. (Green Violet).

#27 *Ionidium n.sp.?* (*lineare*) Torr., Ann. Lyc. Nat. Hist. N.Y. 2:168.1827.

Ionidium lineare Torr., in Torr. & Gray, Fl. No. Am. 1:145.1838. "On the Red River, Arkansas, *Dr. James!*"

The type was collected "on rocky declivities of hills about the northwestern branches of the Red river."888 This collection was made on August 1 near the junction of Garcia Creek with Ute Creek in the steep-sided canyon, about six miles east and a little north of Yates, Harding County, New Mexico.

Many authors, including Morton,889 consider Torrey's species to be a

886MOLDENKE, 232.
887JAMES [3], June 29.
888JAMES [3], August 1.
889MORTON [1], 76; MORTON [2], 62.

synonym of the earlier *H. verticillatus* (Ort.) Baill., whose type locality is Mexico.

Viola pubescens Ait., Hort. Kew. 3:290.1789. (Downy or Smooth Yellow Violet).
#29 *Viola pubescens* Ait., in Torr., Ann. Lyc. Nat. Hist. N.Y. 2:168.1827. "Council Bluffs."
James listed *Viola* among the plants collected on May 29, in the area of Engineer Cantonment, some five miles downstream on the Missouri River from Fort Calhoun, Washington County, Nebraska.[890]

Viola viarum Pollard, in Britton, Man. 635. 1901. (Plains Violet).
#28 *Viola palmata* L., in Torr., Ann. Lyc. Nat. Hist. N.Y. 2:168. 1827. "On the grassy plains of the Platte."
James described this violet as entirely glabrous and referred to it as *Viola palmata,* a species that is out of range in Nebraska.[891]
Viola viarum, also a glabrous species, resembles *V. palmata* and is in good range for James's June 7 collection site near the Elkhorn River, a few miles southeast of Arlington, Washington or Dodge County, Nebraska.
Viola palmata is also cited in the *Account* on June 9.[892] In addition to that plant there are several other plants listed in the same footnote. According to the diary, some of these plants were collected before June 9, others after that date.

Vitaceae

Ampelopsis arborea (L.) Rusby, Mem. Torr. Bot. Club 5:221.1894. (Pepper Vine).
#53 *Ampelopsis bipinnata* Michx., in Torr., Ann. Lyc. Nat. Hist. N.Y. 2:173.1827. "On the Arkansa and Canadian."
James mentioned *Cissus bipinnata* on August 30, the day that the party camped on the Canadian about four miles southwest of Asher, Pottawatomie County, Oklahoma.[893] That is still the farthest west that the species has been found on the Canadian.

[890]JAMES [3], May 29.
[891]JAMES [3], June 7.
[892]JAMES [1], I, 433n.; JAMES [2] in THWAITES [1], XV, 200n.
[893]JAMES [1], II, 150; JAMES [2] in THWAITES [1], XVI, 162; JAMES [3], August 30.

Ampelopsis cordata Michx., Fl. Bor. Am. 1:159.1803. (Raccoon Grape).

#52 Ampelopsis cordata Michx., in Torr., Ann. Lyc. Nat. Hist. N.Y. 2:173.1827. "On the Arkansa."

In the diary for September 11, James mentioned a *Cissus* as part of the undergrowth on the Canadian and Arkansas rivers.[894] At that time the party was on the Arkansas River southwest of Sallisaw, Sequoyah County, Oklahoma. That could be the location of the collection to which Torrey referred; James, however, was in range of this species through all of August from the Texas panhandle down the Canadian River through Oklahoma.

Parthenocissus quinquefolia (L.) Planch., in DC., Mon. Phan. 5:448.1887. (Virginia Creeper).

#54 Ampelopsis quinquefolia Michx., in Torr., Ann. Lyc. Nat. Hist. N.Y. 2:173.1827. *A. hederacea* DC. "With the preceding ['On the Arkansa and Canadian.']."

In his diary for August 30, James listed "Cissus hederacea" (i.e., *Parthenocissus quinquefolia*) and noted that the plant "is found 200 miles above."[895]

It is true that this species is found in Oklahoma along the Canadian River west to Texas. Curiously, *Cissus quinquefolia* is cited in the *Account* as growing with *Cissus hederacea*.[896]

On August 30 the party traveled from near Lexington, Cleveland County, to about four miles southwest of Asher, Pottawatomie County, Oklahoma.

Vitis acerifolia Raf., Med. Fl. ii, 130 (May) 1830. (Bush Grape). *Vitis longii* Prince, Treat. Vine. 184. (Sept.) 1830.

#55 Vitis n.sp., Torr., Ann. Lyc. Nat. Hist. N.Y. 2:173.1827. "Abundant on the Arkansa." This grape, which Torrey described as having "exquisite flavour," is the one that James similarly described in his diary and the *Account* on August 17.[897] *Vitis acerifolia* does not occur along James's route on the Arkansas.

It is on Torrey's #55 that Rafinesque based *V. acerifolia*.

James could have collected the type on the Canadian River through the Texas panhandle to Pottawatomie County, Oklahoma. References

[894]JAMES [3], September 11.
[895]JAMES [3], August 30.
[896]JAMES [1], II, 150; JAMES [2] in THWAITES [1], XVI, 161.
[897]JAMES [1], II, 126; JAMES [2] in THWAITES [1], XVI, 133–34; JAMES [3], August 17.

were made by James in his diary to *Vitis* on August 5 and 17 in the Texas panhandle, and on August 27 in Canadian County, Oklahoma.[898] If the type were collected on August 17, the type locality would be on the Canadian River slightly more than twenty miles downstream from the town of Canadian, Hemphill County, Texas.

Wild grapes are mentioned a few more times as the expedition continued downstream to Ft. Smith. The comments on them in the diary and the *Account* are too brief to enable us to determine which of the several species in the area they might be.

Zygophyllaceae

Kallstroemia parviflora Norton, Ann. Rept. Mo. Bot. Gard. 9:153. 1898. (Water Caltrop).

#57 *Tribulus maximus* L., in Torr., Ann. Lyc. Nat. Hist. N.Y. 2:173.1827. "Station not recorded; probably on the Arkansa."

The Ann. Lyc. reference with James as a collector is cited in Torrey and Gray under *K. maxima*.[899]

Tribulus maximus, as now understood, is far out of range. According to Porter, *K. parviflora* is the only species that occurs along James's route.[900]

James could have made his collection in any of the five states through which he traveled, with the exception of Nebraska.

---

[898]JAMES [3], August 5, 17, and 27.
[899]TORREY AND GRAY [1], I, 213.
[900]PORTER, 66.

APPENDIX ONE

PLANT NAMES COMMEMORATING JAMES BASED ON
COLLECTIONS MADE ALONG THE ROUTE OF THE EXPEDITION[1]

Andropogon jamesii Torr.
Asclepias jamesii Torr.
Aster jamesii O. Kuntze
Caesalpinia jamesii (T. & G.) Fisher
   Hoffmanseggia jamesii T. & G.
Carex jamesii Torr.
Chionophila jamesii Benth.
Cryptantha cinerea (Greene) Cronq. var. *jamesii* Cronq.
   Eritrichium jamesii Torr.
   Cryptantha jamesii (Torr.) Payson
Dalea jamesii (Torr.) T. & G.
   Psoralea jamesii Torr.
   Jamesia obovata Raf.
Desmanthus jamesii T. & G.
   Acuan (as *Acuania*) *jamesii* (T. & G.) Ktze.
Eriogonum jamesii Benth.
Frankenia jamesii Torr.
Jamesia americana T. & G.
Jamesia pauciflora (Torr.) Nees
Mimulus jamesii T. & G. ex Benth.
   This plant was actually collected in Iowa, a short distance downstream
   from Engineer Cantonment.
Oenothera jamesii T. & G.
Paronychia jamesii T. & G.
Penstemon jamesii Benth.
Polanisia jamesii (T. & G.) Iltis
Polygala jamesii Raf.
Senecio filifolius Nutt α *jamesii* T. & G.
Solanum jamesii Torr.
Stellaria jamesiana Torr.

---

[1]Three different genera were named for James. They are *Jamesia pauciflora* (*Stephanomeria pauciflora*) in the Compositae, *Jamesia americana* in the Hydrangeaceae, and *Jamesia obovata* (*Dalea jamesii*) in the Leguminosae.

Telesonix jamesii (Torr.) Raf.
  Saxifraga jamesii Torr.
Vernonia jamesii T. & G.

APPENDIX TWO

TYPES COLLECTED BY JAMES[2]

Acanthaceae
Justicia dubia Raf., a syn.[3] of *Ruellia humilis* Nutt. var. *longiflora* (Gray) Fern.
Aceraceae
Acer glabrum Torr.
Aristolochiaceae
Aristolochia coriacea Raf., a syn. of *A. tomentosa* Sims
Asclepiadaceae
Anantherix angustifolia Raf., a syn. of *Asclepias asperula* (Dcne.) Woods. var. *decumbens* (Nutt.) Shinners
Anantherix ovata Raf., a syn. of *Asclepias viridis* Walt.
Asclepias obtusifolia β? *latifolia* Torr. = *A. latifolia* (Torr.) Raf. and *A. jamesii* Torr.
Asclepias speciosa Torr.
Boraginaceae
Lithospermum decumbens Torr., not Vent., a possible type and probable syn. of *L. caroliniense* (Walt.) Macm.
Myosotis suffruticosa Torr. = *Cryptantha cinerea* (Greene) Cronq. var. *jamesii* Cronq.
Pulmonaria alpina Torr. = *Mertensia alpina* (Torr.) G. Don
Pulmonaria ciliata James ex Torr. = *Mertensia ciliata* (James ex Torr.) G. Don
Capparidaceae
Cleomella angustifolia Torr.
Cristatella jamesii T. & G. = *Polanisia jamesii* (T. & G.) Iltis
Caryophyllaceae
Arenaria obtusa Torr. = *A. obtusiloba* (Rydb.) Fern.
Paronychia jamesii T. & G.
Stellaria jamesiana Torr.
Chenopodiaceae
Atriplex torreyana Raf., a syn. of *A. canescens* (Pursh) Nutt.
Chenopodium hybridum β? *simplex* Torr. = *Chenopodium simplex* (Torr.) Raf.

[2]Bibliographic references and notes on the type localities are given for each taxon in Part 2. "The Botany."
[3]syn. = synonym.

Chenopodium nigrum Raf. = *Suaeda nigra* (Raf.) Macbride

Compositae

Artemisia filifolia Torr.

Aster multiflorus Ait. γ *commutatus* T. & G. = *A. falcatus* Lindley subsp. *commutatus* (T. & G.) A. G. Jones

Berlandiera incisa T. & G., a syn. of *B. lyrata* Benth.

Bidens gracilis Torr. = *Thelesperma gracile* (Torr.) Gray, syns. of *T. megapotamicum* (Spreng.) Kuntze

Gaillardia pinnatifida Torr.

Hieracium runcinatum James = *Crepis runcinata* (James) T. & G.

Inula ericoides Torr. = *Leucelene ericoides* (Torr.) Greene

Linosyris pluriflora T. & G. = *Haplopappus pluriflorus* (T. & G.) Hall

Pectis angustifolia Torr.

Prenanthes runcinata James, not Lag. = *P. pauciflora* Torr. = *Jamesia pauciflora* (Torr.) Nees (also the basis for the genus *Jamesia*) and *Stephanomeria pauciflora* (Torr.) A. Nels.

Prenanthes tenuifolia Torr., not L., a syn. of *Stephanomeria minor* (Hook.) Nutt.

Riddellia tagetinae Nutt. = *Psilostrophe tagetina* (Nutt.) Greene

Rudbeckia tagetes James = *Ratibida tagetes* (James) Barnh.

Senecio filifolius Nutt., a syn. of *S. douglasii* DC. var. *longilobus* (Benth.) Benson

Senecio filifolius Nutt. α *jamesii* T. & G., a syn. of *S. douglasii* DC. var. *longilobus* (Benth.) Benson

Silphium peristenium Raf. = *Engelmannia peristenia* (Raf.) Goodm. & Laws.

Stenotus pygmaeus T. & G. = *Haplopappus pygmaeus* (T. & G.) Gray

Stevia sphacelata Torr. = *Palafoxia hookeriana* T. & G. β *subradiata* T. & G. and *P. sphacelata* (Torr.) Cory

Vernonia altissima β? *marginata* Torr. = *Vernonia marginata* (Torr.) Raf. and *Vernonia jamesii* T. & G.

Zinnia grandiflora Torr.

Crassulaceae

Rhodiola integrifolia Raf. = *Sedum integrifolium* (Raf.) A. Nels.

Sedum lanceolatum Torr.

Sedum nuttallianum Raf., *S. nuttallii* Torrey & James ex Eaton, and *S. torreyi* G. Don, syns. of *S. pulchellum* Michx.

Cruciferae

Iberis candicans Raf. = *Dimorphocarpa candicans* (Raf.) Rollins

Stanleya integrifolia James = *Stanleya pinnata* (Pursh) Britt. var. *integrifolia* (James) Rollins

Cucurbitaceae

Cucumis perennis James, a syn. of *Cucurbita foetidissima* HBK.

Cyperaceae

Carex jamesii Torr., a syn. of *C. nebraskensis* Dewey

Fuirena squarrosa Michx. ε *aristulata* Torr. = *F. simplex* Vahl var. *aristulata* (Torr.) Kral

Euphorbiaceae

Euphoria missurica Raf. (A Nuttall specimen has since been designated the lectotype.)

Euphorbia montana Engelm. var. *robusta* Engelm. (Specimens of James and Fremont have been designated syntypes.)

Stillingia sylvatica L. var. *salicifolia* Torr.

Tragia ramosa Torr.

Fagaceae

Quercus undulata Torr.

Frankeniaceae

Frankenia jamesii Torr. (*Wright 626* has since been designated the lectotype.)

Geraniaceae

Geranium caespitosum Torr. = *Geranium intermedium* James

Gramineae

Agrostis airoides Torr. = *Sporobolus airoides* (Torr.) Torr.

Agrostis caespitosa Torr. = *A. torreyi* Kunth and *Muhlenbergia torreyi* (Kunth) Hitchc. ex Bush

Agrostis cryptandra Torr. = *Sporobolus cryptandrus* (Torr.) Gray

Andropogon glaucum Torr. = *A. torreyanus* Steud., *A. jamesii* Torr., and *A. saccharoides* Sw. var. *torreyanus* (Steud.) Hack.

Aristida fasciculata Torr., a syn. of *A. adscensionis* L.

Pleuraphis jamesii Torr. = *Hilaria jamesii* (Torr.) Benth.

Uniola stricta Torr. = *Distichlis stricta* (Torr.) Rydb.

Hydrangeaceae

Jamesia americana Torr. (Also the basis for the genus *Jamesia*).

Hydrophyllaceae

Phacelia integrifolia Torr.

Krameriaceae

Krameria lanceolata Torr.

Labiatae

Scutellaria ambigua Nutt. β *missouriensis* Torr. = *S. parvula* Michx. var. *missouriensis* (Torr.) Goodm. & Laws.

Scutellaria resinosa Torr.

Teucrium laciniatum Torr.

Leguminosae

Acacia cooleyi Eaton = *Desmanthus jamesii* T. & G. and *D. cooleyi* (Eaton) Trel.

Astragalus hypoglottis β *polyspermus* T. & G., a syn. of *A. agrestis* Dougl. ex G. Don

Astragalus mollissimus Torr.

Dalea formosa Torr.

Darlingtonia intermedia Torr., a syn. of *Desmanthus illinoensis* (Michx.) MacM. ex Robins. and Fern.

Hoffmanseggia jamesii T. & G. = *Caesalpinia jamesii* (T. & G.) Fisher

Petalostemum macrostachyum Torr. = *Dalea cylindriceps* Barneby

Psoralea jamesii Torr. = *Jamesia obovata* Raf. (Also the basis for the genus *Jamesia*) and *Dalea jamesii* (Torr.) T. & G.

Lupinus decumbens Torr., a syn. of *L. argenteus* Pursh

Prosopis glandulosa Torr.

Trifolium dasyphyllum T. & G.

Trifolium nanum Torr.

Liliaceae

Ornithogalum bracteatum Torr. = *Fenelonia bracteata* (Torr.) Raf. (Also the basis for the genus *Fenelonia*), syns. of *Lloydia serotina* (L.) Sweet

Loasaceae

Petalanthera hispida Nutt., a syn. of *Cevallia sinuata* Lag.

Malvaceae

Malva pedata β *umbellata* T. & G. = *Callirhoe macrorhiza* Gray, syns. of *C. alceoides* (Michx.) Gray

Malva involucrata T. & G. = *Callirhoe involucrata* (T. & G.) Gray

Sida stellata Torr., not Cav. = *Sphaeralcea stellata* (Torr.) T. & G. and *Sphaeralcea angustifolia* (Cav.) G. Don var. *cuspidata* Gray

Nyctaginaceae

Oxybaphus multiflorus Torr. = *Mirabilis multiflora* (Torr.) Gray

Onagraceae

Gaura coccinea Nutt. ex Pursh var. *integerrima* Torr.

Gaura linifolia Nutt. ex James = *Stenosiphon linifolius* (Nutt. ex James) Heynh.

Gaura mollis James

Gaura parvifolia Torr. = *Gaura coccinea* Nutt. ex Pursh var. *parvifolia* (Torr.) Rickett

Gaura villosa Torr.

Oenothera coronopifolia T. & G.

Oenothera jamesii T. & G.

Oenothera lavandulifolia T. & G. = *Calylophus lavandulfolius* (T. & G.) Raven

Papaveraceae

Argemone alba James, not Raf., a syn. of *A. polyanthemos* (Fedde) G. B. Ownb.

Pinaceae

Pinus flexilis James

Plantaginaceae

Plantago eriopoda Torr.

Polemoniaceae

Cantua longiflora Torr. = *Ipomopsis longiflora* (Torr.) V. Grant

Cantua pungens Torr. = *Leptodactylon pungens* (Torr.) Nutt.
Polygalaceae
Polygala jamesii Raf., a syn. of *P. alba* Nutt. and *P. torreyi* G. Don
Polygala torreyi G. Don, a syn. of *P. alba* Nutt.
Polygonaceae
Eriogonum jamesii Benth.
Eriogonum tenellum Torr.
Eriogonum umbellatum Torr.
Polygonum viviparum β *capitatum* Torr., a syn. of *P. viviparum* L.
Primulaceae
Androsace carinata Torr.
Primula angustifolia Torr.
Ranunculaceae
Aquilegia coerulea James
Psycrophila auriculata Raf. = *Caltha auriculata* (Raf.) Merrill, syns. of
     Caltha leptosepala DC.
Ranunculus amphibius James
Rosaceae
Cercocarpus montanus Raf.
Geum virginianum β *trilobum* Torr., a syn. (?) of *Sibbaldia procumbens* L.
Potentilla leucophylla Torr., not Pall., a syn. of *P. hippiana* Lehm.
Potentilla nivalis Torr., not Lapeyr. = *Geum turbinatum* Rydb. and *Geum
     rossii* (R.Br.) Ser. var. *turbinatum* (Rydb.) C. L. Hitchc.
Rubus deliciosus Torr.
Rubus Idaeus var. *americanus* Torr., a syn. of *R. occidentalis* L.
Spiraea monogyna Torr. = *Physocarpus monogynus* (Torr.) Coult.
Salicaceae
Populus angustifolia James
Saxifragaceae
Saxifraga jamesii Torr. = *Telesonix jamesii* (Torr.) Raf.
Tiarella bracteata Torr. = *Heuchera bracteata* (Torr.) Ser.
Scrophulariaceae
Capraria pusilla Torr., a syn. of *Mimulus floribundus* Dougl.
Castilleja occidentalis Torr.
Chionophila jamesii Benth. (Also the basis for the genus *Chionophila*).
Mimulus jamesii T. & G. ex Benth. = *M. glabratus* HBK. var. *jamesii* (T. &
     G.) Gray
Penstemon alpina Torr. = *P. glaber* Pursh var. *alpinus* (Torr.) Gray
Penstemon ambiguus Torr.
Penstemon jamesii Benth.
Penstemon torreyi Benth.
Veronica plantaginea James = *Besseya plantaginea* (James) Rydb.
Solanaceae
Physalis lobata Torr.

Solanum flavidum Torr., a syn. of *S. elaeagnifolium* Cav.
Solanum hirsutum James, not Dunal, a syn. of *S. triflorum* Nutt.
Solanum jamesii Torr.
Solanum torreyi Gray, a syn. of *S. dimidiatum* Raf.
Ulmaceae
Celtis reticulata Torr.
Umbelliferae
Eryngium diffusum Torr.
Oreoxis humilis Raf. (Also the basis for the genus *Oreoxis*).
Verbenaceae
Verbena stricta Vent. β *mollis* Torr. = *V. mollis* (Torr.) Raf., syns. of *V. stricta*
     Vent.
Zapania cuneifolia Torr. = *Phyla cuneifolia* (Torr.) Greene
Violaceae
Ionidium lineare Torr. = *Hybanthus linearis* (Torr.) Shinners
Vitaceae
Vitis longii Prince = /or a syn. of *Vitis acerifolia* Raf.

Sources Cited

AELLEN AND JUST   Aellen, Paul, and Theodor Just. "Synopsis of the American Species of the Genus *Chenopodium* L." *American Midland Naturalist,* 30 (1943), 47–76.

AMMERMAN   Ammerman, Elizabeth. "A Monographic Study of the Genus *Palafoxia* and Its Immediate Allies." *Annals of the Missouri Botanical Garden,* 31 (1944), 249–78.

BARKLEY   Barkley, Theodore M. "Senecio." In *North American Flora,* Series II, Part 10 (1978), 50–139.

BARNEBY [1]   Barneby, Rupert C. "Atlas of North American *Astragalus.*" *Memoirs of the New York Botanical Garden,* 13 (1964), 1–1188.

BARNEBY [2]   ———. "Daleae Imagines." *Memoirs of the New York Botanical Garden,* 27 (1977), 1–891.

BASSETT   Bassett, I. J. "Taxonomy of *Plantago* L. in North America: Sections Holopsyllium Pilger, Palaeopsyllium Pilger, and Lamprosantha Decne." *Canadian Journal of Botany,* 45 (1967), 565–77.

BENSON [1]   Benson, Lyman. "Supplement to a Treatise on the North American Ranunculi." *American Midland Naturalist,* 52 (1954), 328–69.

BENSON [2]   Benson, Maxine L. "Edwin James Scientist, Linguist, Humanitarian." Ph.D. diss., University of Colorado, Boulder, 1968.

BENSON [3]   ———, ed. *From Pittsburgh to the Rocky Mountains: Major Stephen Long's Expedition, 1819–1820.* Golden, Colorado, Fulcrum, 1988.

BENTHAM   Bentham, George. "Scrophulariaceae." In De Candolle *Prodromus,* 10 (1846), 186–586.

BRITTON AND BROWN   Britton, Nathaniel L., and Addison Brown. *An Illustrated Flora of the Northern United States, Canada, and the British Possessions.* New York, Charles Scribner's Sons, 1913.

BRITTON AND ROSE   ———, and Joseph N. Rose. *The Cactaceae.* Washington, The Carnegie Institution of Washington, 1919.

BROWN   Brown, Roy C. "Biosystematics of *Psilostrophe* (Compositae: Helenieae). II. Artificial Hybridization and Systematic Treatment." *Madroño,* 25 (1978), 187–201.

BUTTERS AND ST. JOHN
Butters, Frederic K., and Harold St. John. "Studies in Certain North American Species of *Lathyrus*." *Rhodora,* 19 (1917), 156–63.

CARLETON
Carleton, M. A. "Observations on the Native Plants of Oklahoma Territory and Adjacent Districts." *Contributions from the U.S. National Herbarium,* 1 (1892), 220–32.

CARLSON
Carlson, Gayle F. "Archeological Investigations at Fort Atkinson." *Nebraska State Historical Society Publications in Anthropology,* No. 8 (1979), 1–12.

CHITTENDEN
Chittenden, Hiram M. *The American Fur Trade of the Far West.* Stanford, California, Academic Reprints, 1954.

CLAUSEN
Clausen, Robert T. *Sedum of North America North of the Mexican Plateau.* Ithaca, N.Y., Cornell University Press, 1975.

CORE
Core, Earl L. "The North American Species of *Paronychia*." *American Midland Naturalist,* 26 (1941), 369–97.

CORRELL AND JOHNSTON
Correll, Donovan S., and Marshall C. Johnston. *Manual of the Vascular Plants of Texas.* Renner, Texas Research Foundation, 1970.

CRONQUIST [1]
Cronquist, Arthur. In Arthur Cronquist, Arthur H. Holmgren, Noel H. Holmgren, James L. Reveal, and Patricia K. Holmgren. *Intermountain Flora.* Bronx, The New York Botanical Garden, 1984.

CRONQUIST [2]
———. *Vascular Flora of the Southeastern United States.* Vol. I: *Asteraceae.* Chapel Hill, University of North Carolina Press, 1980.

CRONQUIST [3]
———. In C. Leo Hitchcock, Arthur Cronquist, Marion Ownbey, and J. W. Thompson. "Vascular Plants of the Pacific Northwest." *University of Washington Publications in Biology,* 17, Part 5 (1955), 1–343.

CUTRIGHT
Cutright, Paul Russell. *Lewis and Clark: Pioneering Naturalists.* Urbana, University of Illinois Press, 1969.

DAVIDSON
Davidson, John F. "The Genus *Polemonium* (Tournefort) L." *University of California Publications in Botany,* 23 (1951), 209–82.

DIETRICH AND RAVEN
Dietrich, Werner, and Peter H. Raven. "An Earlier Name for *Oenothera strigosa* (Onagraceae)." *Annals of the Missouri Botanical Garden,* 63 (1976), 382–83.

DORN
Dorn, Robert D. "*Chenopodium simplex,* An Older Name for *C. gigantospermum* (Chenopodiaceae)." *Madroño,* 35 (1988), 162.

DORR
Dorr, Laurence J. "Revision of *Callirhoe*." *Memoirs of the New York Botanical Garden,* 56 (1990), 1–74.

DOTT
Dott, Robert H. "Lieutenant Simpson's California Road

Across Oklahoma." *The Chronicles of Oklahoma,* 38 (1960), 154–79.

FERNALD Fernald, Merritt L. *Gray's Manual of Botany.* 8th ed. New York, American Book Co., 1950.

FERNALD AND GRISCOM ———, and Ludlow Griscom. "Notes on *Diodia.*" *Rhodora,* 39 (1937), 306–8.

FISHER Fisher, E. M. "Revision of the North American Species of *Hoffmanseggia.*" *Contributions from the U. S. National Herbarium,* 1 (1892), 143–50.

FLORES Flores, Dan L. *Jefferson & Southwestern Exploration.* Norman, University of Oklahoma Press, 1984.

FOREMAN Foreman, Grant. "An Unpublished Report by Captain Bonneville with Introduction and Footnotes." *The Chronicles of Oklahoma,* 10 (1932), 326–30.

FULLER AND HAFEN Fuller, Harlin M. and LeRoy F. Hafen, eds. *The Journal of Captain John R. Bell.* Glendale, Calif., The Arthur H. Clark Co., 1973.

GAISER Gaiser, Lulu O. "The Genus *Liatris.*" *Rhodora,* 48 (1946), 331–82.

GLEASON [1] Gleason, Henry A. "Change of Name for Certain Plants of the 'Manual Range.'" *Phytologia,* 4 (1952), 20–25.

GLEASON [2] ———. *The New Britton and Brown Illustrated Flora of the Northeastern United States and Adjacent Canada.* Lancaster, Penn., Lancaster Press, 1952.

GOETZMANN Goetzmann, William H. *Exploration and Empire.* New York, Alfred A. Knopf, 1966.

GOULD Gould, Charles N. *Oklahoma Place Names.* Norman, University of Oklahoma Press, 1933.

GRAY [1] Gray, Asa. *Synoptical Flora of North America.* Vol. I, Part I, Fascicle I. Edited by Benjamin L. Robinson. New York, American Book Co., 1895.

GRAY [2] ———. *Synoptical Flora of North America.* Vol. I, Part I, Fascicle II. Edited by Benjamin L. Robinson. New York, American Book Co., 1897.

GRAY [3] ———. *Synoptical Flora of North America.* Vol. I, Part II. New York, Ivison, Blakeman, Taylor, and Co., 1884.

GRAY [4] ———. *Synoptical Flora of North America.* Vol. II, Part I. New York, Ivison, Blakeman, Taylor, and Co., 1878.

GRAY [5] ———. "Botanical Contributions.—1. Reconstruction of the Order Diapensiaceae.—2. Revision of the North American Polemoniaceae.—3. Miscellaneous Botanical Notes and Characters." *Proceedings of the American Academy of Arts and Sciences,* 8 (1870), 243–96.

GRAY [6] ———. "Plantae Fendlerianae Novi-Mexicanae." *Memoirs of the American Academy of Arts and Sciences,* New Series, 4 (1849), 1–116.

GRAY [7] ————. "Revision of the North American Rununculi." *Proceedings of the American Academy of Arts and Sciences,* 21 (1886), 363–78.

GRAY [8] ————. "*Rubus deliciosus* Torr." *American Journal of Science,* Series III, 6 (1873), 389.

HALL Hall, Harvey M. "The Genus *Haplopappus.* A Phylogenetic Study in the Compositae." *Carnegie Institution of Washington,* Publication No. 389 (1928), 1–391.

HARRINGTON Harrington, Harold D. *Manual of the Plants of Colorado.* Denver, Sage Books, 1954.

HELLER Heller, Amos A. "New Plants from Western North America.—I." *Bulletin of the Torrey Botanical Club,* 25 (1898), 193–201.

HEMPHILL Hemphill, W. Edwin, ed. *The Papers of John C. Calhoun,* Vol. VII. Columbia, University of South Carolina Press, 1973.

HITCHCOCK Hitchcock, C. Leo. "A Revision of the North American
[1] Species of *Lathyrus.*" *University of Washington Publications in Biology,* 15 (1952), 1–104.

HITCHCOCK ————. In C. Leo Hitchcock, Arthur Cronquist, Marion
[2] Ownbey, and J.W. Thompson. "Vascular Plants of the Pacific Northwest." *University of Washington Publications in Biology,* 17, Part 2 (1964), 1–597.

HODGE Hodge, Frederick W., ed. *Handbook of American Indians North of Mexico.* Smithsonian Institution Bureau of American Ethnology *Bulletin 30.* Part 2. Washington, D.C., Government Printing Office, 1910.

HOLLON Hollon, W. Eugene. *The Lost Pathfinder: Zebulon Montgomery Pike.* Norman, University of Oklahoma Press, 1949.

HOLMGREN Holmgren, Noel H. In Arthur Cronquist, Arthur H. Holmgren, Noel H. Holmgren, James L. Reveal, and Patricia K. Holmgren. *Intermountain Flora.* Bronx, The New York Botanical Garden, 1984.

HOLZINGER Holzinger, John M. "List of Plants Collected by C. S. Sheldon and M. A. Carleton in Indian Territory in 1891." *Contributions from the U.S. National Herbarium,* 1 (1892), 189–219.

HOPKINS AND Hopkins, Christine O., and Will H. Blackwell, Jr. "Synopsis
BLACKWELL of *Suaeda* (Chenopodiaceae) in North America." *Sida,* 7 (1977), 147–73.

ISELY [1] Isely, Duane. "Leguminosae of the United States: II. Subfamily Caesalpinioideae." *Memoirs of the New York Botanical Garden,* 25 (1975), 1–228.

ISELY [2] ————. "Legumes of the United States: II. *Desmanthus* and

Neptunia." *Iowa State Journal of Science,* 44 (1970), 495–511.

JACKSON [1]   Jackson, Donald. *Thomas Jefferson and the Stony Mountains.* Urbana, University of Illinois Press, 1981.

JACKSON [2]   ———, ed. *The Journals of Zebulon Montgomery Pike.* Norman, University of Oklahoma Press, 1966.

JAMES [1]   James, Edwin, comp. *Account of an Expedition from Pittsburgh to the Rocky Mountains, Performed in the Years 1819 and '20, Under the Command of Major Stephen H. Long.* Readex Microprint, 1966.

JAMES [2]   ———, comp. *Account of an Expedition from Pittsburgh to the Rocky Mountains, Performed in the Years 1819, 1820. Under the Command of Maj. S.H. Long. . . .* In THWAITES [1], Vols. XIV–XVII, 1905.

JAMES [3]   ———. "Notes of a part of the Exped. of Discovery Commanded by S. H. Long Maj. U. S. Eng., 1820." Unpublished diary.

JAMES [4]   ———. "Catalogue of Plants collected during a Journey to and from the Rocky Mountains during the summer of 1820." *Transactions of the American Philosophical Society,* New Series, 2 (1825), 172–90.

JAMES [5]   ———. "Remarks on the Sandstone and Floetz Trap Formations of the Western Part of the Valley of the Mississippi." *Transactions of the American Philosophical Society,* New Series, 2 (1825), 191–215.

JAMES [6]   ———, comp. *Account of An Expedition from Pittsburgh to the Rocky Mountains, performed in the years 1819 and '20, under the command of Major Stephen H. Long.* Philadelphia, Penn., H. C. Carey and I. Lea, 1823.

JAMES [7]   ———, comp. *Account of an Expedition from Pittsburgh to the Rocky Mountains, performed in the Years 1819, 1820. under the command of Maj. S. H. Long, of the U. S. Top. Engineers.* London, Longman, Hurst, Rees, Orme, and Brown, 1823.

JOHNSTON [1]   Johnston, Ivan M. "Studies in the Boraginaceae.—II." *Contributions from the Gray Herbarium of Harvard University,* New Series #70 (1924), 3–61.

JOHNSTON [2]   ———. "Studies in the Boraginaceae.—XXIII A Survey of the Genus *Lithospermum.*" *Journal of the Arnold Arboretum,* 33 (1952), 299–366.

JONES   Jones, Almut G. "The Taxonomy of *Aster* Section *Multiflori* (Asteraceae). I. Nomenclatural Review and Formal Presentation of Taxa." *Rhodora,* 80 (1978), 319–57.

JONES AND JONES   Jones, G. Neville, and Florence F. Jones. "A Revision of the Perennial Species of *Geranium* of the United States and Canada." *Rhodora,* 45 (1943), 32–53.

LAGASCA [1]   Lagasca, Mariano. *Genera et Species Plantarum.* Madrid, 1816.

LAGASCA [2]   ———. *Elenchus Plantarum.* Madrid, 1816.

LONG   Long, Stephen H. "Report of the Western River Expedition by S. H. Long, T. Engr. to Hon. J. C. Calhoun, Secretary of War, dated Philadelphia, February 20, 1821." In *Bulky File, Case 1, Drawer 4, NA Box 13,* in RG77, National Archives.

MCDERMOTT [1]   McDermott, John F. "Samuel Seymour: Pioneer Artist of the Plains and the Rockies." *Annual Report Smithsonian Institution,* Publication 4025 (1950), 497–509.

MCDERMOTT [2]   ———, ed. "The Western Journals of Dr. George Hunter, 1796–1805." *Transactions of the American Philosophical Society,* New Series. 53 (1963), 1–133.

MCNEILL,   McNeill, J., I. J. Bassett, and C. W. Crompton. "*Suaeda*
BASSETT, AND   *calceoliformis,* the Correct Name for *Suaeda depressa* Auct."
CROMPTON   *Rhodora,* 79 (1977), 133–38.

MATTHEWS,   Matthews, James F., Donna W. Ketron, and Sandra F. Zane.
KETRON, AND   "The Reevaluation of *Portulaca pilosa* and *P. mundula* (Por-
ZANE   tulacaceae)." *Sida,* 15 (1992), 71–89.

MEEUSE AND   Meeuse, A. D. J., and A. Smit. "A New Combination in
SMIT   *Krascheninnikovia.*" *Taxon,* 20 (1971), 644.

MERRILL   Merrill, Elmer D. *Index Rafinesquianus.* Jamaica Plain, Mass., The Arnold Arboretum of Harvard University, 1949.

MILLER AND   Miller, Kim I., and Grady L. Webster. "A Preliminary Revi-
WEBSTER   sion of *Tragia* (Euphorbiaceae) in the United States." *Rhodora,* 69 (1967), 241–305.

MOLDENKE   Moldenke, Harold N. "Materials Toward a Monograph of the Genus *Verbena.* XXVI." *Phytologia,* 11 (1965), 219–87.

MORTON [1]   Morton, Conrad V. "Taxonomic Studies of Tropical American Plants." *Contributions from the U.S. National Herbarium,* 29 (1944), 1–86.

MORTON [2]   ———. "Some Types and Range Extensions in *Hybanthus* (Violaceae)." *Phytologia,* 21 (1971), 56–62.

MUNZ   Munz, Philip A. "Aquilegia: The Cultivated and Wild Columbines." *Gentes Herbarum,* 7 (1946), 1–150.

MURPHY   Murphy, Robert C. "The Sketches of Titian Ramsay Peale (1799–1885)." *Proceedings of the American Philosophical Society,* 101 (1957), 523–31.

NESOM   Nesom, Guy L. "Synopsis of *Chaetopappa* (Compositae-Astereae) with a New Species and the Inclusion of *Leucelene.*" *Phytologia,* 64 (1988), 448–56.

NICHOLS AND   Nichols, Roger L., and Patrick L. Halley. *Stephen Long and*
HALLEY   *American Frontier Exploration.* Newark, University of Delaware Press, 1980.

NUTTALL [1]   Nuttall, Thomas. "Descriptions of new Species and Genera of Plants in the natural Order of the Compositae, collected in a Tour across the Continent to the Pacific, a Residence in Oregon, and a Visit to the Sandwich Islands and Upper California, during the Years 1834 and 1835." *Transactions of the American Philosophical Society,* Series 2, 7 (1840–41), 283–453.

NUTTALL [2]   ———. "A Catalogue of a Collection of Plants made chiefly in the Valleys of the Rocky Mountains or Northern Andes, towards the sources of the Columbia River, by Mr. Nathaniel B. Wyeth, and described by T. Nuttall." *Journal of the Academy of Natural Sciences of Philadelphia,* 7 (1834), 5–60.

NUTTALL [3]   ———. "A catalogue of a collection of plants made in east-Florida, during the months of October and November, 1821, By A. Ware, Esq." *American Journal of Science and Arts,* 5 (1822), 286–304.

NUTTALL [4]   ———. "A Description of some new species of Plants, recently introduced into the gardens of Philadelphia, from the Arkansa territory." *Journal of the Academy of Natural Sciences of Philadelphia,* 2 (1821), 114–23.

NUTTALL [5]   ———. *The Genera of North American Plants.* Philadelphia, D. Heartt, 1818.

NUTTALL [6]   ———. "Collections towards a Flora of the Territory of Arkansas." *Transactions of the American Philosophical Society,* New Series, 5 (1835–36), 139–203.

O'KANE, WILKEN, AND HARTMAN   O'Kane, Steve L., Jr., Dieter H. Wilken, and Ronald L. Hartman. "Noteworthy Collections." *Madroño,* 35 (1988), 72–74.

OSTERHOUT [1]   Osterhout, George E. "Rocky Mountain botany and the Long Expedition of 1820." *Bulletin of the Torrey Botanical Club,* 47 (1920), 555–62.

OSTERHOUT [2]   ———. "What is *Geranium caespitosum* James?" *Bulletin of the Torrey Botanical Club,* 50 (1923), 81–84.

OWNBEY   Ownbey, Ruth P. "The Liliaceous Genus *Polygonatum* in North America." *Annals of the Missouri Botanical Garden,* 31 (1944), 373–413.

PAYSON   Payson, Edwin B. "A Monograph of the Section *Oreocarya* of *Cryptantha.*" *Annals of the Missouri Botanical Garden,* 14 (1927), 211–359.

PENNELL [1]   Pennell, Francis W. "Scrophulariaceae of the Central Rocky Mountain States." *Contributions from the U.S. National Herbarium,* 20 (1920), 313–81.

PENNELL [2]   ———. "The Scrophulariaceae of Eastern Temperate North

America." *Academy of Natural Sciences of Philadelphia, Monograph* 1 (1935), 1–650.

PILGER Pilger, Robert. "Plantaginaceae." *Das Pflanzenreich,* 102 (1937), 1–466.

PILZ Pilz, George E. "Systematics of *Mirabilis* Subgenus *Quamoclidion* (Nyctaginaceae)." *Madroño,* 25 (1978), 113–32.

PORTER Porter, Duncan M. "The Genus *Kallstroemia* (Zygophyllaceae)." *Contributions from the Gray Herbarium of Harvard University,* No. 198 (1969), 41–53.

PURSH Pursh, Frederick. *Flora Americae Septentrionalis.* London, White, Cochran, and Co., 1814.

RAFINESQUE [1] Rafinesque, Constantin S. "Twenty New Genera of Plants from the Oregon Mountains &c." *Atlantic Journal,* 1 (1832), 144–46.

RAFINESQUE [2] ———. *Autikon Botanikon,* Lithoprinted, Ann Arbor, Michigan, Edwards Brothers, Inc., 1942.

RAVEN AND GREGORY Raven, Peter H., and David P. Gregory. "A Revision of the Genus *Gaura* (Onagraceae)." *Memoirs of the Torrey Botanical Club,* 23 (1972), 1–96.

REVEAL Reveal, James L. "On the Names in Fraser's 1813 Catalogue." *Rhodora,* 70 (1968), 25–54.

RICHARDS Richards, Edward L. "A Monograph of the Genus *Ratibida.*" *Rhodora,* 70 (1968), 348–93.

ROBBINS Robbins, G. Thomas. "North American Species of *Androsace.*" *American Midland Naturalist,* 32 (1944), 137–63.

ROE Roe, Frank Gilbert. *The North American Buffalo.* Toronto, University of Toronto Press, 1970.

RYDBERG [1] Rydberg, Per A. *Flora of Colorado.* Fort Collins, Colorado, The Agricultural Experiment Station, 1906.

RYDBERG [2] ———. *Flora of the Rocky Mountains and Adjacent Plains.* New York, published by author, 1922.

RYDBERG [3] ———. "Notes on Two Western Plants." *Bulletin of the Torrey Botanical Club,* 24 (1897), 90–92.

RYDBERG [4] ———. "Studies on the Rocky Mountain flora." *Bulletin of the Torrey Botanical Club,* 37 (1910), 443–71.

SHINNERS Shinners, Lloyd H. "Revision of the Genus *Leucelene* Greene." *Wrightia,* 1 (1946), 82–89.

SMITH Smith, Albert C. "Notes on North American Araliaceae." *Brittonia,* 2 (1936), 247–61.

STAFLEU AND COWAN Stafleu, Frans A., and Richard S. Cowan. *Taxonomic Literature.* 7 vols. Utrecht, Netherlands, Bohn, Scheltema and Holkema, 1976–88.

STEYERMARK [1] Steyermark, Julian A. *Flora of Missouri.* Ames, Iowa State University Press, 1963.

STEYERMARK [2] — ————. "The First Recorded Occurrence of *Distichlis spicata* in the Central Interior of the United States." *Rhodora,* 42 (1940), 22–24.

STROUD — Stroud, Patricia Tyson. *Thomas Say: New World Naturalist.* Philadelphia, University of Pennsylvania Press, 1992.

THWAITES [1] — Thwaites, Reuben G., ed. *Early Western Travels, 1748–1846.* 32 vols. Cleveland, Ohio, The Arthur H. Clark Company, 1904–1907.

THWAITES [2] — ————. *Original Journals of the Lewis and Clark Expedition 1804–1806.* 8 vols. New York, Dodd, Mead and Co., 1904–1905.

TIDESTROM — Tidestrom, Ivar. "Flora of Utah and Nevada." *Contributions from the U.S. National Herbarium,* 25 (1925), 1–663.

TORRES — Torres, Andrew M. "Taxonomy of *Zinnia.*" *Brittonia,* 15 (1963), 1–25.

TORREY [1] — Torrey, John. "Descriptions of some new or rare Plants from the Rocky Mountains, collected in July, 1820, by Dr. Edwin James." *Annals of the Lyceum of Natural History of New York,* 1 (1824), 30–36.

TORREY [2] — ————. "Some Account of a Collection of Plants made during a journey to and from the Rocky Mountains in the summer of 1820, by Edwin P. James, M.D. Assistant Surgeon U. S. Army." *Annals of the Lyceum of Natural History of New York,* 2 (1827), 161–254.

TORREY [3] — ————. *Botany of the Boundary. Report on the United States and Mexican Boundary Survey,* Vol. II, Part I, 34 Cong., 1st sess., House Executive Document No. 135, 1859.

TORREY [4] — ————. "Catalogue of Plants collected by Lieut. Fremont in His Expedition to the Rocky Mountains." In Fremont, John C., *A Report on an Exploration of the Country lying between The Missouri River and the Rocky Mountains, on the line of The Kansas and Great Platte Rivers,* 27 Cong., 3d sess., Senate Executive Document, No. 243, 1843.

TORREY [5] — ————. "Description of the Plants Collected During the Expedition." In Marcy, Randolph B., *Exploration of the Red River of Louisiana in the Year 1852,* 32 Cong., 2d sess., Senate Executive Document, No. 54, 1853.

TORREY [6] — ————. "Descriptions of some new Grasses collected by Dr. E. James, in the expedition of Major Long to the Rocky Mountains, in 1819–1820." *Annals of the Lyceum of Natural History of New York,* 1 (1824), 148–56.

TORREY AND GRAY [1] — ————, and Asa Gray. *A Flora of North America.* 2 vols. New York, Wiley & Putnam, 1838–43. Reprinted, New York, Hafner Publishing Co., 1969.

TORREY AND GRAY [2]
————. "A Revision of the Erigoneae." *Proceedings of the American Academy of Arts and Sciences,* 8 (1870), 145–200.

TRENTON AND HASSRICK
Trenton, Patricia, and Peter Hassrick. *The Rocky Mountains. A Vision for Artists in the Nineteenth Century.* Norman, University of Oklahoma Press, 1983.

TUCKER [1]
Tucker, John M. "Studies in the *Quercus undulata* Complex. V. The Type of *Quercus undulata.*" *American Journal of Botany,* 58 (1971), 329–41.

TUCKER [2]
————. "Major Long's Route from the Arkansas to the Canadian River, 1820." *New Mexico Historical Review,* 38 (1963), 185–219.

TURNER
Turner, Billie L. "Revision of the United States Species of *Neptunia* (Leguminosae)." *American Midland Naturalist,* 46 (1951), 82–92.

TURNER AND MORRIS
————, and Michael I. Morris. "Systematics of *Palafoxia* (Asteraceae: Helenieae)." *Rhodora,* 78 (1976), 567–628.

WAHL
Wahl, Herbert A. "A Preliminary Study of the Genus *Chenopodium* in North America." *Bartonia,* 27 (1954), 1–46.

WATSON [1]
Watson, Sereno. "Bibliographical Index to North American Botany." *Smithsonian Miscellaneous Collections,* Publication 258 (1879), 1–476.

WATSON [2]
————. "Revision of the North American Chenopodiaceae." *Proceedings of the American Academy of Arts and Sciences,* 9 (1874), 82–126.

WATSON [3]
————. "Revision of the North American Liliaceae." *Proceedings of the American Academy of Arts and Sciences,* 14 (1879), 213–88.

WEBB
Webb, Ardis. *The Perry Park Story.* Denver, Colorado, published by author and Olin Webb, 1974.

WEBER [1]
Weber, William A. *Rocky Mountain Flora.* Boulder, Colorado Associated University Press, 1976.

WEBER [2]
————. *Colorado Flora: Western Slope.* Boulder, Colorado Associated University Press, 1987.

WEDEL
Wedel, Waldo R. *An Introduction to Pawnee Archeology.* Smithsonian Institution Bureau of American Ethnology *Bulletin 112.* Washington, D.C., Government Printing Office, 1936.

WHALEN
Whalen, Molly A. "Systematics of *Frankenia* (Frankeniaceae) in North and South America." *Systematic Botany Monographs,* 17 (1987), 1–93.

WHEELER
Wheeler, Louis C. "*Euphorbia* Subgenus *Chamaesyce* in Canada and the United States Exclusive of Southern Florida." *Rhodora,* 43 (1941), 97–154.

WHERRY
Wherry, Edgar T. "New Phloxes from the Rocky Mountains

and Neighboring Regions." *Notulae Naturae of the Academy of Natural Sciences of Philadelphia,* 146 (1944), 1–11.

WOODSON   Woodson, Robert E., Jr. "The North American Species of *Asclepias* L." *Annals of the Missouri Botanical Garden,* 41 (1954), 1–211.

WOOTON AND   Wooton, E. O., and Paul C. Standley. "Flora of New Mexico."
STANDLEY   *Contributions from the U.S. National Herbarium,* 19 (1915), 1–794.

YUNCKER   Yuncker, Truman G. "Revision of the North American and West Indian Species of *Cuscuta.*" *Illinois Biological Monographs,* 6 (1921), 1–141.

INDEX TO SCIENTIFIC NAMES

INDEX TO COMMON NAMES

GENERAL INDEX